FIFT

FASCINATING

FACTS

ABOUT THE

ISLE OF WIGHT

by

John Dowling

Published by Island Tourist Products
Wootton, Isle of Wight.
Tel: 01983 884411
© 2007

ISBN 978-1-906296-00-1

First published in 1984 by
The Museum of Smuggling History, Ventnor, Isle of Wight

This new edition first published in 2007

British Library Cataloguing in Publication Data
A catalogue record for this book is available from the British Library

ISBN 978-1-906296-00-1

Printed by The Grosvenor Press, Shanklin, Isle of Wight

CONTENTS

INTRODUCTION

The Isle of Wight has a fascination all of its own. Over a million people each year visit Britain's "Holiday Island" in search of sun, sea and sand, but few realise the fascinating facts that are hidden in their surroundings.

With an area of just over 155 square miles the Island is the smallest county in England, and is the largest of the islands in the Channel: also, with a population of around 135,000 it is the largest political constituency in the country.

While carrying out research into the history of the Island I came across many interesting stories, some humorous, some historical, and all of them fascinating. These I now present for you as "Fifty Fascinating Facts about the Isle of Wight".

TO FREE A KING

The Isle of Wight was used to welcoming Royal visitors, yet in 1647 one arrived who was to receive less hospitality than he had anticipated.

Charles I had escaped from Hampton Court and fled to the Isle of Wight, hoping for protection by its governor, Colonel Robert Hammond, who was the nephew of the King's chaplain. He arrived in November 1647 and at first was allowed the freedom of the Island, living at Carisbrooke Castle and hunting in the Royal Forest of Parkhurst, but things were about to change.

Soon the King's chaplains, Dr. Sheldon and Dr. Hammond, were "no longer permitted to exercise their functions" and then his servants Ashburnham and Legg were forbidden to wait on him. As the screws tightened, so he was eventually confined to the Castle, where Colonel Hammond had converted the barbican to a bowling green and had a summer house built, and there he took his exercise: bowling, walking the ramparts and reading.

In December 1647 there was an abortive attempt to rescue the King by Captain Burley of Yarmouth Castle, who was executed, but dispatches were still carried to and from the King by his servant Henry Firebrace and by his laundry-woman, Mrs. Wheeler, who smuggled out messages to Royalist supporters.

An escape attempt was planned and Firebrace suggested a saw to cut through the bars of the window in the room in which the King was confined at night. Charles felt this was unnecessary, as he had managed to get his head between the bars and judged that "where the head would pass, the body would easily follow". Firebrace was to give the signal and the King would then slip through the window and descend by a cord to the courtyard. He would climb the outer wall and be lowered by rope to the ground, where he would find Mr. Worsley and Mr. Osborne ready mounted and with a spare horse, pistol and boots. They would then ride off to rendezvous with Mr. Newland, who had organised a large boat to take the King to safety.

All had been arranged: ropes, boots, pistols and boat. Then Firebrace gave the signal. The King managed to get his head through the bars, but when he tried to ease himself and the rest of his body through the narrow opening, he found himself stuck between the bars, unable to go forward or back! After much discomfort he released himself and remained inside his room and the escape attempt was called off.

On a second attempt some time later, the window bars were cut and the King could have escaped from his room, but seeing more people below than had been arranged, he decided to abandon this attempt as well. A wise move, since the plan was to shoot him when he left the castle. Worsley and Osborne rode through a hail of bullets to their rendezvous at the coast, but the master of the ship refused to let them on board without the King. Luckily they managed to escape in a small boat they acquired at Chale.

There was one further chance of escape for Charles, but he turned it down. During the 60 day "Treaty of Newport" he was under house arrest in the old Grammar School, a building which still exists to this day, and he was urged to make a run for it, on the principle of "rather a King in exile than a dead King". Charles refused, saying he had given his word to remain in Newport until the proceedings were over.

Shortly after the Royal prisoner was taken by military officers to Hurst Castle and then on to London to face execution in Whitehall.

————➤•○•◀————

THE FIRST MARCONIGRAM

Guglielmo Marconi was born in 1874 and at the age of twenty began his experiments in wireless telegraphy at his parents' villa near Bologna, Italy. By 1896 he decided that his system had commercial properties and offered it to the Italian Post Office who declined to test his equipment, so in that year he moved to London and gave several demonstrations of his invention to the public.

He wanted to prove that he could transmit messages across a stretch of open water, so in 1897 a 40 metre mast was installed outside the Needles Hotel at Alum Bay as a transmitting station, with a receiving station at the Haven Hotel, Poole, which was 30 kilometres away.

A small tug was hired which steamed to and fro' across the Solent for several weeks. Bad weather tossed the small vessel about and the cabin which contained Marconi's equipment was sometimes knee deep in water; however, transmissions of up to 30 kilometres were recorded, which confirmed its durability under adverse conditions.

Some of his ship to shore demonstrations were mainly for publicity purposes: a link was established between Queen Victoria's Island home at Osborne and the Royal Yacht anchored off Cowes, where the Prince of Wales was convalescing after a fall.

3

A gardener asked Marconi to change his route through the Royal estate to his transmitter to avoid "violating the Queen's privacy" and when Marconi refused, and the Queen was informed, she is reputed to have said "Get another electrician".

"Alas, your majesty, England has no Marconi" was the reply and the Queen relented and gave an audience to the Italian.

In 1898, while Marconi was giving a demonstration of sending messages from the Needles to the mainland, Lord Kelvin sent some messages to be forwarded to his friends and insisted on paying a shilling for each message. Despite being in violation of the Post Office monopoly on inland communications, this became the first ever use of wireless telegraphy for commercial purposes, with the sending of the very first "Marconigram".

<hr />

THE PETRIFIED FOREST

The Victorians "discovered" the Isle of Wight as a holiday island and England's health resort, yet their predecessors in the Georgian Era has already found the Island to be a naturalist's paradise, abounding in many types of flora and fauna and a living museum of geology.

One of these naturalists, Thomas Webster, discovered the "Pine Raft" at Hanover Point, near Brook, when he visited the Island between 1811 and 1813. He found masses of black rock resembling trees that appeared to have been charred and embedded in the clay. In some parts wooden fibre was still evident, whereas in others the wood had been converted into a substance resembling the mineral jet.

Webster lifted some seaweed and was surprised to find that all the rocks were composed of fossilised wood, from tree trunks 8 to 10 feet long and 2 feet in diameter, through a range of different sized branches, right down to small twigs. The knotty bark and wooden fibre was very distinct, and in Webster's own words "the whole exhibited a beautiful example of the astonishing processes of nature in converting vegetables into coal".

During the passage of time, sea and sand have taken their toll on Webster's Pine Raft, but evidence of it can still be seen at low tide near Hanover Point, and at nearby Compton Bay several examples have been found of carbonised hazel nuts, which have become known locally as "Noah's Nuts".

QUARR ABBEY

Baldwin de Redvers, the fourth Lord of the Isle of Wight, founded the Cistercian Abbey of Quarr in 1132, in conjunction with Abbot Gervase of Savigny.

When monks came to the Island, their first task was to dig stone out of the ground to build the abbey; this stone was in a shallow seam 3-4 feet thick and was dug out of pits in the ground using the open cast method. Taking advantage of the nearby stream and a plentiful supply of oak bark used in the process, they constructed a tannery and also a corn mill at Wootton – the present Sloop Inn used to be the miller's house.

The monks also introduced the technique of "fulling" to the Island (a method of cleaning wool using a solution of fuller's earth which they obtained locally) and built a fulling mill at Haseley-in-Arreton.

Baldwin, the founder of the Abbey was buried with his wife in the church, as was the daughter of Edward IV. There is a legend that Queen Eleanor, the wife of Henry II, was imprisoned at the Abbey and was buried in a gold coffin in a spot still known as Eleanor's Copse.

The Abbey had several agricultural holdings on the Island known as Granges, and by the mid 1500s owned seven windmills and watermills including the Wootton tide mill and the fulling mill at Haseley-in-Arreton.

Then came the dissolution of the monasteries and the abbey was sold to a Mr. Mills of Southampton, who demolished it, much of the stone being used to build Yarmouth Castle. It may be that this was just because the stone was available on the Island, but what a supreme irony for bluff King Hal – to demolish a monastery in order to build a castle to defend yourself against the very foreigners you have just alienated!

Why the name Quarr? This simply comes from the stone-pits in the ground in which the monks used to quarry the stone to build their "Quarry-Abbey".

A WATERTIGHT AGREEMENT

The history of brewing on the Island probably goes back 1000 years, when the ale houses each brewed their own beer for sale to their customers. By the early 1600s brewhouses had been set up to supply a larger area than one single alehouse. Jermyn Rychardes owned the brewhouse at Brading (then a harbour) and made a fortune from selling beer to the fleet of ships anchored in St. Helens Roads; Mew Langtons brewery in Newport, founded in 1643, supplied a large export market through the trading ships which called at Cowes and several small breweries produced enough ale to supply a number of local inns.

By the 1800s there were seven public breweries on the Island, including Shanklin Brewery, Sprakes of Chale Green, the Eagle Brewery, Ryde and the Castle Brewery, Sandown.

The last brewery to survive on the Island was Burts of Ventnor, established in the 1840s, where until recently beer was brewed in the traditional manner using only spring water, malt, hops, and sugar, with finings added at the time of distribution.

The spring water issues from the foot of St.Boniface Down and makes its way beneath the town to emerge as Ventnor Cascade, formerly driving a small corn mill where the Winter Gardens now stand.

The curious fact about the brewery goes back to 1850 when the owner, James Corbould, made an agreement with Thomas Page of the Ventnor Water Company on behalf of their "heirs, executors, administrators and assigns" that the brewery should receive its water at a preferential rate. The agreement was that the brewery could draw an unlimited supply of untreated spring water, which would be piped to its premises in the High Street, at the rate of 6d (2 $^1/_2$p) a year for the next 1000 years!

Truly a watertight agreement.

The brewing tradition continues with the Ventnor Brewery at the former Burts premises producing a number of fine ales including "Ventnor Golden", but sadly the agreement with the water company seems to have lapsed with the change of ownership.

THE FIRST PIER

In these days of ferries, hovercraft, and catamarans we tend to accept travel to and from the Island as a matter of course, but 200 years ago it was a different story.

You could make the journey by a Portsmouth Wherry, also known as a "sea cab", which must have been a trial in bad weather, or on the sailing packet that called at Ryde two or three times a week, which made for a smoother crossing, but also had its problems.

Novelist Henry Fielding visited Ryde in 1754 and described his experiences in his book "A Voyage to Lisbon". At the time passengers for the Island disembarked from their ship to a smaller boat, and when nearer the shore were carried to the beach by horse and cart, sedan chair, or by two longshoremen, with arms linked, forming a "human chair".

Cowes was the main trading port at the time and landing space must have been at a premium; Ryde was the obvious landing point for what were then referred to as "parties of pleasure", but how to provide a safe and convenient way of landing passengers from the sailing packet?

The gently sloping sands prevented ships approaching the shore, and there was no natural harbour, so in 1812 it was decided to build a pier, so that passengers could disembark from their ship, and then walk or be driven to the shore.

Promenade piers became very fashionable in Victorian society, and the first one on the mainland was Brighton Chain Pier, which opened in 1822; but the wooden pier at Ryde, opened in 1814, can rightly claim to be the first seaside pier in Great Britain.

THE CURATE'S INVENTION

The Reverend Legh Richmond was Curate in charge of Brading and Yaverland from 1797 to 1805 and is commemorated by a brass tablet in the south aisle of the historic Church of St.Mary in Brading.

During his time as curate at Brading he wrote "Annals of the Poor", a series of stories with a moral message, including the "Dairyman's Daughter" (Elizabeth Wallbridge) and the "Young Cottager" (Little Jane); his accounts were based on the lives of real people, and Little Jane is buried in the churchyard at Brading. These stories were best-sellers in Victorian times, containing interesting descriptive accounts of Shanklin Chine and other beauty spots in the area, and "Annals of the Poor" can still be found on the shelves of the public libraries in the Island.

However, Legh Richmond was responsible for inventing something that churchgoers all over the country now take for granted, as is revealed in this contemporary quotation; "... at the front of the gallery (he) exhibits an ingenious contrivance of his, which by means of little sliding boards inscribed with letters and figures shows the congregation the psalms to be sung, and the versions".

This, then, was the legacy left by the Curate of Brading: a book based on members of his flock, which is still being read nearly 200 years after his death; and a hymn and psalm indicator which can be seen in churches of all denominations throughout Great Britain.

THREE HOURS TO NEWPORT

A journey from Yarmouth to Newport in the 1850s was a much more drawn-out affair than it is today. A coach and horses would depart from Yarmouth three times a week (it went to Freshwater on the other two weekdays) and the trip to Newport would take three hours each way!

The coach was drawn by a pair of horses and it was covered with canvas, with a ventilation system of flaps at each end, which could be raised or lowered according to the weather. There were wooden benches upholstered with leather for the comfort of the passengers, and the floor was covered with clean straw in the winter, and sweet smelling hay in the summer.

One of the reasons why the journey was a lengthy one was that the coach would stop at any point along the way to pick up passengers, since there were no regular "stops" as we know them, and also to pick up parcels to be delivered. Another reason was the number of gates along the way.

The road then ran through private land, and at each boundary of every field there was a gate to open to let the coach through, and to close afterwards. Hassell, on his driving tour of the Isle of Wight in 1790, found 52 gates between Yarmouth and Newport and consequently most private coaches in those days had a seat at the rear for the gate-boy, whose sole function was to open and close the gates.

There were redeeming features of the journey: the coach would always stop at three inns along the way to water the horses, and since the inns were open all day, the passengers presumably availed themselves of their hospitality as well. In addition, the fare for this six hour round trip was just one shilling return.

USELESS EUSTACE

The vineyard at Barton Manor is on the site of the model farm created by Prince Albert, when Barton was part of the Royal estate at Osborne. The farm however, has a much longer history than this, dating to Saxon times over 1000 years ago. Shortly after the Norman Conquest, when the fertile lands of the Isle of Wight had been distributed amongst the followers of William the Conqueror, the owner of the land caused Barton Oratory to be built as a place of worship and a place where prayers could be said for him and his family.

All such religious houses were forfeit, either at the suppression of alien priories in 1414 or with the dissolution of the monasteries by Henry VIII, and either became possessions of the Crown or were sold to private individuals. Thus it was that the owner of Barton Farm in the time of Charles I was one Eustace Mann.

Now these were troubled times, with the Civil War looming, and if the Crown fell and parliament took over the running of the country, then the price of belonging to "the common-wealth" might be the loss of land and possessions and this worried Eustace.

Clearly if his house and land were forfeit he could do nothing about it, but he did have a considerable sum of money salted away for a rainy day and the skies were becoming cloudy.

He decided to hide his money away until the political situation became more settled, and went and buried his fortune in Barton Wood. Eventually, the monarchy was restored and he went to collect his nest egg, but, sad to say, he had hidden his money so well that even he couldn't find it!

As far as is known, the cache of gold was never found, and rests today in a piece of woodland still known as "Money Coppice".

—————➤◦◀=————

NEWPORT'S FRENCH BLONDE

The Industrial Revolution which swept through Great Britain at the end of the eighteenth century hardly affected the Isle of Wight. The Island was prosperous in its own right and had a very favourable balance of payments, selling more goods than it bought, which was largely due to its positions as grocer, dairyman, and butcher for Nelson's navy, as well as a considerable merchant fleet.

"Manufactories" were a common sight on the mainland, following mechanisation of many traditional handcrafts such as spinning and weaving, yet in this time of social upheaval and mechanical innovation, the Isle of Wight was to see only one factory.

Freeman and Nunn began lace making by machine at their premises in London in 1811. Patterns for these operations were such a closely guarded secret and such was the degree of industrial spying in those days, that the firm decided to split up its operations and move half its machinery to Tewkesbury in Gloucestershire, and half to Newport in the Isle of Wight.

Broadlands, the actual building which housed the factory, can still be seen in Staplers Road, Newport, and is now the Island's office of the Department of Social Security.

At its peak, Freeman and Nunn's Lace Manufactory employed between 600 and 700 people, and produced lace of such fine quality that its patented lace known as "French Blonde" was once said to cost a pound weight of silver for every pound of lace.

CROMWELL'S CHURCH

The old church of St. Mary, West Cowes, was built in 1657 and served as a place of worship for 200 years, until it fell into disrepair and the decision was made to demolish it and build a new church. This was completed in 1867 and the foundation stone was laid by a local dignitary, Miss Ward of West Hill.

The Victorians were responsible for destroying a lot of our historic churches on the grounds that the old crumbling buildings should be taken down and elegant new ones put in their place.

Regrettable though this is, we should have more cause to regret the passing of the old St. Mary's Church in Cowes than any of the rest. Why? Because it was built in 1657 between the time of Charles I and the restoration of the monarchy by Charles II and it is believed to have been the only church to have been built during the Protectorate of Cromwell.

THE FIRST WORKHOUSE

The Island's "House of Industry" was established in 1770 by the gentlemen of the Island for the "reception of the poor, and ease of the poor rates". Before this time each parish was responsible for taking care of its own poor, and it was decided that a central poor-house would spread the burden of caring for the poor evenly across the whole Island.

Having decided to build this institution, an agreement was made with the Crown to lease 80 acres of His Majesty's forest at Parkhurst on a 999 year lease at an annual rent of £8.17.9 $^1/_2$d a year!

The building, when completed, consisted of workshops, a master-weaver's room, spinning room and tailor's shop, a shoemaker's shop, dairy, brewhouse, washhouse, laundry, woodhouse and store-rooms. The idea was to give inmates work to do so that they could earn a living rather than rely upon charity, and by 1781 the House of Industry was manufacturing sacks for corn, flour and biscuits (no doubt to help the British Fleet which anchored off the Island), and stockings for the inmates. In addition, there were school rooms, sick-wards and a chapel.

The average number of residents was between 500 and 600, and a sample breakdown of 550 in the late 18th century is given below:

64	Men
136	Women
84	Girls (9 and over)
95	Girls (under 9)
55	Boys (9 and over)
116	Boys (under 9)

The House of Industry at Parkhurst, or Forest House as it became known locally, was a blueprint for numerous schemes all over the country, and was actually the first workhouse in Great Britain.

THE BUGLE

Inn signs give a fascinating insight into the history and traditions of the area in which they appear. The Stag at Parkhurst reveals that the forest at Avington, later known as Parkhurst Forest, was a renowned area for hunting; the Sportman's Rest at Porchfield, The Hare and Hounds at Arreton, and the Falcon Inn at Ryde reflect the same sporting interest.

Clearly, being an agricultural neighbourhood, the Island had its share of pubs with names associated with farming, such as the Wheatsheaf at Newport, the Barley Mow at Shide, and the White Horse at Whitwell. In addition, with Queen Victoria's choice of Osborne as a holiday home, there were numerous pubs and inns named after her and her family: the Prince Regent and the Victoria at Cowes, the Victoria at East Cowes and the Prince of Wales opposite the gates of Osborne House, the Prince Regent and the Victoria in Newport, and the Prince of Wales and Prince Albert in Ventnor, several of which are no longer with us.

There are pubs which have names associated with the defence of the Island such as the Battery at Seaview, and the Volunteer in Ventnor, but one inn sign appears more in the Isle of Wight than in any other area.

There were at one time at least five inns named "The Bugle" on the Island. The one in Ryde was demolished in 1827, the Bugle at Carisbrooke is no longer there, and the building which housed the Bugle Hotel in Newport is now a shop and office development, but there still remain two pubs called "The Bugle", at Brading and Yarmouth. The inn sign usually shows a military bugle or bull's horn and this gives a clue to the name.

The reason why there were more pubs of this name in the Isle of Wight than any other area is because a "bugle" was the local name for a type of wild bull found in the Island, and the bugle horn is a symbol for this beast which at one time was a well known Island breed.

RYDE TRAMWAY

Ryde Pier was opened in 1814 and at that time visitors to the town disembarked from their vessels at the pier head, with a coach and horse waiting to take them along the pier to the esplanade. The growth of tourism was such during the early Victorian era that, by the mid nineteenth century, there were ten steamers a day arriving at Ryde from Portsmouth and it was necessary to find a means of transporting numbers of people from the pier head to the esplanade en masse.

In 1864 a separate pier was constructed alongside the existing one to contain a tramway (named after James Outram, who had introduced the system in the Yorkshire Collieries) which could transport people along the pier in coaches.

A steam locomotive "The Vectis" was given extensive trials on the new tramway but was found to create a disturbing amount of vibration and the service was eventually opened using a horse-drawn tram. There were some curious features of the new tramway, not least of which was that in the Strand area of Ryde it went straight through a large building called Holywell House! The house is now known as Harcourt flats, and the archway through the right hand end of the building has been filled in, but it is still possible to see the route of the original tramway.

The most important development in the history of Ryde tramway was when the system was electrified in 1886. It then became one of the first electric railways in the world, even pre-dating the London Underground by some years.

With tramways closing all over the country, the Ryde system stood little chance of remaining in operation, particularly in competition with a rail/bus network that covered not just Ryde but the whole Island, and in 1969 the last tram trundled along the pier, the last journey for one of the first electric passenger-carrying services in Great Britain.

THE NEWTOWN MACE

Newtown's history goes back as far as 1254, when it was known as Novum Burgum de Franchville, meaning Free Town. The name "Newtown" came into being in the mid 1300s, possibly after the destruction of the town by French raiders, but the names "Newtown" and "Franchville" were used side by side for the next 300 years.

John Churchill was the Member of Parliament for Newtown in 1678, and he went on to become the famous Duke of Marlborough, remembered in the names of many streets and buildings in the Isle of Wight.

The town later became important for its salterns, where salt was produced and exported to the mainland, and for its oyster fisheries; in addition in 1840 Newtown was regarded as one of the best harbours in the Island and was a safe anchorage for vessels of up to 500 tonnes.

Indeed, the town seal depicted an ancient one-masted vessel on the sea, with the sail furled and a pennant flying. The other details were a lion on the ship, and on the right, above the sail, a mullet. On the left was a crescent, with an escutcheon of St. George below the sail, and round the sail, the words:
S:COMITAS:DE:FRANCHVILLE:DE:LILE:DE:WHYT.

In the town hall, built in 1699, there existed the town mace which bore the seal of Edward IV, and in 1855 the British Archaeological Society visited Newtown and assembled at the Town Hall in order to study the town's regalia. While they were examining the town mace the seal fell out and it was found to have the seal of Edward IV on one side, and that of Oliver Cromwell's "Commonwealth" on the reverse.

This is curious since the seal must have been reversed in order to engrave the commonwealth emblem on it, then turned again on the restoration of the monarchy, to show the original motif.

The irony of this is told in the words of the first edition of the Post Office Directory for the Island in 1871: "(it was) ... either for economical considerations,...or a presentiment that the sway of the commonwealth would not endure".

———⇒►◦◄⇐———

ALUM BAY SANDS

The visitor to the Isle of Wight soon becomes aware of the coloured sand found in the cliffs at Alum Bay, even if he has not been to the Needles to view them himself from the chair lift or the beach. Almost every gift shop from one end of the Island to the other displays a range of sand pictures using the different coloured sands to form a picture, and numerous clear glass containers of various shapes filled with the strata of the Island's natural colours. However few visitors realise that the sands of Alum Bay once had a national, rather than a local, importance.

The bay takes its name from the amount of natural alum that used to be found on the beach, which was gathered and exported in a small way to chemical works. Attention soon turned from the relatively minor importance of the alum to the commercial potential of sand found in the area, which by 1842 was described as "the finest sand in the kingdom".

In the early 1800s the sand was quarried at Alum Bay and taken by horse and cart to the sand house on the quay at Yarmouth. There it was loaded into coastal schooners, which carried 200 tonnes each and taken to Runcorn to make plate glass.

Perhaps even more incredible is the fact that the fine white sand from the bay, which proved the best for the manufacture of porcelain, was taken by ship to the porcelain factories of London, Bristol, Worcester, and even the West Indies.

This trade was at its height in the mid 1800s, until the Great Exhibition in 1851. Amongst the exhibitors at this world trade fair were French sand merchants who showed their product to the glass and porcelain makers, and Alum Bay was deserted in favour of the finer quality French sand.

The decorative use of sand had not been overlooked, and even in 1839 we find the author Barber saying, "various ornaments for the mantel-piece are made from these coloured sands using phials and bottles", and fortunately we are still able to enjoy the coloured sands of Alum Bay to this day.

BLACKGANG

The southern tip of the Isle of Wight, from Chale round St.Catherine's Point to Shanklin, is well known for the landslips which have occurred in the past two hundred years. Between layers of sandstone there exists a strata of blue slipper clay, or gault, and this has caused massive landfalls when the pressure above the clay has become too much for it to bear, giving this part of the Island its dramatic craggy scenery. There were landslips at Bonchurch in 1810 and 1818, but probably the most significant was that at Chale in 1799, which created the giant fissure we know as Blackgang Chine.

The Dabell family had brought the Flemish lace-making industry from France to the East Midlands of England in 1633, and two hundred years later one of their descendants, Alexander Dabell, had come to the Island from Nottingham to join the growing lace industry in Newport. However, in 1843 he decided to establish himself in business, and bought Blackgang Chine from the owner of the Blackgang Hotel. The agreement was that Mr. Dabell should acquire all the land within the distance of a stone's throw from where he stood, and in this way he became the owner of a tract of land, a shepherd's hut and the Chine itself.

Alexander Dabell constructed the pathway through the Chine to allow visitors to view the awe-inspiring scenery of the "Back of the Wight", and he was no doubt inspired in this by the idea of Mr. Colenutt, who had opened Shanklin Chine to the public some years earlier. At Blackgang there was no admission charge to the Chine, but visitors had to pass through the bazaar and were expected to make a small token purchase there to help defray expenses.

By 1879 the Dabell family had acquired several interests in the area: Alexander owned the Chine and Blackgang Bazaar: Charles was the local butcher and dairyman, George was the manager of the Blackgang Hotel and the only other hotel in the district, The Clarendon, was managed by Miss Dabell.

The family is still connected to the Chine to this day, but nowadays there are more man-made amusements to supplement the scenic views which were so popular a century ago. The bazaar is still there to tempt visitors to take away souvenirs, and the Chine is a well known attraction on the Island, all thanks to the landslip of 1799 and the foresight of Alexander Dabell.

HOLY STONES

The Saxon name for St. Helens was Eddington, which means Eadwine's Farm; the Doomsday Book refers to it as Etharin, and in 1270 it was known as Hertham, so why do we call it St. Helens?

A priory was founded here about the year 1100 and in the fourteenth century a church was built which was dedicated to St. Helena, the village taking its name from the patron saint of the church.

The original church was built on the Duver (pronounced Duvver) which is a local name for a stretch of sand by the sea; we find the same name in Ryde, where the Duver gave its name to one of the principal roads, Dover Street.

St. Helens was destined to become the meeting place of the British navy; vessels would assemble in the sheltered anchorage off the coast known as St. Helens Roads, and Henry VIII's navy used St. Helens as an anchorage where the ships could be supplied with fresh meat, milk, eggs and beer, and could also take on barrels of the local water, which had the reputation of being able to travel to the West Indies and back and remain as sweet as the day it was collected.

The old church at St. Helens had been built on the sandy Duver and within a couple of centuries the sea had advanced across the sand and caused the building to become unstable. However, the church still had its uses although not as a place of worship; the tower of the church was later reinforced and used as a sea-mark for vessels heading for a safe anchorage in St. Helens Roads.

In addition, the stones from the ruined church were found to be ideal for the sailor's task of scrubbing the wooden decks of the ships, and the expression "holystoning the decks" persists to this day, commemorating the crumbling masonry of St. Helens Church.

⎯⎯⎯⎯⎯≫-◦-≪⎯⎯⎯⎯⎯

THE CASTLE WELL

Carisbrooke Castle was probably the central fortress of the Romans when they occupied the Isle of Wight; certainly, after the Normans had established themselves here, the Castle was the seat of government and the refuge for the rulers of the Island in the event of a siege. The most essential thing for a besieged garrison was a supply of fresh water and for this reason a well was sunk as early as 1100.

Carisbrooke Castle continued its role as a stronghold for several hundred years and in 1587 the well house and wheel were rebuilt, the wheel being 15.5 feet in diameter, and the depth of the well 161 feet. It is not known who walked the treadmill in the early days, possibly the soldiers who were stationed there, but for the past 150 years water has been drawn up from the well by means of donkeys working the wheel, a method which may well be unique in Britain.

These donkeys have acquired a reputation for longevity and long service, several of them having worked for 26 years in the castle. One old veteran achieved 40 years of service, and may well have continued had he not fallen to his death from the ramparts, but even he was superseded by a donkey that died in 1771 after 47 years work in the castle.

The most unusual donkey to work the huge wheel was one who lived during the time of the Duke of Gloucester, uncle to George III. The old Duke was most impressed with the animal and the task it performed, and decided to award it a pension! The donkey was to receive an annuity of a penny loaf a day as long as it lived and apparently went on to enjoy its "daily bread" from its Royal patron for several years.

17

As a footnote, there is a fine example of local decorative brickmaking to be seen set in a wall in Church Litten, in Newport, in the form of a tableau depicting the well-house at Carisbrooke Castle and one of its celebrated donkeys.

THE AGE OF STEAM

The Isle of Wight was in the right place at the right time during the golden age of steam. During the early 1800s the railway system was expanding in all directions from London, enabling people to travel easily to the coast, and steamers enabled the general public to travel across the Solent to reach England's "Garden Isle". It was unique in the south of England as a health resort, recommended by the most eminent doctors in the land and, to cap it all, Queen Victoria decided in 1845 to have her country residence on the Island.

The opening of the London and South Western Railway in 1840 meant people could travel from London to Southampton in three hours, followed by a one hour trip across the water to Cowes and, as one writer observed at the time, "an influx of visitors will, doubtless, constantly arrive". We tend to think of regular travel services as a modern innovation, yet in 1840 six steamers a day made the crossing from Southampton to Cowes and back and three more left Cowes for Portsmouth, calling at Ryde en route.

Steam powered vessels reached their peak at this time, and from the crowded port of Cowes, nearly 150 years ago you could travel almost anywhere. Every Monday, Wednesday and Friday a steamer left for Poole and on the same days another left for Yarmouth and Lymington. There was a twice weekly service to Plymouth and another to Weymouth, which on its return went on to London; even the London to Dublin steamer called at Cowes to pick up passengers and goods!

Ryde also offered a regular service to the mainland, docking at Portsmouth, and also a once weekly trip to Brighton. It is interesting to note that in 1834 the return fare from Ryde to Portsmouth was 1 shilling and sixpence (7 $\frac{1}{2}$p) for a place on the quarterdeck and 1 shilling (5p) for the fo'csle; the price was still the same in 1851 and was actually maintained until 1880.

The distinction of providing the first passenger service round the Island must go to Cowes. Local landowner and businessman George Ward started the Cowes to Southampton steam packet service in 1820 and by 1842 was advertising the first-ever round the Island trip. The time needed to make the voyage was six to seven hours and the fare for this day out – just 5 shillings (25p).

THE SALT POT

When the Isle of Wight was originally split up into manors in the eleventh century, care was taken that each manor, however far inland, should have at least one piece of land which bordered on the sea, so that it could claim ownership of anything washed up on its shores, which was known as "wreck of the sea". This accounts in part for the fact that both Ryde and Ventnor were once in the parish of Newchurch, even as late as 1866.

Whoever had the rights to the wreck of the sea from Chale Bay was sitting pretty, due to a combination of the prevailing southwesterly winds and the Atherfield Ledge (a treacherous bank of rocks to the south-east of the bay). In 1314 the "St. Mary", a ship of Bayonne laden with 174 tuns (barrels) of wine from the Duchy of Aquitaine, was wrecked on the Atherfield Ledge. The crew were saved but the ship was lost and its cargo was washed ashore, being duly claimed by the Lord of the Manor, Walter de Godeton.

Walter was no doubt very pleased with his catch until he found out that the wine actually belonged to the Monastery of Livers in Picardy. He was charged by the church with having unlawfully seized the wine and fined 227 $\frac{1}{2}$ marks (just over £150 – a king's ransom in those days). To add to his troubles he was threatened with excommunication for having taken wine belonging to the Church, but could redeem himself if he built an oratory on top of St. Catherine's Hill.

The tower he built stood 35 feet 6 inches high, was octagonal on the outside and had four sides within, and a succession of solitary monks lived there in piety until the reign of Henry VIII, preserving a light to warn ships of the rocks below, making this the country's third oldest (though not very effective) lighthouse.

The Salt Pot, as it is still known locally, was restored by Sir Richard Worsley and still stands alone on the summit of St. Catherine's Hill as a memorial to Walter de Godeton and the power of the Church in Medieval England.

———►·0·◄———

FROM FLYING BOAT TO HOVERCRAFT

The boatbuilding firm of S. E. Saunders was founded in the 1830s at Streatley-on-Thames and in 1901 moved to a boatyard at Cowes in the Isle of Wight. This was the dawn of the age of flying and in 1913 the company began a joint project with Sopwith Aviation of Kingston-upon-Thames to produce a boat that could fly.

The structure of the craft was made at Kingston and the hull, constructed of Saunders' patented "Consuta" material of plywood stitched together with copper wire, was built at Cowes.

The craft, constructed using traditional boatbuilder's skills, became known as the "Bat Boat" after Rudyard Kipling's visionary thought of a motor boat with wings, and was exhibited at the Olympia Aero Show in 1913.

Winston Churchill, as First Lord of the Admiralty, was keen to promote naval aviation and flew in the Bat Boat, which later took part in a sponsored competition at Hamble to find a practical amphibian aircraft.

The official observer was Lieutenant Spenser Grey of the RNAS Station at Calshot, who found he could operate the retractable wheels by means of a well aimed kick! One of Saunders' competitors on the Hamble called his own flying boat an "aerial yacht", but the Bat Boat was primarily a military aircraft, going on to develop bombing techniques in the years leading up to the First World War.

In 1947 the company, then Saunders-Roe, continued its military role by producing the world's first fighter flying boat and in 1958 work began on Sir Christopher Cockerell's invention of the hovercraft....still, in a sense, "a boat that flies".

20

The prototype SRN 1 Hovercraft was built in 1959, the year that Westland Aircraft took over the company, and in 1962 came the SRN 2, the world's first all metal hovercraft.

In August of that year the SRN2 made an eleven day trial run carrying fare paying passengers between Ryde and Southsea, thus becoming the first commercially operated hovercraft in the world.

━━━►►◦◄◄━━━

THE ALEXANDRIAN PILLAR

Visitors to the south of the Island will see, on the summit of St. Catherine's Down, two landmarks that can be seen from some miles away. One is the ancient lighthouse, the story of which is told elsewhere in this book; the other is the Hoy Memorial, or Alexandrian Pillar.

Michael Hoy was a merchant and businessman who had spent many years in Russia, and in the early nineteenth century was living at The Hermitage, in the lee of St. Catherine's Down. The pillar he erected on top of the down in 1814 is 72 feet high and surmounted by a ball. It has stood for 180 years and has managed to escape the fate of other monuments on the Island; the old oratory nearby on St. Catherine's Down eventually fell down, and the Worsley memorial on Stenbury Down was reduced in size when it was struck by lightning.

The Alexandrian Pillar still stands, but what does it stand for? The inscription at the base of the column explains its purpose. "In commemoration of the visit of his Imperial Majesty Alexander I, Emperor of all the Russians, to Great Britain in the year 1814 and in remembrance of many happy years of residence in his dominions, this pillar was erected by Michael Hoy".

Unfortunately, relations between the two countries deteriorated to the extent that Britain declared war on Russia on March 28th 1854, the beginning of the Crimean War. It is ironic that on the south face of the memorial which celebrates the visit of the Emperor of all the Russias in 1814, there is a tablet in memory of the British soldiers who died in the Crimea just forty years later, fighting against the army of the Czar.

━━━►►◦◄◄━━━

THE SALE OF THE ISLAND

Vespasian and the 2nd Roman Legion conquered the Isle of Wight in 43AD after overcoming southern Britain and establishing bases in Wessex. Surprisingly, no central control of the Island was set up, except for possession of the fort at Carisbrooke; perhaps this was all that was needed in Roman times.

Indeed after the Romans left some 400 years later, the Saxons, Jutes and Danes who invaded the Island and plundered its wealth made no move to establish a governing body – they simply used it as a convenient point from which to launch raids on the adjacent English mainland and to provide their raiding parties with the necessities of life.

However, in 1066 William the Conqueror presented the rich and fertile lands of the Isle of Wight to William Fitz-Osborn, who had been his principal military adviser and Marshal of his army at Hastings. A central administration was set up and for over 200 years the Island had Norman "Lords of the Isle of Wight" who ruled their domain, almost as an independent kingdom, from the seat of government at Carisbrooke Castle. The last of the Norman rulers was Isabella de Fortibus, Countess of Albermarle and Lady of Wight, who held court at Carisbrooke from 1262 to 1293. During this time the English King made several approaches to Isabella with a view to buying the Island from her, but each was turned down.

In 1293, during the reign of Edward I, Isabella went to her palace at Stockwell, south of London, and the King heard that she was on her death-bed. He promptly sent the Bishops of Durham and Coventry to Stockwell in order to persuade her to sign a sale agreement, which she did the day before she died.

A sum of money was duly paid to a group of merchant bankers in the wool manufacturing town of Spene, near Newbury, and the agreement was "The Conveyance of Lordship and Lands in the Isle of Wight" for the sum of 6,000 marks, and this was how the King of England acquired the Island for a sum which was the equivalent of just £4,000.

<hr />

PALMERSTON'S FOLLIES

Napoleon III became Emperor of France in 1851 and this gave rise to a fear that the French would invade England. Despite the fact that there had been no French incursions into English territory for nearly 300 years, this threat was taken seriously and when Lord Palmerston became Prime Minister in 1859, he started an extensive defence programme.

It was thought that any invasion would have to cross the Channel and pass by the Isle of Wight, so existing defences were strengthened, and new ones built to protect the Needles Passage at the western end, and Spithead to the east.

Eight forts and batteries existed to cover the Needles Passage, including Fort Warden (now a country park), Golden Hill Fort and Fort Victoria, which are open to the public. The garrison at Freshwater was linked by the newly built Military Road to the large barracks at Niton, and movement of troops along this road would protect the south-west coast of the Island from direct attack. The barracks at Niton no longer exist, but there is a reminder of them in the road name, "Barrack Shute".

Battery Gardens in Sandown marks the site of Sandham Fort built by Henry VIII, and later rebuilt by Charles I, but Palmerston had the new Sandown fort built in the Yaverland area of Sandown Bay where it still stands today, giving its name to Fort Street and the former Fort Tavern, now known as Caulkheads. In addition, there are five other batteries and gun positions covering the south east coast of the Island. The original plan was to continue the Military Road from Niton to Sandown, but this extension never materialised.

Five gun batteries covered the Spithead approach, one of these being remembered in the name of the Battery pub at Seaview, and this was the extent of the land based defences.

In addition to these, a number of forts were constructed which stood on the seabed, including St. Helens Fort and No Mans Land Fort, which is remarkable for it's 570 feet deep well from which is drawn fresh water. These forts, which can still be seen today, were known as "Palmerston's Pups", possibly from the expression "to buy a pup", i.e. to make a mistake.

Certainly the people of Palmerston's time felt that he had protected them against a threat of invasion which had not existed and christened his extensive defences in the Isle of Wight "Palmerston's Follies".

SIR ROBERT HOLMES

Robert Holmes was born in Ireland and made his reputation as a seafaring man. In 1661, as Admiral Sir Robert Holmes, he was sent to Guinea in West Africa to deal with the Dutch who had seized British gold mines there. He successfully defeated the intruders and brought back to England a large quantity of gold, which was minted into coins worth 21 shillings. These coins were soon christened "guineas" after their country of origin.

Hearsay evidence suggests that three years later he was off again, this time to the American colonies where his old foes, the Dutch, had assumed control over one of the major towns on the eastern seaboard. Apparently Holmes ousted the lowlanders from the town they had christened New Amsterdam and the name was soon changed to New York.

Unfortunately, although this delightful story fits in with Holmes' swashbuckling image, it is not true. In fact, he was back in West Africa at the time. Sir Robert served a token sentence in the Tower on his return, as a result of a Dutch protest that he had been none too gentle with their citizens in Africa, but Charles II was obviously pleased with him as he appointed him Governor of the Isle of Wight.

Sir Robert Holmes lived for almost thirty years on the Island and while he was here he became virtually a licensed pirate. He had a roving commission to patrol the shores of southern England and to capture, destroy or plunder any foreign ships which approached our coasts. On one occasion he captured a ship on its way from Italy to the French Court and laid claim to all the goods it was carrying.

The biggest prize on this ship was an unfinished statue in white marble of the French King, Louis XIV. The sculptor had been allowed to complete the statue from the neck down from a portrait, but the King insisted that his features were sculpted from life in order to obtain a perfect likeness. Sir Robert took a fancy to this statue and was fortunate enough to have captured the sculptor as well. He decided that the statue would be completed, but since it was now his, the head on the statue would not be of King Louis, but his own!

The Italian sculptor chipped away for some time, and sure enough Sir Robert's features appeared instead of those of Louis XIV. If you go to Yarmouth Church you will see a large white marble statue, which is clothed in the full regalia of the King of France, yet has the face of the roguish Sir Robert, and could it be that there is still a hint of a smile on his face which has lasted for three hundred years?

APPULDURCOMBE HOUSE

Appuldurcombe House stands as a roofless ruin near Wroxall, (although it has undergone extensive renovation of the 1701 South front), protected from the prevailing south westerly winds by Stenbury Down, itself crowned by a ruined memorial to the Worsley family. The Worsleys owned Appuldurcombe for centuries but its history goes back many years before the family acquired the ancient house.

The Saxons called this area Apuldor-cumb (the valley of the apple trees) and this accounts for the local pronunciation of the name – Applercombe; shortly after the Norman conquest this orchard in a valley was given to the Abbey of Montebourg in Normandy, and the first task of the monks who lived here was to build the Priory of Appuldurcombe.

The monks lived and worked there for 300 years until the suppression of alien priories by Henry V, of Agincourt fame, whence the land was leased to the Fry family and eventually passed into the hands of the Worsleys.

In 1710 the priory, along with the old house which stood on the site, was demolished and the building of the new Appuldurcombe House began, the task finally being completed in 1773. An obelisk commemorating the Worsley family was built of Cornish granite at the top of Stenbury Down in 1774. This was struck by lightning in 1831 and reduced to its present size.

The completed house had several distinguishing features, from its entrance near Godshill via the Freemantle Gate (which can still be seen today, a couple of fields away from the house) to the gardens laid out by Capability Brown, and stocked with deer. One curious fact remains: the house contained 365 windows to correspond with the number of days in the year; there were 52 rooms as there are 52 weeks of the year, and the number of staircases was seven, the number of days in the week.

THE ISLAND'S KING

Following the sale of the Isle of Wight to the Crown in 1293, the administration of the Island was still in the hands of the "Lords of the Isle of Wight", although these did not have the absolute power of the Norman rulers.

Henry VI became King of England in the early fifteenth century, but for years the country was ruled on his behalf by a regent, until he became old enough to take command. The expression "wisdom comes with age" may not have applied in Henry's case, but when he took over the helm he decided to do some king-making of his own and during the time when Humphrey Duke of Gloucester was Lord of the Island, he decided to create a King of the Isle of Wight.

His choice fell upon Henry Beauchamp, the 21 year old Duke of Warwick, who was the son of Richard, Earl of Warwick, the former Regent of France. In 1444 Beauchamp was duly crowned King of the Isle of Wight by the King's own hand, but was King in name only, having no power to accompany his title.

During his short life he collected more titles, became the premier Earl of England, Duke of Warwick, and was granted Bristol Castle. On top of this, his kingdom in the Channel was extended to include the islands of Jersey and Guernsey, but he was not to enjoy his reign for long.

A feeble man, both in mind and body, his life came to an end at the age of 22 at his castle in Henley, Worcestershire. He was buried in the church of the Monastery of Tewkesbury in 1445, the first (and last) King of the Isle of Wight.

———◦———

GEORGE MORLAND IN YARMOUTH

George Morland was a well known artist in the late eighteenth century, specialising mainly in animal paintings and scenes of country life. He was sufficiently important to have a painting hung in the National Gallery, but led a dissolute life which caused him to be almost permanently in debt. It was this that caused him to come to the Island.

In 1799 Morland stayed at a house in Cowes belonging to a London surgeon named Lynn, but when his creditors followed him there he fled to Yarmouth and lodged at the house of a well known local smuggler whose name was George Cole, afterwards moving on to the George Inn where he befriended the landlord, Mr. Plumbley.

A description of his breakfast at the George is well worth recording. This consisted of a beefsteak, accompanied by a drink known as purl, which was a mixture of hot strong ale, gin, spices and sugar.

One day, after enjoying such a meal, Morland was sitting in the Square at Yarmouth idly sketching the castle, when he found himself arrested by General Don, the Commander of the District. He was marched from Yarmouth to Newport by a lieutenant and eight soldiers of the Dorset Militia and, after being jeered and insulted by the local people along the way, arrived confused and exhausted at Newport.

He was brought before the court and evidence was produced in the shape of an unfinished sketch of a spaniel which Morland had in his possession when he was arrested and which the prosecutor assured the magistrates was a map of the Island. On top of that he been making a plan of Yarmouth Castle and there was no doubt that he was in fact a French spy!

Poor George must have felt he didn't have a friend in the world, but he reckoned without his landlord, Plumbley. In addition to his role as an innkeeper, Plumbley was also Captain of the Isle of Wight Volunteers, also known as the Isle of Wight Fencibles, and on hearing of Morland's plight he rode full tilt from Yarmouth to Newport.

Local legend had endowed the journey with a charisma almost akin to Turpin's ride to York. Realising there was no time to lose, Plumbley apparently jumped all the 50 or so fences between Yarmouth and Newport and arrived breathless at the court in time to secure Morland's release.

After hearing Plumbley's evidence, the magistrates decided to release Morland, but only after they had cautioned him and instructed him not to do any more sketching while on the Island!

━━━►○◄━━━

SEA BATHING

The Victorians revelled in the delights of bathing in the sea at their favourite holiday resorts of Cowes, Ryde, Sandown, Shanklin and Ventnor and each town boasted not only bathing in the open sea, but also hot and cold sea-water baths near the beach. However, the novel idea of immersing the body in salt water had begun before the Victorian era.

As early as 1824 Cowes had offered fashionable walks along the newly constructed Parade, and also several bathing machines in which to undress and enter the sea in privacy, although because of the steep descent from the promenade to the sea, the machines had to be lowered by means of a windlass until they reached the water.

In the same year, Ryde was said to have fine white sand, extremely pleasant when bathing, and several well attended machines. The bathing machines at Ryde were of the more conventional sort, virtually a cart which would be wheeled down to the beach and into the sea so that the occupants could then take to the water. Some of these machines were fitted with a canopy at the seaward end known as a modesty hood, so that ladies could enter the sea from the machine without being seen.

Ventnor, Shanklin and Sandown soon followed the trend, so that by the mid 1800s every popular beach had its collection of bathing machines and even Victoria herself enjoyed the new fad of sea bathing from her private beach at Osborne, although was said not to be amused when on one occasion the water covered her head.

The bathing machine with its modesty hood was typical of the Victorians' desire for public privacy and the preservation of dignity and decorum. They even went so far as to introduce a rule that ladies should bathe at one end of the beach and gentlemen at the other and that no bather should approach within 50 yards of a bather of the opposite sex!

ST. JAMES'S DAY

Yarmouth Church is dedicated to St. James and the town is thought to be unique in the country for celebrating St. James' Day, 25th July.

Sadly the tradition seems to have declined, but there were fairs on St. James' Day from the Middle Ages to the early part of the last century, giving the townspeople an opportunity to have a day off and let their hair down.

In addition, two courts were held on 25th July to settle the town's affairs: one was the Court Leet, which will be referred to elsewhere, and the other was the Court de Pie Poudre, a corruption of the French "Pieds Poudreux" meaning "dusty feet", and referring to tramps or wayfarers. The Court of Pie Poudre was held in Yarmouth from 1609 to the early eighteenth century, and the mayor presided over it, settling disputes and minor troubles and dealing with any problems with wayfarers and travelling folk.

The annual St. James' Day Fair was a time of great celebration for the local people; a time to dress up in their finery, to indulge in games and pastimes, examine the wares of the various pedlars and to eat, drink and be merry. The day was a full one and a long one, with plenty of revelry, and nobody really minded if you overstepped the mark and drank a little too much.

There was a quaint custom which died out some 100 years ago, of hanging a pole outside the town hall with a stuffed glove on the end. This was the symbol of an open hand, signifying that on that one day the authorities would not be too strict on minor breaches of the law and you had an "open hand" to behave in any way you pleased.

THE FIRST CARNIVAL

Street carnivals are now common all over the country and most cities, towns, and even villages have a day set aside each year (often a Bank Holiday) when the local people dress up in costume and deck their lorries and tractors as colourful floats which parade through the streets. In a way, this replaces the old country fairs, which provided an opportunity for the local people to have a get-together and display themselves in their finery. However, to the Isle of Wight must go the distinction of holding the first street carnival.

One of the reasons is that the Island was the holiday home of Queen Victoria and a favourite resort of fashionable Victorians; indeed, with Brighton and Torquay it was one of the first holiday resorts in Britain and all the more popular for being an island.

Ventnor developed in popularity through the nineteenth century, and held its own carnival in 1889, a tradition that has carried on to the present day, with the exception of the war years. It was pipped at the post by the bustling town of Ryde, which in the mid 1880s organised the very first street carnival in the country, the forerunner of the many hundreds which exist today.

A LAMB FOR A HARE

The Isle of Wight has long been famous for its wildlife; naturalists have come here because of the variety of wild plants, insects, and animals, and it has been the hunting ground of the rich, the famous and the royal. Charles I hunted deer in the Royal forest of Parkhurst, and Henry VIII visited the Island to follow his favourite sport of hawking; indeed, Henry had written to the Worsleys of Appuldurcombe and instructed them to ensure that nobody poached "fesant or partriche" from their estate and to punish any offenders.

On the death of Richard Worsley in 1565, Sir Edward Horsey became Captain of the Isle of Wight. Sir Edward was a seafaring man from an old Dorset family, who rose to fame when he rid the Channel of French ships "with which it had been much infested".

In common with the rest of the Elizabethan notability he was very keen on hawking and hunting and it came to his notice that the Island had "infinite of coneys (rabbits), but not one hare".

Feeling the need to remedy this in 1574 he offered a young lamb in exchange for every hare fit for breeding and such was the response, that he was able to stock the Isle of Wight with hares for the first time.

The species has survived for over 300 years, providing sport for its human hunters and food for its natural enemy, the fox. To this day the descendants of Sir Edward Horsey's hares can be seen in the fields and lanes of the Island.

═══►•◄═══

THE SHALFLEET GUN AND BELLS

With the construction of the "Mary Rose", Henry VIII had effectively laid the foundations for the Royal Navy; the Service which would grow to become the protector of Britain's interests all over the world. But it would be some years before Britannia ruled the waves and the people of southern England, and particularly the Isle of Wight, were vulnerable to attack from their long-time enemies, the French.

The Island would have been an ideal base from which to launch a full scale attack on the nearby mainland and there had been several French invasions of the Island from 1340 to 1545. Therefore, in the sixteenth century every parish was issued with a brass cannon, which was kept in a small gun-house or underneath the church. Examples of these guns were found at Brighstone, Chale, Niton, Shorwell and Shalfleet and they were mainly one to six pounders, made in the reigns of Edward VI and Elizabeth I.

The gun carriage had to be provided by the parish, as did the ammunition, and local farmers provided the horses to pull the carriage; the local people were drilled in the use of the guns and, with frequent exercises, this sixteenth century "Dad's Army" became quite expert in aiming and firing the cannons.

The guns were never used against an enemy, possibly due to our supremacy at sea preventing troops being landed, and they eventually became redundant. In 1812, the people of Shalfleet wanted to build a steeple that was lacking from their church, and despite renewed fears of a French invasion of the Island, decided to sell the village gun. Finding that they were still short of the required amount of money, they also sold the bells that would have rung from the steeple!

This gave rise to a local saying:

"Shalfleet poor and simple people,
Sold the bells to build the steeple".

WINDMILLS AND WATERMILLS

The Isle of Wight was once the centre of a worldwide trade in flour which was distributed through its trading ports of Newport and Cowes. At one time there were 38 watermills and 7 windmills in the Island, all grinding corn to be used by the Royal Navy (which picked up all its supplies on the Island), the merchant fleet and the convict ships which made the Isle of Wight their last port of call before their long voyage to the Colonies. In addition flour was exported to London and many ports in the Channel, sometimes using corn imported from as far away as Devon when even the rich fields of the Island could not cope with the demand.

There is only one remaining example of an Island windmill and that is the one at Bembridge which is maintained by the National Trust; these mills were never very popular despite the advantage of sea breezes, since there was a plentiful supply of water power.

Watermills driven by natural springs, streams and rivulets tended to have a small capacity and existed mainly to supply local needs, such as flour to provide bread for the immediate neighbourhood. A fine example can still be seen in working order at Calbourne.

The third kind of mill is the tide mill, which supplied most of the Island's overseas trade, and for this reason it was usually sited at a port or on a tidal river. The principle of the tide mill was that the mill-pond would fill up as the tide rose and the water-wheel was driven as the tide fell and the pond emptied.

Sadly there are no working examples of this type of mill left on the Isle of Wight but some buildings are still to be found. The mill at Wootton Bridge has now been pulled down, but the Sloop Inn used to be the miller's house and the millpond can be seen on the opposite side of the road. The building which housed Yarmouth tide mill can still be seen, but of our greatest example there is now no trace.

In 1790 a Newport baker, William Porter, built the East Medina tide mill to supply his bakery in Newport, and a large export trade. The mill became known as one of the great tide mills of England, in conjunction with its counterpart on the west bank of the river.

Both mills supplied flour to provision the convict ships on their way to Australia, and with typical Isle of Wight impishness the one on the eastern side was christened by local people "Botany Bay Mill" and the western one was nicknamed "Port Jackson" after the former name for Sydney.

THE FERRY TO THE ISLE OF WIGHT

"The engine moans, the Captain groans
and it's all systems go,
But after fifteen minutes
You think you'll have to row
The seagulls carry nylon ropes
In case you need a tow
When you travel on the ferry
to the Isle of Wight"

(from the song "The Ferry to the Isle of Wight" by Tony Malo).

Many unkind things have been said about the ferry crossing to the Island from the adjacent mainland ports of Portsmouth, Southampton and Lymington, not the least of which is the fact that, mile for mile, it is possibly the most expensive sea crossing in the world. Travellers who are incensed at the cost of the journey may not be aware of the primitive travel arrangements which existed in years gone by.

The first crossings were by small, open-decked sailing vessels known as Portsmouth Wherries, or sea cabs, and these offered little comfort to passengers to and from the Island, particularly during heavy rain or when storms lashed the Island during the autumn.

The first attempt at providing shelter to the passengers was a tarpaulin strung across the deck to the stern of the boat, and this must have afforded some protection, at least from the rain.

By 1840, six steamers a day left Southampton for Cowes and there were comparable "sailings" serving the Ryde to Portsmouth route, with prices at this time of one shilling for a place on the fo'csle and two shillings for the best cabins. These ships were all passenger ferries as we know them, but they did incorporate a rather curious means of a vehicle ferry.

For a price of £1 for a four wheel carriage, and half of that for a two-wheeler, coaches and their horses (at an additional rate of 5 shillings each) would be towed in a barge behind the steamer. When the steamer neared its destination, the barge would be cast off and brought to shore or pierhead on the tide, with additional help from a man in the stern with a pole.

If this method of ferrying vehicles seems to belong to a bygone age, it is a sobering thought that carriages and horses, and eventually motor cars, were still carried in this way between Portsmouth and Ryde as recently as 1927, and the service continued on the Lymington to Yarmouth route until the year 1937.

THE NEEDLES

Although the name "Wight" is derived from an Old English word meaning "rising from the sea", the Island was once joined to the mainland by a chalk ridge which existed between Freshwater and Studland in Dorset.

About 5000 B.C. this ridge was breached by the sea and, through erosion and the sinking of the bed of the Solent River, an island was created. Over the centuries, this left a jagged ridge of chalk at each end of the breach; at Swanage we have the Old Harry Rocks and at Freshwater we have the Needles.

These rocks have always been a hazard to shipping, particularly sailing ships trying to round the Island while being driven by a south westerly gale, but it was 1785 before the first lighthouse was built, and even then it was erected on top of the cliffs 715 feet above sea level!

Fortunately a new lighthouse was constructed in 1859 on the outermost rock, which warns all shipping of the dangerous coastline.

But the question remains "why the Needles?" One Victorian linguist decided that it was a corruption of the German "Nieder fels – under the cliff" yet although we have absorbed words from the Gauls, Saxons, Danes and French who have invaded us during our history, the Isle of Wight shows no sign of any German speaking invaders from whom we could have learnt the phrase.

The answer is clear: there used to be a Needle Rock, a conical pillar of chalk standing 120 feet high, and known to mariners as "Lot's Wife" which gives its name to the Needle Rocks.

This pillar was undermined by the waves and finally fell into the sea during a storm in 1764 with a crash that could be heard in Portsmouth, leaving us with no reminder of "Lots Wife" except the name, "The Needles".

<hr/>

A TAILOR'S TALE

During the reign of Queen Anne there lived in Bonchurch a young orphan boy by the name of "Hobby" Hobson. He had the good fortune to be apprenticed to a tailor in Niton, where he was taken in as one of the family.

One day, a squadron of men'o'war was passing the "back of the Wight" and the boys from the tailor's shop went down to the seashore to look at the ships. Young Hobby was so impressed by the sight of the fleet that he took a small boat that was beached on the shore, rowed out to the flagship of the squadron which was commanded by an admiral, and was accepted as a volunteer for Her Majesty's Navy.

He had cast his rowing boat adrift and also left his hat on the seashore in his excitement, and because of this it was presumed that he had been drowned, which upset the tailor and his wife, who had grown very fond of their young apprentice.

The fleet soon sailed away and was shortly engaged in action against the French. The fighting was very fierce, with the flagship locked yard-arm to yard-arm with that of the enemy.

After two hours, Hobson asked of a fellow sailor how long the action would last and was told "until that white flag is struck from the masthead"; in other words, until the French battle flag was removed from her flagship's mast.

"Oh, if that's all, I'll see what I can do" said the tailor's apprentice, and clambering up the rigging of his own ship, crossed unnoticed to the rigging of the French ship, bringing back the flag from the main top gallant mast head.

In the confusion which followed, the French were driven off and beaten and, despite the opinions of several English officers who felt that this was not the way to win a battle, young Hobby was promoted by the Admiral for his ingenuity. In the words of the day he "rose rapidly in his profession" to the rank of Admiral and was knighted by Queen Anne for his exploit of breaking the Vigo boom.

Some years later a party of naval officers arrived in Niton and, stopping at the tailor's house, asked for a simple meal. Bacon and eggs were all that could be offered, but they sat and enjoyed this, along with wine that had been brought by the officers. One or two hints were dropped, but the tailor did not realise why his humble home had been chosen by the officers, until one of them began humming the verse of a ballad, at which the tailor's wife exclaimed "it's all for the world like our poor Hobby". At which "poor Hobby", now Admiral Hobson, introduced himself and much was the rejoicing in the house at this happy reunion.

BONCHURCH POND

In the seventeenth century the whole area which we know as Bonchurch consisted of three farms: Marepool Farm and Mackett's Farm, both owned by Joseph Hadfield, and Bonchurch Farm, which in 1826 was converted by its owner, Mr. Surman, into East Dene.

On Hadfield's land there was an osier bed, or withy bed as they are known in the Island, from which the local longshoremen would collect lengths of willow to make and repair their crab and lobster pots. There was a feeling in the village that the swamp-like nature of the withy bed was the cause of many diseases and fevers which were prevalent amongst the local inhabitants, and they were quite pleased when Mr. Hadfield (who became known as the Father of the Undercliff) announced his intention to remove the osier bed.

Hadfield duly had the willows grubbed from the area and, taking advantage of the natural springs which existed, converted the swamp into the now famous Bonchurch Pond.

The numerous distinguished Victorians who visited Bonchurch in the next few decades enthused about the picturesque scenery of the village and particularly the pretty little pond which was now its centrepiece. Visitors still come to see the village pond today, and few now realise that it is not a natural landmark, but a man made piece of scenery, created out of a swamp which once yielded the materials of the crab fishermen's trade.

===>-o-<===

THE GUN AND THE BULLRING

These are two separate facts but they both concern the town of Brading.

Brading Town Gun

In the sixteenth century each town and village on the Island was provided with a cannon made of brass with which to defend itself from the French, who were expected to invade at any time.

The Brading Town Gun was a traditional brass cannon made in 1549, and bore the inscription "John and Robert Owine, brethen, made this pese 1549 Brerdynd". Brerdynd is a corruption of the Old English name for Brading, which is "Breordingas" or "the people living by the ridge" (i.e. Brading Down).

The gun was regularly taken from its gun-shed for exercises and target practice during the sixteenth and seventeenth centuries, but like the other town guns it fell into disuse as the power of the Navy increased and invasion became less likely. In fact, it never fired a shot in anger; not until the passing of the Reform Bill, that is.

The Reform Bill finally became law in 1832, and the town of Brading decided to celebrate by firing the town gun.

The old gun, which had not been used for many years was taken out of the gun-shed and dusted off, and with much effort the townspeople dragged it to the top of Brading Down. Preparations were made to fire the shot that heralded a new era in British politics but, to quote a contemporary source, "when the match was applied, the gun, behaving like a true Tory, exploded" and put paid to the town's celebrations!

The Bullring

Although the name persists in many places in Great Britain, few towns can claim that they still have their original bullring. The Bull Ring at Brading is a large cast iron ring set in the High Street, and it was to this ring that a bull used to be tethered when the "sport" of bull baiting was practised.

It was customary in those days to accompany these events with ceremonial behaviour and the Island's diarist Sir John Oglander gives an account for this from the mid 1600s.

It was an old custom for the Governor of the Isle of Wight to give £5 to provide a bull for baiting and, after it was killed, the meat was given to the poor. The Mayor and Corporation attended in full ceremonial dress and brought with them the town mace and regalia. The bull was tethered to the ring and the first dog to be set on it was the "Mayor's dog" which was dressed in ribbons. A barbaric custom indeed, but a piece of history even so, and the Bull Ring at Brading serves as a reminder of less enlightened times in our past.

THE TWO COWES

The town of Cowes is known the world over as a yachting centre and for a week in August it becomes the Mecca of the international yachting fraternity. Approached from the sea, the western end of the town, with its spacious parade and comfortable hotels, gives an impression of Victorian elegance; indeed Cowes has been chosen as the headquarters of the Royal Yacht Squadron, that most elite club patronised by Royalty and the nobility, which had included amongst its members Queen Victoria's Consort, Prince Albert.

The heart of the town, radiating out from the ferry terminal which was once the Fountain Hotel quay, is a mass of narrow streets crowded with pubs, eating places, bookshops and yacht chandlers that preserve their Victorian heritage – just look at Pascall Atkey's shop in the High Street.

But why the name Cowes? In the Middle Ages no town existed here, just a cluster of fishermens cottages at the mouth of the river Medina which divided the forest land covering the north of the Island into Alvington on the west and Bowcombe to the east. Richard Worsley in his "History of the Isle of Wight" states that "West Cowes was without a name until Henry VIII built here" and this is one clue to the origin of the name of the town.

In 1539, as part of his defence measures, Henry VIII commissioned the building of castles at the mouth of the Medina. That on the west bank was built with stone from the suppressed Abbey of Beaulieu and the eastern one was built on the site of the religious house of Shamblord. They soon became known as the West Cowe and the East Cowe and this was attributed to the fact that a "cowe" in the sixteenth century was the name for a fort or blockhouse.

However, there is an even simpler explanation. Many places take their names from their geographical features, such as Sandbanks in Dorset, and the same principle applies to Cowes. Sixteenth century mariners had identified sand bars in the Medina estuary and at this time such obstacles were often given the names of animals (Horse Ledge is one example). The Medina sand bars were given the name "The Cows" or "The Cowes" as it was then spelt and these hazards to shipping gave their name to the towns which developed at the mouth of the river.

THE CONEYMAN

Rabbits were introduced into the Isle of Wight at the time of the Norman Conquest, possibly to stock the Island with game for the benefit of the noblemen who would hunt them with hawk and hound, but more likely the result of them being brought to the Island as a source of live fresh food and having been allowed to escape.

The rabbits, or coneys as they were known in medieval times, flourished in their Island home; so much so that they provided food both for the Lord of the Manor and the serfs who worked for him, and also the Abbeys and Monasteries which existed here at that time. Not only that, many found their way to the London markets through the efforts of the Coneyman.

Now the Coneyman made frequent journeys from London to the Isle of Wight to buy rabbits and since he was the only person making a regular crossing of the Solent who had a connection with London, he became the postman for the Island, taking letters from the local gentry and delivering them to a London post-house.

You may wonder why the Coneyman took so much trouble to make what was, in those days, a difficult journey across to the Island just to collect rabbits, when there were hunting grounds nearer home, such as the Surrey hills and the South Downs.

The answer is simple: unlike the rest of the country, from the Norman Conquest to the time of Henry VIII, there were no foxes on the Isle of Wight to control the number of rabbits. So great was the desire to preserve the rabbit population that at one time the offence of letting a fox loose was punishment by transportation to the Colonies!

<hr />

POT POURRI

The Isle of Wight is rich in local sayings and pastimes, and has had a number of distinguished visitors who have left their mark on the Island. Many have been mentioned elsewhere, along with other fascinating facts, but the remainder are grouped here under the title of "Pot pourri".

Natives of the Isle of Wight refer to themselves as "Caulkheads", as opposed to the visitors arriving during the summer season, who are known as "Grockles" (a term shared by other resorts throughout south west England), whereas mainland people who decide to settle on the

Island are referred to as "Overners". This is a parallel to the phrase used for settlers in the Isle of Man, who are known as "come over Stayovers".

"When the furze is not in bloom,
Kissing is not in fashion".

That is an Island saying that may well be remembered by older Islanders, and the subtlety of it lies in the fact that broom, or furze, blooms throughout the year!

I was playing darts in a pub in Wroxall one night and a man who had lived in the village for many years said to me "You want 81 – Deep Snow". I asked him what he meant, and he said that 81 was always referred to as "Deep Snow" because of the unusually heavy snowfall on the Island over a hundred years ago in 1881. Hence "81 – Deep Snow".

The Isle of Wight is one of the few places in the country where the game of "Rings" is still played, and in the Ventnor area there is a thriving Rings League. Each flexible ring is four inches in diameter and players throw three rings each at a board which has fifteen numbered hooks on it. Those rings that stay on the hooks deduct an appropriate number from the score, similar to the scoring in darts.

The next item of pot pourii is the park at Watchingwell. For many years it was thought that Woodstock Park in Oxfordshire was the first park in England, but the Worsley "History of the Isle of Wight" shows that Watchingwell Park, belonging to the nuns of Wilton, existed before Woodstock and although it can no longer be seen, it was the first park in the whole of England.

Finally, to the distinguished visitors. Queen Victoria and Prince Albert chose the Isle of Wight as their favourite retreat and because of this, the Island had more Earls, Lords and general nobility per square mile than any other place in Britain. Tennyson lived here for many years, Keats wrote Endymion on the Island, and Dickens wrote several works while staying at Bonchurch.

Lewis Carroll stayed at Sandown and collected much of his material for "Alice" on the beach. Darwin began his "Origin of the Species" while staying at the Kings Head Hotel in the town and Isaac Pitman wrote his shorthand dictionary during his stay here.

These are but a few of the distinguished people who have found the Isle of Wight an ideal place for relaxation, an escape from busy town life and a source of inspiration for their writing, and detailed accounts of the work of these authors and others who have lived here are to be found in the libraries and bookshops on the Island.

BRADING HAVEN

Brading is now a small inland village on the road between Sandown and Ryde and there is little to suggest that at one time the village was a thriving market town and a seaport of some importance.

A thousand years ago there was a large harbour here, known as Brading Haven, with St. Helens and Bembridge forming the mouth; in fact, the name Bembridge stems from an old British word meaning "the land within the bridge" and at this time Bembridge was cut off by the sea at high tide, only being joined to the rest of the Island by the causeway built at Yarbridge in 1336.

There is a Roman villa at Carisbrooke and also one at Brading and the significance of the sites is that both were accessible from the sea; the villa at Carisbrooke is close to the river Medina, and Roman ships could tie up at Brading quay, less than a mile from the Brading Villa.

Despite the town's usefulness as a port, there have been numerous attempts throughout the centuries to bridge the gap between St.Helens and Bembridge. When Sir William Russell, Lord of Yaverland, constructed the Yar Bridge he reclaimed part of Brading Haven and in 1562 another section was walled in by George Oglander and German Richards, with some further reclamation in 1594.

The finances of the next attempt are rather interesting. The job was commissioned by Bevis Thelwall and Sir Hugh Myddleton, who was famous for his work on the New River project in London. They paid £2,000 for the land rights, £4,000 for the Dutch workmen involved and £1,000 for a dwelling house, barn and mill and the work was completed in 1620. The soil of the reclaimed land proved to be light running sand, and when the inland spring water joined the high spring tide, the waters met under the earthworks and the wall was breached, causing the project to be abandoned at a cost of £7,000.

The harbour was eventually reclaimed nearly 250 years later by Jabez Balfour in 1880, the same year that the Brading Roman Villa was discovered, but to this day the remains of the old harbour wall can still be seen behind Brading's narrow High Street.

THE FIRST CANNED BEER

One of the first public breweries on the Isle of Wight was that established by the Mew family at Newport during the reign of Charles I. The brewery's central position in the Island's capital meant that it could supply many inns around the town and also in the surrounding villages.

At the end of the eighteenth century brewing was in full swing at Newport, with the company owning another brewery at Lymington. By the early 1800s business had expanded dramatically, mainly due to the trade in Army canteens both in Britain and in other parts of the world, such as China and India.

The Mews were in a perfect spot for supplying the Army's needs; at one time there had been 10,000 troops stationed on the Island in the garrisons at Freshwater, Niton and Sandown and at the large Albany Barracks just along the road from Newport. In addition, the brewery's location on the River Medina meant that barrels could be loaded onto barges and sent a few miles down the river to the port of Cowes, which in the seventeenth and eighteenth centuries was a major victualling centre for the Royal Navy and the merchant fleet prior to their voyages all over the world.

However, in the late 1800s the brewery, then known as Mew-Langtons, began using a revolutionary new method of storing beer which we now treat as commonplace. Screw top cans were used instead of fragile bottles to supply the troops in India with their India Pale Ale (IPA), making Mew-Langtons the first brewery in the world to produce canned beer.

YARMOUTH'S CROOKE

A Court Leet was held in Yarmouth at the annual St. James' Day Fair for 150 years, until the custom was wound up in 1862. At the Court, the Mayor would select twelve citizens not holding any office who would then examine the town's affairs, check weights and measures, and certify the town's accounts.

There was no fee for attending the Court Leet but, after the day's business had been conducted, the Mayor and his twelve citizens would adjourn to one of the local inns and the town would treat them to a dinner in payment for their services. The bill for the dinner was usually quite high, and the amount of food and drink consumed on these occasions was phenomenal.

It was customary to invite to the dinner any persons of note who happened to be in the town, and in 1784 the Mayor was pleased to offer an invitation to a naval officer, Lieutenant Charles Cunningham Crooke, whose ship HMS Expedition was tied up at the quay, waiting for wind and tide.

The members of the Court duly adjourned to a hotel to enjoy the Court Leet Dinner and, as was the custom, took with them an oak chest containing all the town's documents, including its original charter, subsequent charters and all the town's records.

As may be imagined, the dinner was a lengthy affair with much ale and wine being consumed and it was some hours before it was noticed that Lieutenant Crooke had departed and the town chest had vanished! A visit to the quay confirmed that his ship had weighed anchor and sailed away.

There seemed no doubt that Crooke had taken the chest and with it all the town's deeds. There was some speculation that he thought the box contained the remainder of the wine from the meal and, finding that it contained only documents, tossed it over the side of the ship; perhaps he felt the contents would be valuable, who knows?

My opinion is that he expected to find gold in the box and was disappointed.

The town sued him for £10,000 or the return of the box, but was awarded only £500 by a jury; the town chest was never recovered and Yarmouth now has only a manuscript copy of its original charter and no original records of the town's affairs before the year 1784.

⟹►◦◄⟸

ST. BONIFACE DOWN

The church in Bonchurch is dedicated to St. Boniface, a monk who was martyred in Holland in 755 and whose name refers not to his benign countenance, but to the Latin words meaning "a doer of good". The old church of St. Boniface was built around 1070 by a French nobleman Johannes de Argentine and Bonchurch was made a parish at that time by Walkelyn, the Bishop of Winchester.

In times gone by it was customary to visit the wishing well on the summit of the hill above St. Boniface Cottage, a natural spring which was supposed to be magical, appearing as it did so many hundreds of feet above sea level. The tradition was that if you could reach the top of the down without looking back and wish while drinking then your wish would come true.

For many years the well was visited by young people from the village on St. Boniface Day and on that occasion the well was always decked with flowers. Sadly, the tradition has now died out (either from a disbelief in superstition or a lack of will to climb the steep slopes of the Down) and even the well seems to have given up the ghost, having dried up after providing a constant supply of water for many years.

Old photographs of Ventnor taken just before the First World War show St. Boniface Down rising majestically behind the town completely devoid of trees. Nowadays the slopes of the Down are a mass of foliage and you may ask how this came about in the space of 85 years or so. It appears that the lower parts of the Down were covered with trees when Ventnor was first developed as a resort, but these were soon removed, either for building purposes or for firewood. Then, within living memory, a man with a purpose appeared, who walked for hours on the Down with his pockets full of acorns, planting them every few feet as he went!

Some people prefer the Down as it used to be, but I congratulate this unknown conservationist for the work that he did. There is concern at the moment that the upper, unwooded part of the Down is being defaced by its use for motor cycle scrambling and that this causes pathways to be dug in the face of the Down. I make no comment except to refer to an account of the Down in 1849 in which the writer gratefully notes that: "The practice of peasant lads descending the Down on the skull of a horse has now become obsolete" showing that the concern of local people about the natural beauty of the Down dates back many years.

⟾•◦•⟸

SIR RICHARD WORSLEY

Richard Worsley was born in 1751, the son of Thomas Worsley. He is mainly remembered as the man who completed the rebuilding of Appuldurcombe House, where his family had lived for several hundred years, and as the publisher of the first History of the Isle of Wight, which was a compilation of his own work and information collected by his father and grandfather. Yet there is another story hidden beneath these facts of Worsley's life which will now be revealed.

44

In 1770 he embarked upon his Grand Tour of Europe, the customary way for the sons of gentlemen to learn about life and the rest of the world, and he returned from this in 1772 a changed man.

His tutor, Edward Gibbon, is quoted as saying "From an honest, wild, English Buck, he is grown a philosopher...he speaks in short sentences, quotes Montaigne, seldom smiles, never laughs, drinks only water, professes to command his passions and intends to marry in five months".

In 1773 he completed the rebuilding of Appuldurcombe House, which had begun in 1710, but his plan to marry within five months was not to be; perhaps he was waiting for "Miss Right" to come along. In 1775 "Miss Right" appeared in the shape of Seymour Dorothy Fleming whom he married for love....and a dowry of £80,000!

Worsley's "History of the Isle of Wight" was published in 1781, but perhaps he spent too much time in his study working on this project, because in 1782 he sued for divorce on the grounds of his wife's 27 lovers. He filed a suit against the last known offender, Captain M. G. Bisset of the Hampshire Militia, claiming £20,000 damages. The Court heard his case but, suspecting connivance, reduced the amount payable.

Sir Richard Worsley was awarded damages amounting to just one shilling.

━━━━━►•◄━━━━━

SHANKLIN CHINE

Shanklin dates back to before 1066 and owes its name to the old English words "Scenc Hlinc", which means "the cup in the rising ground". The cup in question is now known as the Chine, which is another old English word meaning " a chink or fissure". For hundreds of years Shanklin was simply a small hamlet by the sea with a manor house and a church and a few villagers earning a living from farming and fishing.

The Chine has the distinction of being one of the places chosen for the last French invasion of England. When Henry VIII and his fleet (including the flagship Mary Rose) were at Portsmouth awaiting an attack, the French sheltered beneath Culver Cliff on the Island and made token invasions at Bonchurch and Shanklin Chine, hoping to draw out the English fleet; a tactic which was unsuccessful. The French were driven back and their leader at Shanklin, the Chevalier d'Eulx, was killed.

The village went back to its quiet existence and even as recently as 1801 the population numbered only 105. Around this time the only resident of the Chine was the innkeeper whose family had owned the inn for over 200 years and who paid one shilling a year for the right to graze his cow on the open land at the top of the Chine.

Then in 1817 Mr. W. Colenutt built a house on the beach which is still known as the "Fisherman's Cottage" and also constructed a path through the Chine, which would allow visitors to observe this wonder of nature at first hand for a small fee. The same Mr. Colenutt went on to introduce the first bathing machine to the beach and his efforts were a major influence in turning Shanklin into a seaside resort.

The Chine was referred to by Victorian tourists as "savagely grand" and "terrifically sublime" and far superior to the gloomy and foreboding aspect of its fellow Chine at Blackgang, which was known for its "dreary wildness". Today Blackgang is far more popular, but for the Victorian visitor Shanklin Chine, with its cascade of water, had the greater appeal for its scenic beauty, and the number of people coming to see it during the 1800s turned the tiny village into a thriving seaside town.

Shanklin Chine was chosen as the site for the beginning of PLUTO, the Pipeline Under The Ocean, which was to provide fuel for the Normandy landings on D-Day. Dummy fuel tanks were built along the Esplanade which attracted enemy bombs, but the fuel was safely pumped from the foot of the Chine across the Channel to provide the life-blood for the vehicles involved in the invasion.

SMUGGLING

Smuggling was rife along the south coast of England in the eighteenth century, from the Romney Marsh down to Devon and Cornwall, but few people realise how important the Isle of Wight was to the "free-traders" and the extent of the traffic in contraband on our little island.

Curiously, the historians of the time make no mention at all of the free trade, despite the fact that smuggling probably reached its peak during this period.

The dubious distinction of being the Island's first recorded smuggler must go to a member of the clergy! Thomas Symonde, Rector of Freshwater, was caught smuggling wool to France on St.Valentine's Day 1395 and was duly fined by his bishop. However the eighteenth century was the hey-day of the smuggler in the Isle of Wight. An increasing number of goods were subject to a heavy import duty and those goods could be readily obtained from the French ports of Roscoff and Barfleur. Most of the smuggling runs were carried out during the fishing season between May and September, when small boats leaving and returning to the Island would arouse less suspicion.

Superb sailors and oarsmen they must have been, finding their way to remote beaches on the southern coast of the Island in the dead of night, bringing not only brandy, tea and tobacco but also lace, silks, scent and jewellery.

Fortunes of £40,000 are said to have been made from smuggling as long ago as 1722 and the Island soon became a clearing house for goods brought over from France. The coastline was difficult to patrol with an under-manned Customs service and, once on the Island, the goods could easily be carried across the Solent to destinations on the mainland. An exciseman estimated that in 1836 10,000 tubs of spirits were being landed on the Isle of Wight, with only about 1,000 destined for local consumption.

Everyone must have been aware that smuggling went on; the landed gentry who put up the money to buy the goods, the fishermen who carried it across the Channel, the farm workers who carried the contraband away from the shore and even the farmers who were required to provide pack-horses for transportation were rewarded with a barrel left on their doorstep the next day. Yet despite this huge trade in illicit goods contemporary historians fail to mention smuggling, either as a crime or an occupation. I think the answer is that the smuggler, who brought brandy, tea, tobacco and other household commodities, was accepted as part of everyday life, much the same as the farmer and the fisherman, and was so commonplace that he did not warrant special attention.

1870 saw the end of traditional smuggling at Ventnor, when Noel Wilkins was caught on the beach with tubs of smuggled spirits and was duly sentenced for his crime.

For many years Ventnor has also housed the Smuggling Museum in the Botanic Gardens, a unique collection of artefacts showing methods of smuggling through the centuries, from the wool smugglers of long ago to the modern drug smuggler.

Smuggling has changed through the years and this eighteenth century version of the "black economy" bears little resemblance to the occasional run of drugs and illegal goods that we sometimes see today. However while there are prohibitions and goods which have a heavy duty, the smugglers will be at work and who can watch every yacht and fishing vessel that passes the Isle of Wight?

His hand sho   to
flinch, nor t   he
wrenched again at her hair, pulling her head
relentlessly towards him. When her face was an inch
from his own he spoke with soft fury. 'I don't want
you here. It would suit me very well to slit your
throat and leave you. But I suppose you want to live,
get back to that civilised little husband of yours. So
you do it on my terms. Now, you want to argue?'

'No.' It was no more than a croak. Langeveldt let
her go. She sat shaking, rubbing her head, amazed
that her hair was still attached. Oh God, how to cope
with this man?

'Why are you so cruel?' she asked.

He looked at her with bleak detachment. 'Cruelty
is something you don't begin to understand,' he said
calmly.

Dark Sunrise

Elizabeth Walker

HEADLINE

Printed and bound in Great Britain by
Collins, Glasgow

HEADLINE BOOK PUBLISHING PLC
Headline House
79 Great Titchfield Street
London W1P 7FN

Running through the night like a thief, like a beggar,
Once long ago it was I who ran.
Now I stand alone in the dark, in the danger;
African night you may do what you can.

What do you want here, English lady,
Far from your home and the warmth of your bed?
Why do you long for the arms of your children –
Know you not that the spirits feed on the dead?

Your hair is like a curtain, soft and scented,
It trails in my mouth like a thread of pain.
Here in the night is a thing undreamed of
Quiet on the earth like the healing of rain.

Lie in the night and know I am with you,
Turn your ear to my heart, not the lion's wild roar.
He only cares if you stray, if you falter,
I shall enfold you. I am here; I am sure.

Harsh is the land and harsher my loving,
Lighting a flame in the glow of your eyes.
Stand with me here as we look to the eastward,
Waiting for morning and a Dark Sunrise.

Chapter 1

The day was blue and held the promise of warmth. Thin mist pearled the grass and from the ancient trees, heavy with leaf, came the bright, clear song of many birds. Thrush; starling chatter; a blackbird's faultless aria. Sarah watched with rueful interest as a bee, out too early, blundered into a dewy rose and buzzed in consternation.

'At least you have something to do,' she admonished. 'You've no right to complain.'

Oh, but that was a foolish thing to say. What, truthfully, could she complain about? That at last she had time on her hands? A month, two months ago she would have given anything for a morning such as this, house clean, garden tidy, Emma at school and Joanne at the nursery. Time to do what she wanted. Time to realise she did not know what she wanted a small voice insisted, but she turned resolutely back to the bee. There at least was a woman of purpose: she did not stand around in sunny gardens and wonder why life seemed so flat. She got on and did what had to be done, to and fro, flower to flower, back and forwards to the hive, content to know that she was useful and necessary. When at last she failed to make it home and lay exhausted in the grass she would be secure in the knowledge that her life had been spent gainfully. The bee hummed off towards the dahlias, now past their best, and mumbled amongst them. She seemed an old bee, experienced and worldly-wise, wasting no time in idleness. This one would not survive the winter, thought

Sarah. To die without a single mark left on the world to show that here you had laboured. It was enough for a bee.

But who should feel melancholy on such a day? Even as she watched the mist vanished like a wraith of night, the flowers turned their faces to the sun and swallows came to drink from the pool. She was so lucky to have her garden. Douglas had not wanted to live here, he would have preferred something smaller and more central, but she loved Wimbledon. With the common so close it gave her a feeling of the country. It reminded her of her childhood, a muddy, messy, chicken-keeping time that she remembered with affection. Sometimes, in town, she felt light-years away from a blade of grass, although of course it was lovely to have the shops and the theatre. Douglas liked the town.

So, this house had been a compromise. It was a pity in a way that he had insisted on a gardener, as well as Mrs Burton to help with the house. Without them she might have had more to do. But that was silly, because after all, she didn't really want to fill her life with housework and weeding, she wasn't a bee. She was – what? Sarah Hamilton, wife and mother. Bored wife and mother.

She wondered about a cup of coffee, or possibly a sandwich, though she wasn't hungry. There was some shopping she could do: Douglas's blue suit needed cleaning and she could always pop into the library. Yes, that would be best. After all, tomorrow was her meals-on-wheels day and on Friday she and Douglas were going out to dinner, just the two of them. It was her birthday, on Friday. Another year gone.

She went quickly indoors and up to the dressing room, determined to snap herself out of this mood. Her hair was caught in a ribbon at the back of her head and she pulled it free, letting it fall about her face in a dark, misty cloud.

She looked no older now than she had when she married and she knew that the years had given her a certain style. Other women often asked where she bought her clothes and Sarah always told them, but somehow when they wore the same things they always looked different. She had a flair for dress, she could put a blouse and a skirt together, add a scarf, and it looked – right. Dashing. Other women just wore blouses and skirts. Before she married she had thought she might do something in fashion, buying, possibly, or even design, because she was fairly arty, but of course once she met Douglas that was it. He was lovely, Douglas. He took such care of her.

The vacuum cleaner begun to hum in the hall, which meant that Mrs Burton would soon be upstairs. Flinging open her wardrobe Sarah pulled out the stonewashed jeans that Douglas hated because they looked as if they had indeed been through an avalanche, threw on a red, lacy T-shirt and tied her hair in a wispy knot on top of her head. Not today svelte Mrs Hamilton of the shantung suit but Sarah Melling as was, who used to make her own dresses, paint messy pictures and eat ice creams in the street.

As always there was absolutely nowhere to park. After an irritable ten-minute cruise she shoe-horned the Rover into a space suitable for a Mini and locked it with a flourish. The day was definitely improving, there weren't many women who could have parked that car. A man digging the road saw her and whistled, a great echoing whistle that made everyone turn to look. Sarah pretended she hadn't heard and sauntered on, allowing her bottom the tiniest possible wiggle. Oh, there was something to be said for sunny days and a home and a husband, a security that allowed you to enjoy whistles like that since there was no need to do anything about them. It hadn't been all fun when she was single. Men had often seemed to threaten her, to ask more than she was prepared to give. Life itself had seemed daunting, an insoluble problem which she had to face with no idea where to start. The relief that marriage had brought! The loss of independence had been a price she was happy to pay.

She had forgotten to bring Douglas's suit. Damn. Still, she would be coming in on Wednesday for the girls' ballet class and if she took it out of his wardrobe and put it in hers he might never know. As far as Douglas could see if he had asked her once that was more than enough and although he would be quite patient when he discovered her lapse it would have something of the patience of God faced with the foibles of an eternally backsliding humanity. Sometimes, in the early days, she had snarled at him when he began his homilies, but it had never been worth it. He believed he was right, he repeatedly said so, and after a while the whole argument seemed too tedious for words. The result had been a satisfactory compromise, which was after all the basis of most happy marriages. He believed she did just as he said and she made sure he never knew that she did not.

Today the sun was so warm that you could believe it would be summer forever. She wandered up and down the street, vaguely looking for some T-shirts for the girls, but there was nothing but jumpers and woolly tights. Anyway they didn't really need them, both the children had far more clothes than they could possibly wear. She supposed they were very indulged, but it seemed not to have done them any harm. There were never two such lovely, bouncy, smooth-skinned girls as hers, all hair and giggles, with a sweet politeness of manner that, if she had but known it, was a direct copy of her own. Yes, she was very, very lucky.

The library seemed dark and cool in contrast to the baking pavement outside. These same shelves that she knew so well could still occasion a spark of anticipation, because who knew what might have come home to roost since last she was here? Sarah knew she read too much, Douglas often said so, but then he did not read a great deal himself. The *Financial Times* and the *Economist* were his bedtime reading while she devoured everything from the trashiest romance to weighty historical biography. But today there seemed nothing worthy of her attention. It could be like that sometimes, almost as if you were tired of escape and wanted something real to happen, as if you would like it if it did. In the end she took *Emma* to read yet again, a book on houseplants and some stories for the children. Nothing now to do but make her way home and perhaps think about sunbathing in the garden. And she had neglected her painting recently; perhaps she could start another study of the pool. If she painted outdoors there would be no cloying smell of turpentine for Douglas. It annoyed his sinuses and made him quite miserable.

As she made for the door her eye caught a poster, stylishly drawn, showing a figure seated at an easel. 'Do you paint?' it asked. 'Amateur or would-be professional, this is the course for you. A weekend in the country, expert advice and tuition from established artists. Find out where your art is heading. Enquire at the desk for details.'

A tremor of excitement caught at her throat. The poster seemed to be speaking directly to her. Where was she heading, in her art or anywhere? She had no idea at all. In the past, before her marriage, she had wanted to go to art school but everything about the idea had horrified her mother. Depraved hippy types with rope sandals and greasy hair, that was how she saw art students and there was no way any daughter of hers was going to join them. Good heavens, they probably had diseases.

Sarah's father had died only months before. It seemed too much to pile yet another blow on her mother's suffering head and in the end the dreamy, shy girl Sarah had allowed herself to be persuaded. She had married Douglas instead.

She rushed home clutching her explanatory leaflet and buoyed up with enthusiasm. Two nights away, that was all, she would be back by Sunday evening and if her mother came over there would be no problem about the children. She could even leave all their meals in the freezer, perhaps a lasagne for Douglas and her mother and that baked bean and mince thing for the children; they could eat it with French bread and that would be no trouble. She could make a salad and a roast that they could have cold – oh, it was easy. Gingerbread in the cake tin, shortbread in the biscuit barrel and Mrs Burton popping in on Sunday morning to straighten things up. Nobody could possibly complain.

When she rang the course centre they were charming, helpful and welcoming. Yes, of course she could make a provisional booking, she sounded exactly the sort of person they wanted. Lots of married women came and most of them took their art seriously, as she wished to do. Enjoyment came from determined effort.

'I'll confirm as soon as I've made arrangements,' assured Sarah. 'The children and so on – but I'm sure I can sort it out. Thank you. I'll let you know. 'Bye.'

That was the first step, then. Her mother was out when she phoned, so instead she cooked and baked furiously, stuffing the freezer with more food than her family could possibly eat in a fortnight. Why had she not thought of this before? It was the parable of the talents all over again, she would make a life for herself using the gifts she had. Just imagine, she might have gone on and on moping around telling herself she wasn't miserable when all the time the answer lay in her own capable hands. She might even make a career of it, only a little career, working from home, of course. The possibilities made her head swim. Then her mind stopped in its headlong imagining as a horrible thought struck her. Suppose they were not such wonderful gifts after all? Suppose all she could produce were third-rate seascapes that would moulder in the attics of relatives because they were too terrible even to be hung in the loo.

An image of the tutor looking pityingly at her work rose before her. He might be so appalled he would not even dare say so, but would take refuge in platitudes and metaphorical pats on the head. It would be absolutely awful. In a panic she abandoned a casserole half-made and went to rummage in the attic, finding canvases she thought she had forgotten until she saw them again and remembered the exact moments of planning, construction and final, almost pleased conclusion. Was she wrong or were they possibly quite good? Douglas always said they were far too flamboyant and it might be true. They were – exotic. Almost tropical, using the colour sense she carried over to her dress. But sometimes the drawing was poor and she needed help with perspective. Would they understand what it was she wanted? They must. Hardly able to contain herself she skipped downstairs and went to fetch the girls.

Emma had fallen over in the playground and skinned her knee. 'It hurted and I cried,' she said gloomily. 'And Miss Mills couldn't find a plaster.'

'We'll put some cream on it at bedtime,' assured her mother, negotiating a tentative path through the after-school traffic jam.

Elizabeth Walker

'Alexander bit me,' confided Joanne, revealing a plump arm with the occasional toothmark.

'Don't tell Daddy,' warned Sarah, well aware that disclosures of that type caused Douglas to come out in a rash of fee-paying prospectuses. He agreed with Sarah that it was better for their children to spend at least part of their childhood somewhere other than a middle-class ghetto, but evidence of assault on his lovely, chubby baby would have her in the convent nursery class before you could turn round. And they were far too keen on discipline for Sarah's liking, who could see no reason why three-year-olds should spend half an hour a day reciting numbers which they would learn in an instant when they were five. She preferred them to count snails in the sandpit. Douglas would certainly not agree, so she avoided the argument, and fortunately the girls were receptive to embargoes on tales to Daddy. Sometimes it worried Sarah that she was educating them in deceit, but since it was either make them promise not to tell or never let them eat lollies in the car, paddle in the park, do somersaults on the climbing frame or go to the hamburger place on the nights when Daddy was away, there really seemed to be no choice. And she was sure that they realised Daddy only wanted the very best for them all.

Her thoughts turned back to her painting weekend.

'Mummy will be going away for two nights soon,' she said cheerfully. 'Grandma will look after you, and Daddy. You won't mind, will you?'

'But you can't,' said Emma in shocked tones. 'We need you.'

'Not all the time you don't, darling. Sometimes it's nice for mummies to get away. And Grandma will give you lots of lovely food and I'll bring you both a present.'

'I want a tractor,' said Joanne happily, secure in the knowledge that someone, somewhere, always looked after her.

'Of course you can have a tractor, darling,' promised Sarah easily, although Douglas hated the girls to have toys meant for boys.

'Daddy won't let you,' said Emma, and turned to gaze out of the window. 'You won't bring anything 'cos Daddy won't let you go.'

'Don't be silly, love. It's not a question of Daddy letting me go – I've arranged it. And anyway, I'm Mummy, I don't have to ask.' That was right, she was Mummy, she didn't need people's permission to do things. Anyway, Douglas couldn't object, she was organising everything beautifully.

'He won't let you,' said Emma again and Sarah could have slapped her. Honestly, anyone would think she was five years old too.

When the children had changed and were playing outside Sarah went again to the phone.

'Hello, Mother? It's me.'

'Darling! I'm so glad you rang, I was beginning to think you'd forgotten me.'

'I rang yesterday.'

'Yes, dear, but you were in such a hurry. Still, I know how it is when you're young, never any time for anyone. When you get to my age of course it's different, no-one needs you any more and when you're on your own –'

'I do need you actually,' broke in Sarah, refusing to be drawn into the long and familiar routine of pacification. Her mother was annoyed because she hadn't been invited to Sunday lunch for a fortnight, but it was entirely her own fault. A widow, she had taken to town life with more enthusiasm than Sarah could ever muster. Mrs Melling shopped and played bridge, took senior citizen tickets to the theatre, gave sherry parties for her more elegant friends. It all cost a great deal more than she could afford, and when the bank began to grumble she appealed, as always, to Douglas. He paid up like a Trojan for Douglas was never mean, he had no need to be. But it infuriated Sarah, who loathed the way her mother treated Douglas, like some sort of bran tub, a prize every time. Still, now she could return to favour and be of some use.

'I want you to come and hold the fort for me. Just for a weekend, Friday to Sunday.'

'What? Are you and Douglas going away? How lovely. I should love to look after the children –'

'Not Douglas. Me. An art weekend. I've arranged it.'

There was a stunned silence. Then: 'Have you asked Douglas?'

'Well – no, not yet. I thought I'd arrange everything first. It's only a weekend after all. Tuition in a country house, with real artists. The lady was awfully helpful and I'm so looking forward to it. They make an assessment of your potential, see if you could possibly make a career out of it and so on. I mean I don't want a career really, but I would like to know if I was any good. It would be something to do.'

'He won't like it, Sarah. Especially not artists, you know what he thinks of them. And personally I couldn't agree more, very free-living types artists are. And they simply do not wash. If you must paint you're better off at home with a book out of the library to help you, and there's that programme on television, you could watch that, it's bound to give you some ideas –'

Sarah sucked in her breath with annoyance. Why did her mother always think she was useless at things, that's what she meant – don't try, you'll only make a mess of it.

'Mother, you're being ridiculous. All I want you to do is say you'll come and keep house. The food's all ready. Mrs Burton will come in, it'll be easy. Please, Mother.'

There was a sigh and a pause. Then her mother said, 'Sarah, you know I will. But I'm sure it's not a good idea. After all you know how cautious Douglas is, at least you ought to by this time. A very sensible sort of man I've always thought him. I don't think he'll let you go.'

'Oh, for goodness sake, why does everyone behave as if I'm some kind of lapdog? I'm a grown woman and I can do as I like, provided I don't let everyone down. And I'm not. Really. I've arranged everything and I'm only asking for two whole days to myself. Is that too unreasonable? That I should do what I want, by myself, just for once?' She was almost shouting down the phone.

'Dear me, you are getting yourself in a state. Well, go ahead and ask him then. But don't say I didn't warn you.'

Sarah slammed the phone down with a bang. Her mother never saw her as anything but a child, needing constant guidance and supervision. Susie had undoubtedly done the right thing, taking off for Africa as soon as the wedding ring was firmly in place, leaving her unfortunate sister to shoulder the responsibilty of a restless, feckless widow who couldn't believe that her children had grown up. She flounced off into the kitchen to prepare dinner, longing for Douglas to come home so that she could tell him about it.

Douglas was late that night. The children were in bed and the garden was in twilight before she heard his step in the hall. A stocky man, not very tall, with a square, firm face and dark hair tinged with grey. He wore glasses and he looked hot and cross.

11

'I have been in that train for over an hour,' he fumed, flinging his briefcase into a corner. Sarah retrieved it and set it on a chair.

'Come into the garden, darling. I've made some cocktails – I thought you might be a bit frazzled. Or would you like to pop up and change: you look all sticky.'

'I think I'll change. Honestly, you would think it would be possible to run a train on time occasionally, but it's never the same two days' running. It's the snow, or the rain; today I suppose the lines have melted or something and I shall never know why everyone always commits suicide on the District Line –'

Sarah followed behind, letting him fume and bluster while she picked up socks and handed clean ones, took away a dirty shirt and found one newly ironed on its hanger. Gradually he calmed down until at last, when they were seated on the terrace in the dusk, he smiled. The heavy contours of his face lightened and a touch of humour sparked in his eyes.

'Am I being a pain?' he asked suddenly.

'Yes, but I don't mind. Have you had a hard day?'

'The very worst. The latest estimate for that rig's in. It's way over budget and no-one seems to know why. Stock market's going up and down like a yo-yo and we've a dealer in Hamburg having a fit because he's got his decimal point wrong and thinks he's lost half a million. God, I can do without days like today.'

Sarah grinned and leaned forward to pour her husband a drink. It seemed to her that the oil market lurched from one crisis to another, with no constant except the large salary cheques that continued to come their way. She popped a cherry in Douglas's glass and leaned back in her chair, wondering if this was the moment to tell him her plan. She had dressed with care, a calf-length full linen skirt and a blouse of pale blue silk with a cowl neck. Soft, feminine clothes that Douglas would like.

'Harry Rogers' wife came in today,' he said suddenly.

'Isn't she the one with the very exclusive dress shop?'

'Yes, that's her. I don't know how he puts up with it. One of the most overpowering women I have ever met, and she can hardly ever be home. They've two children, you know, both at boarding school. They'd have to be, she's no time for them, or for Harry if you ask me. Sometimes I thank my stars that I've got you, Sarah.' He reached out and took her hand.

Sarah gulped. Oh well, it was now or never. She let her long, slender fingers toy with his square ones, moving her body slightly so that her breast was outlined against her blouse.

'Do you think I'm a flighty piece, darling?' She was being a little girl for him, teasing with a hint of sex.

He stroked her wrist and said, 'You? My little homing pigeon, pretty and sweet and loving, that's what you are.'

'Mother thinks I am. She thinks you won't ever let me out of your sight.'

She stretched a leg and leaned back, knowing that she was buying his agreement with the promise of things to come.

'What are you after, you little baggage?'

'Will you let me leave you for a weekend? I'll make it up to you, I promise. You'll see.'

Douglas sat up and dropped her hand. 'A weekend? Sarah, what on earth are you on about?'

'Friday evening to Sunday afternoon, that's all. It's an art weekend, and I do so want to go. You've no idea how bored I've been recently and it's exactly what I want. They assess how good you are and what you should consider doing and – look, here's the leaflet.' She thrust it at him, surprised to see her hands trembling with eagerness. Douglas scanned it briefly.

'Really, Sarah! If you ask me you've fallen for one of the oldest tricks in the book. Of course they'll say you're wonderful, provided they can get you to sign up for a dozen more weekends at God knows what price. I should have thought you'd know better. Anyway, what's this sudden enthusiasm for art, may I ask?'

Foolishly tears pricked her eyelids and she blinked furiously. 'It's not a sudden enthusiasm, you know I've always been good at painting and things. I enjoy it. And now the children are at school I thought – I do so want to go, Douglas. All the food's in the freezer and Mother will come, and Mrs Burton can pop in on Sunday and –'

'Darling, darling, darling.' Douglas caught her hands and drew her to him, letting her bury her face in his chest. 'You've been getting in quite a state, haven't you? Do you really mean to tell me that you would rather spend a few days in the company of a bunch of hippies, half of them smoking pot if I'm any judge, than be with your husband and children? I find it hard to believe.'

'Well, of course I don't – and it's only two days – Douglas, I want to go!'

'Dear, dear me. Poor Sarah. I should have realised, darling, it's been awful for you since Joanne went to nursery. You're lonely, poor sweet. How would you like a holiday? We could go back to John's villa in Genoa or –'

'I don't want a holiday, I want this course!' Sarah pulled away and glared at him. Douglas blinked in surprise. 'It's only two days and it would be fun,' she insisted, her voice shaking with the threat of tears. 'It would be my own thing to do by myself. Who knows, I might even be able to make something of it if I got some advice.'

'Whatever do you mean? Sell things or something?

Sarah darling, I'm not about to put you on the breadline, however many fur-trimmed jackets your mother buys.'

'But it's not the money!' All at once the impossibility of explaining it to him became overwhelming. She flopped back into her chair and said dully, 'You won't let me go. Will you?'

Douglas looked bewildered. 'But – there's no reason for you to go. Oh, it's my fault I suppose, I've protected you from so many things you would hate. You don't understand what the world's like, my darling. At a place like that a woman like you – beautiful, innocent – men would take advantage of you. You could be very upset, and I should hate that. Believe me, Sarah, I'm right.'

She clutched at a straw. 'If you just came and looked at the place. The lady on the phone sounded so nice –'

'I don't doubt it for a moment. And the man in charge would be nice too, he'd be very nice to you and before you knew it you would be in a situation that you simply wouldn't know how to handle.'

'Douglas, I am not a child!'

'And that, my darling, is why I simply cannot let you go.'

There was a long, tense silence. Then Sarah said in a thin, high voice, 'Am I never to be allowed out, then? Never permitted to go anywhere without a chaperone?'

'Now you're being silly. If it was necessary, if Susan was ill or anything, then of course you would have to go. But something like this – Sarah, come back. Please, Sarah, if you only give yourself time to reflect –'

The French door slammed with a bang, and all the glass shook. With the air of a man who is much tried, Douglas poured himself another cocktail.

In bed that night Sarah lay rigid, refusing to ler her skin

come within inches of Douglas. He was determinedly cheerful, whistling and humming until she could have brained him with the bedside lamp. That he wanted her, she knew with the instinct of long years of marriage, but when he reached as always for her breast she did not welcome him. Nonetheless, he pulled aside the silk of her nightgown and nuzzled her.

'You're tickling me,' she said sharply. He was always so gentle that sometimes he made her flesh jump. He ran a hand up her thigh and she cringed away from his probing fingers, as unwilling a partner as it was possible to be. But her husband persisted, sure that he would rouse her to warmth, taking so long that she almost screamed with irritation. He would not stop and so she must pretend. She spread her legs and moaned a little, hearing him grunt with satisfaction before he levered himself on top of her. Then it was possible to let her thoughts wander, and as Douglas thrust and heaved she suddenly remembered her course, that tomorrow she would have to endure the humiliations of cancelling the booking, telling her mother and even confessing to her daughter that Mummy wasn't to be allowed out. With a sudden sob she buried her face in Douglas's shoulder.

Afterwards, he tried again to woo her. 'It was good for you, darling, I can tell. You liked it, didn't you?'

'Yes, yes I liked it. I'm sleepy Douglas, let me go to sleep.'

'I am right, you know. It's only because I care so much about you, Sarah. If you only knew how much you mean to me you wouldn't want to go.'

'I know, I know. Let me go to sleep.'

'But if you'd try to see my view of things –'

'For Christ's sake, Douglas, will you shut up and let me go to sleep!'

He recoiled as if savaged by his favourite spaniel and, sighing deeply, retreated to his own satin pillow.

There was an atmosphere at breakfast. Even the children noticed and bent their heads low over their plates.

'Your meals-on-wheels day isn't it, darling?' queried Douglas.

'Yes. It is, on Tuesdays.'

'Why don't you try and get another day as well? It's useful, meals-on-wheels, and you always say how much the old people appreciate it.'

Sarah laughed without humour. 'If you must know they frequently say the food's disgusting, we're late in coming and why don't we supply beer. And half the old boys make suggestive remarks. I'm surprised you think it's a suitable occupation for me at all.'

'Sarah, try not to snap in front of the children,' remonstrated Douglas, pointedly lifting his paper. Nonetheless he popped a kiss on to her silent but furious head as he left.

The children were quiet on the way to school, Joanne trying to escape from her seat belt and Emma unravelling her hem by means of a piece of dangling thread.

'Stop it, Emma, don't you care if you arrive in rags?' snapped Sarah, catching sight of her in the driving mirror, and watched her small daughter look crushed. In a family which almost never rowed a disagreement such as this morning's was traumatic. When they parted she gave them each an extra big hug.

'I'm sorry I was cross. I won't be tonight, I promise.'

The little girls flung their arms around her and clung, bringing tears to her eyes. She hurried off, gulping.

* * *

The phone was ringing as she let herself back into the house. It was her mother.

'Darling, the most terrible thing has happened.'

Sarah's mind spun wildly. Surely next door's cat hadn't dug up yet another row of her mother's carrots? 'Mmmmm?' she replied non-committally, knowing it would infuriate her mother.

'Sarah, don't you care about your sister? There's been a revolution!'

'What? In Zimbabwe? Mother, are you sure?' Sarah looked desperately round to see if she could catch sight of the paper. A revolution in an erstwhile colony would certainly make headlines.

'Of course I'm sure, although why they can't call it Rhodesia like they used to I shall never know. Not there though, next door. In Mandoto. It was on the radio.'

'Oh. There. Well, I suppose it will mean refugees and things. What has it got to do with Susie?'

'It is right next door! God knows what might be happening, shelling and rockets, they might even cut food supplies, and there is Susie, pregnant, alone, in the midst of it. I don't know when I've been so worried.' Mrs Melling dissolved into hiccupping sobs.

'Now, now, Mother, there's no need to get in a state,' soothed Sarah, wondering why she sounded so like Douglas. 'Africa's much bigger than you think it is. Susan has Jerry with her, they live in a town and I'm sure the mining company will fly them out if there's the least danger.'

'It's all right for you with Douglas to take care of you but Jerry's not at all reliable. He should never have taken her there in the first place, everyone knows what happens to decent people in these revolutions and the baby's due in eleven weeks' time. I've tried to phone the Embassy but

18

the line's engaged and you know how hard it is to phone Susie. I don't know which way to turn.'

'Look, why don't you let me deal with it,' soothed Sarah. 'You go out to lunch with Madge, somewhere quiet and sunny, and during the day I will try and telephone Susie. I'm sure I'll be able to find out something.'

'Well, that's very kind of you, dear, but I do wish you'd ask Douglas. He knows about these things and when *he* rings up people make an effort. So ask Douglas, darling, please.'

Sarah promised that she would and put down the phone. At least she had been spared the horror of telling her mother about the art course, although she felt a familiar annoyance at having her own offer of help so summarily rejected. Only Douglas could do anything, only Douglas could help. Pretty, silly Sarah was no use at all.

The room smelt of roses and polish. Absently she twitched the fringe of a rug and smoothed two cushions, letting her eye dwell on the symmetry of soft curtain, shining parquet and rosewood desk. There was a photograph in a silver frame of herself and the children; Emma demure in lace, Joanne just a baby. So peaceful. So English. And Susie was so far away.

She was late for her meals-on-wheels duty, but that would have to wait. For once Douglas had forgotten to take the *Telegraph* with him, which was some measure of his discomfiture this morning. Sarah scanned it quickly, searching for the piece on Mandoto. Only a paragraph on the front page, but inside there was a feature giving the details. Mandoto had been granted independence some three years ago, and all had seemed quiet until the last few months. It appeared that an old tribal feud had been rumbling unresolved and when the Prime Minister, of one tribe, fired members of his cabinet, who were of another, the trouble began. Now a general in the army had seized power, assassinated the president and half the government and was attempting to gain control of the provincial towns, still loyal to the old régime. Fighting had broken out throughout the country.

Sarah chewed at a finger, alarmed despite herself. She and Susan had been very close as girls, although so different. Sue had been the bright bubbly one who changed her boyfriends as rapidly and with as much regret as a chameleon changing colour. Sarah could never be like that, for her boyfriends were always deep in love. When finally she steeled herself to be rid of them it was agony for them both, but what it was about herself that inspired such devotion was a mystery.

'You're too kind and too shy,' Susan had stated. 'You make them want to rescue you.'

'I don't need rescuing,' objected Sarah, but perhaps in a way she had. At least when Douglas appeared with his experience and his charm and his American Express card she felt rather as if she had been fished out of the pond. And now Susan, bright funny Susan who had held Sarah's hand on the night before her wedding and assured her that Douglas was the right choice, now she was alone, and pregnant and in danger.

Sarah rushed to the phone and began the long, tedious business of trying to make a call. It was always difficult, with delays and time differences and elephants breaking the line, but today the operator could make no progess at all. 'If you would try again later, caller,' she urged in her singsong voice, and Sarah agreed that she would. In the meantime there was nothing to do but begin her meals-on-wheels round, however belatedly.

* * *

20

She had noticed before that whenever she was late each and every one of her old people she visited seemed determined to keep her talking. Mrs Tinson wanted help with her knitting, which was really beyond redemption, and the Mandotan revolution had revived memories of the South African war in old Mr Braithwaite. He had rooted out photographs of his time in a cavalry regiment, a thin, totally unrecognisable figure in a white pith helmet standing next to a glum-looking horse.

'Never known heat like it,' he said with relish. 'Burn the flesh off a man it would. Them natives don't feel it though, oh no, running about like spring chickens when we were on our knees. And bloodthirsty –' he lowered his voice conspiratorially '– think nothing of life, them black boys don't. Slit your throat as soon as look at you. Tell you, I wouldn't like to be out there, what with a revolution and all. It only takes one spark and they're away.'

'My sister's in Africa now as a matter of fact,' said Sarah.

'Tell her to get back home I would, missus, before it's too late,' he warned with gloomy triumph, and Sarah retreated, clutching her plates.

When at last she reached home she sank exhausted into a chair. Then she roused herself, determined to have made some progress before Douglas came in. Still no connection, or any prospect of one according to the operator, and none of the Embassies was answering the phone. Was that a good or a bad sign? she wondered, aimlessly pottering in the kitchen. She had prepared so much food yesterday that she need not cook for days, and Mrs Benson had tidied the fridge, a job Sarah had been saving for this very afternoon. She repotted a plant that was looking cramped and hung around the radio, waiting for the news bulletins. There was no further news so she tried the phone again, without success. Later on, she fetched the girls from school and bought some plums, before returning to her vigil. It was a relief when Douglas came home.

She lifted her face for a perfunctory kiss. 'Douglas, have you heard? There's a revolution in Mandoto. I've been trying to phone Susie all day but I can't get through. Mother's having a fit and the radio says there is fighting near the border. Douglas, what can we do?'

'I really hold no brief for quelling revolutions, my dear,' said Douglas with a deliberate chill.

'Are you still cross about this morning? If so, I think it's jolly petty of you. This is important.'

'I happen to think harmony in the home is pretty important too,' he retorted and went upstairs to change. Sarah followed him, aware that he would be difficult until at last she climbed down. Suddenly the art course and all it represented seemed trivial in comparison to what might happen to Susie. The sooner she pacified Douglas the better. She picked up his jacket and dusted the collar before putting it on a hanger.

'I am sorry about this morning, darling – I was tired, I think. It's the weather, it's so close. I don't think I slept very well.'

'You know how I hate us to squabble in front of the children, Sarah.'

'Yes, Douglas, I know. I'm sorry.'

He gave her a warm smile and dropped an arm around her shoulders. 'Now, let's see what we can do about Susie, shall we?'

He rang somebody he knew in Salisbury, Harare as it was now, a colleague in the oil business. Sarah sat nervously by his side, her whole body tense. It seemed there was trouble up country, some band of Mandotan guerrillas had crossed the border fleeing from the troops and that confusion was making communications difficult. But the man would try and get in touch and would let them know as soon as there were any developments. Douglas thanked him and rang off.

'I'd better ring Mother,' said Sarah, looking anxious.

'Ask her to stay the night on Friday: she can babysit. It's your birthday, remember?'

'So it is. I don't feel very festive at the moment, I'm afraid.'

Douglas stroked her hair. 'Little worrier. We'll hear something soon, you'll see.'

'Our wine list, sir. May I recommend the burgundy, it is particularly fine.'

Douglas pursed his lips and looked sceptical. 'Not a year I favour, I'm afraid. I would prefer champagne, but this looks very disappointing.'

Sarah sighed and resigned herself to a long wait. Douglas despised all restaurant wine lists on principle and had been known to spend fifteen minutes wrestling with the waiter only to end up ordering Perrier water.

It was a place she hadn't visited before, very exclusive, with brown suede on the walls and a pianist playing late night music next to a miniscule dance floor. Hardly anyone there was under fifty.

'I'd like that fizzy red Italian stuff,' she said suddenly. 'Lambrusco. It's light and it's fun.'

'Good God, Sarah, are you serious?' Douglas looked as if she had just ordered brown ale in a cut-glass decanter. 'I'm sure they won't have it.'

'Lambrusco? Of course, sir.'

'Oh. A bottle of Lambrusco, then.' He waited until the waiter had disappeared and then said, 'When did you have Lambrusco?'

'At the Italian place in town. I went there with Mary. Don't worry, darling, you can hold your nose as you drink it, I won't mind. One comment though and you'll have to pay a forfeit. It's my birthday, remember?'

'I certainly do. And I haven't yet given you my present.' He reached into his pocket for a small, discreet package and laid it on the white cloth. Sarah took it with a delicious tingle of anticipation. She loved presents, especially the moment just before you opened them when it might possibly be something wonderful.

'It must be a watch,' she giggled, wrestling with the paper, green and gold with a jeweller's hallmark. 'It's that shaped box.'

Douglas twitched it from her fingers. 'If you know what it is there's no need to open it then, is there?'

'Don't be mean, darling, let me have it.' She half stood to grab it but he held it from her for just long enough to let the rest of the diners appreciate the scene. Douglas Hamilton with his beautiful wife on her birthday: Sarah sparkling in deep blue crêpe de Chine with only a hint of cleavage, Douglas smooth and executive in his Savile Row suit.

Sarah caught the package and sat down again, her fingers eager. There, on the bed of dark velvet lay an exquisite miniature watch, the face surrounded by clear, white diamonds, 'Good heavens – Douglas, it's beautiful!'

'Not nearly as beautiful as you, my sweet. Do you know that your dress matches your eyes?'

Of course she did, it was why she had chosen it, but she thanked him for the compliment with a smile. 'You shouldn't have bought something so terribly expensive. I shall never dare to wear it.'

'On the contrary, I'd like you to wear it all the time. It's insured.'

Sarah said nothing. Her everyday watch was big and stylish, a useful anonymous accompaniment to her life. This present was more suited to an idle dowager who felt no compunction about wearing diamonds at nine in the morning. At length she commented, 'I think it might seem a little vulgar if I wore it to do the shopping, and anyway it's too beautiful to spoil. I shall keep it for the times when I want to feel extra special. Thank you, darling, it's perfect.' There, that had solved the problem rather neatly. She felt sure of herself, the thoughts in her head for once running in straight lines, no tangles. They had heard about Susie today, safe and sound in Harare where Jerry had despatched her the moment trouble broke. Sarah had sent a telegram asking her to telephone as soon as she could, but heaven knew when that would be. The telephone connections were erratic in the extreme, no-one quite knew why.

They dined on squid and pepper steak and danced to 'String of Pearls'. An attractive couple, she tall in her high heels, he square and stocky. Sarah was a good dancer, good enough in fact to make her husband appear better than he was. He always said he could never dance so well with anyone else. When at last they left for home it was in a mood of sleepy content, and if Sarah was less than happy with her lot she knew better than to say so. The lights were still on downstairs as they turned into the drive.

'Damn, I hoped your mother would be safely tucked up and we'd have the place to ourselves. Have a brandy and a cuddle.' Douglas let his hand rest on his wife's knee.

'She's up late though. I wonder if there's any news.'

Sarah opened the car door and ran quickly to the house.

Mrs Melling was perched on the sofa, her plump face alight with excitement.

'She phoned! Susie phoned!' she said as soon as she saw her daughter. 'It must have cost a fortune, she was on for absolutely ages.'

'Is she all right? What's happening?' Sarah felt an unreasoning irritation that the news should come second-hand, that as always she was denied an active part in something that so directly concerned her. Douglas came in and rested his hands on her shoulders. She resisted the urge to pull herself free.

'She's in hospital,' said Mrs Melling breathlessly. 'Nothing serious, or so she says, but you can never believe Susie about things like that. Do you remember when she hurt her wrist, it was days before she'd go to the doctor –'

Douglas moved to the cocktail cabinet and poured two brandies. 'Just tell us what's the matter with her, Margaret,' he said and directed a laughing glance of conspiracy at his wife. Sarah ignored him.

'It's the baby,' went on Mrs Melling, fluttering her ringed and manicured hands. 'Blood pressure or something. Well, what can you expect, fleeing from an uprising. As I said to her, couldn't Jerry have taken some precautions?'

'Like what?' asked Sarah, looking bewildered. 'Mount a machine gun on the roof, do you mean?'

'Oh, I don't know. Anyway now he's left Susie all alone in the hospital and gone racing back to get shot by some murderous native I don't doubt. Why he can't be with her in Harare I do not know and actually to suggest that you might go out – I told Susie what I thought of that idea. It's quite bad enough having one daughter in danger of her life without sending the other out to join her.'

'Sounds like one of Jerry's mad ideas,' agreed Douglas, handing Sarah her brandy glass. She took it absently.

'As I said to her,' went on Mrs Melling, 'she should come home at once. But she won't hear of it, says the hospital won't allow it and even if they would she's not leaving Jerry. Though what she sees in him I shall never know, he dresses so untidily for one thing –'

'The casual look,' chuckled Douglas. 'Jerry takes it to extremes, I fear.'

It suddenly occurred to Sarah that Douglas should have married her mother, they would have been ideally suited. He would laugh at her and pet her and they would both adore it. She sipped at her thimbleful of brandy, lost in the vastness of the glass, and let it burn her tongue. Douglas usually poured sticky liqueurs for ladies; it had taken years to persuade him that brandy wouldn't make her ill.

'And Susie thought she would like me to go out?' she said thoughtfully. 'For a week or two, that was the idea? To keep her company?'

'Well – yes, darling, but I told her at once that you couldn't. Douglas would never let you go.'

Sarah turned to her husband. 'But Douglas will, won't you, darling? What was it you said – of course I could leave you all if Susie were ill or something of that nature. It must have been prophetic. Mother can come and stay to look after the children and Mrs Burton can easily take care of the house. I get in her way as it is, I think. I should like to spend a fortnight with Susie.'

'Don't be ridiculous.' Douglas was looking annoyed. 'Of course you can't fly off to Africa in the middle of a revolution. Really Sarah, you're becoming quite hare-brained in your schemes.'

'Harare's quite safe, you said so yourself only this

evening. Please, Douglas, don't be difficult. Susie needs me and I want to go.'

'*Me* be difficult! I've had enough of this, Sarah – first the art course and now something far more silly. What is the matter with you? I give you everything you could possibly want only to have you announce that you intend to go and live with a bunch of hippies, and when I won't put up with that you say you want to float off into the middle of nowhere with hardly a care for your family – I wonder if you shouldn't see a doctor, my girl. First the painting rubbish and now this. Absolutely, definitely no.'

Sarah stared at him, his face pink with anger. She knew herself to be white and her stomach began to heave, as it always did when she disagreed with Douglas. She took a sip of her brandy and said again, 'But I want to go. I'm sorry if you don't like it, darling, but I don't think you've any right to say no.' Her hands trembled and she clasped her glass to hide it.

'Sarah, he's your husband,' broke in Mrs Melling. 'Of course he's got the right.'

'Mother, I'm not a pet,' snapped Sarah. 'I want to go and I will!'

'Not if you expect me to pay for the ticket,' said Douglas coolly. His wife stared at him, wide-eyed. 'I see how it is,' she said slowly. 'An endless supply of goodies provided I do exactly as I'm told. How strange that I never saw it before. I *am* a pet to you, a dog that has to be slapped when it gets above itself. Well, even a dog has some rights. Will you sleep in the dressing room or shall I?'

'Don't be so silly!' blustered Douglas. He looked alarmed, as if the situation was getting beyond him. How could it be that Sarah, his Sarah, was being so difficult? 'You're getting this whole thing out of proportion and in the morning you'll be sorry. Now, let's go to bed and forget about it until we can discuss it rather more rationally.'

'Very well,' said Sarah meekly, but inside she burned. She could see he was rattled and a heady sense of dancing on a tight-rope overcame her. One mistake and she would fall, down, down, down into the depths, but in the time of her falling it would be like flying.

Once upstairs, she undressed as if nothing was wrong. Then, while Douglas was in the bathroom, she found sheets and blankets and made up the dressing room couch. It would be an uncomfortable bed but her mother occupied the spare room. When Douglas reappeared he gazed from the couch to her and back again, his eyes widening in disbelief. 'I am certainly not sleeping on that thing,' he said at length, his voice almost shrill. 'We will go to bed as we always do and forget this silliness. I'm sorry you're upset, Sarah, but it's got to stop. Now.'

'All right, then. I'll sleep here,' said Sarah and got between the sheets, turning her face into the pillow and closing her eyes.

Douglas stood gazing down at her, his face a study in bewilderment. Then he turned and stumped off into the bedroom. They both lay for a long time without sleeping.

In the morning Mrs Melling was subdued, Douglas surly and Sarah determinedly bright and smiling. When breakfast was over she got out the car and drove to the travel agent, to make enquiries about tickets. On the way back she stopped at a baker's and bought Douglas's favourite cream cake. The urge to back down was almost overwhelming and the placatory gesture was evidence of it. Still, she wasn't rowing with Douglas, she told herself, she was standing firm on principle. But just the same it wouldn't hurt if she bought him a cake.

'Hello, everyone,' she called when she got home, and saw that they were all in the garden. Douglas sat slumped in a deck chair, surrounded by papers like a circle of fire. The girls avoided him with a caution that spoke of harsh words recently uttered.

'You've been a long time, dear,' said Mrs Melling nervously.

'I had to enqire about tickets to Harare. Oh, and I bought you a present, darling, your favourite cake.'

'You can't bribe me, Sarah,' said Douglas stiffly.

'I would hardly expect to. Not with a cream cake at any rate.' She bent to kiss his cheek and let her breast rest briefly against his shoulder. Douglas lifted his head but she at once withdrew. 'I must go and prepare lunch,' she said lightly and tripped indoors.

When they had eaten Mrs Melling said she thought she would like to go home. 'I think you two ought to have a little chat,' she said meaningfully.

Sarah looked wide-eyed. 'I thought we had that last night. Douglas knows how I feel, I think.'

'You are making it rather obvious,' said Douglas belligerently and rose to his feet, glaring at Sarah with ill-concealed anger. Sarah blushed and would not look at him. It was so hard to sustain this calm and cheerful pose, it would be so much easier to say she was sorry and have everything normal once again. Tears threatened to spill and she searched for a handkerchief.

'Susie needs me,' she sniffed. 'Goodness knows, I don't want to leave you, Douglas, but I can't see your objection. Susie's ill, you've admitted yourself there's no danger and Mother can look after the house. Why can't I go?'

'Because – because she doesn't need you. I need you.

There she is in some expensive hospital awaiting one of the most important experiences of a woman's life and –'

'– quite alone,' interrupted Sarah. 'She doesn't know anyone. Of course she wants her family with her and if I can't go then it ought to be Mother.' She looked expectantly at Mrs Melling who flopped into a chair as if struck by lightning.

'Good heavens. I would, Sarah, you know I would, but I am such a bad traveller. Why, even Susie didn't suggest it, she wanted you, she was adamant.'

Douglas began to look harried. 'I thought you were going home, Margaret,' he said crossly and Sarah stood up.

'I'll run you back, Mother. Come on, girls, you can come for the ride. I think Daddy would like some peace.'

At bedtime Sarah took a long, leisurely bath and drifted into the dressing room wearing only her négligée, a film of white lace. Douglas was there.

'Come to bed, Sarah.'

'I'd like to, Douglas.' She stood before him, hanging her head. Her hair was a cloud about her face, her eyes deep pools. She seemed so fragile, thought Douglas and reached for her. She turned away.

'I'm sorry about last night,' he said suddenly. 'I didn't mean half the things I said.'

The briefest smile. 'I know that, silly. We both lost our tempers. But, Douglas, I do think I ought to go; Susie needs me.'

'And I need you!' It was painfully true, he had thought he was past such embarrassing desire. He could see her nipple, pink and tender, through a hole in the lace. Further down was the shadow of her hair, guardian of that dark and secret place. He tried to look away and could not.

'Please, Douglas. Please.' She turned full towards him, letting the négligée part. As he hesitated, torn and desperate, she began to turn away.

'All right!' he said hoarsely. Surprise made her blink.

'You mean – I can go?'

'Yes. Yes. You can go! For two weeks and two weeks only.'

In a moment she was in his arms, laughing, warm, letting him push her back to the couch where he could plunge into her as she half lay, half sat beneath him. It was over almost as soon as it had begun and Douglas lay sprawled on her, a gasping fish.

'Darling, darling Douglas,' murmured Sarah. It had excited her, the teasing, and she was unsatisfied. When they lay side by side in their bed, Douglas calm in sleep, she tossed uncomfortably. But at least she had won. She was going!

It was arranged that she should leave in ten days' time. As the date drew nearer Sarah's anticipation dissolved into thinly disguised panic. Since her marriage she had travelled no further than Brighton by herself, and that was to see an old school friend who met her at the station. What had possessed her to think she could zoom off round the world at a moment's notice? What would she do if her passport was stolen, if she lost her luggage, her money, her ticket? What if the children forgot her; two weeks is a long time when you're small. The doubts fizzed in her brain and she longed to talk to Douglas about them, but always stopped herself. If he suspected her feelings he would cancel the flight.

A visit to the doctor made her feel still worse, with an

arm full of punctures, a handbag full of pills and a head full of instructions. She wasn't to bathe except in swimming pools; she must be careful of the water, and the food, and the flies; consult a doctor the moment she felt ill, avoid unlabelled alcohol – the list was endless.

'I'm only going to Harare,' she murmured. 'I'm sure it's very civilised.' But it didn't stem the flow of information.

'Disease is rife in the tropics,' he declared with relish. 'Come and see me the moment you return.' She knew he would be disappointed if she didn't catch Lassa fever at the very least.

Her mother was equally gloomy. 'I don't like it at all, Sarah. It isn't right, upsetting Douglas like this. You'll regret it in the end, mark my words.'

'But I told you, Douglas has agreed, and you can't possibly want Susie to be left alone in a strange city. It must be awful.'

'Yes. Poor Susie,' sighed her mother. 'I must buy her a really lovely present. Now, what shall it be?'

'Not anything expensive.' It would not do for Douglas to be confronted with her mother's debts at this most sensitive moment.

'Really, Sarah!' Mrs Melling looked at her in surprise. 'After I bought you that lovely cashmere sweater for your birthday? I pride myself on being fair to my daughters: what I do for you I must do for Susie. It's only right.'

Sarah almost ground her teeth in annoyance but forced herself to speak calmly. 'Of course you must be fair, it's only that I don't want you to bother Douglas for money while I'm away. Do you understand?'

Mrs Melling's surprise turned into outrage. 'I hope I have never put unreasonable demands on my son-in-law! If he wants me to eke out a miserable existence on my pension then of course I must do so, although to see me in rags living on crusts when you are in that enormous house with maids –'

Sarah's head began to throb in time with her arm. 'All right, Mother,' she sighed. 'We're not asking you to starve although goodness knows you ought to be able to manage – all right, all right!' She gave in at the fresh onslaught. 'Just don't ask Douglas until I'm back.'

The last few days were spent shopping for clothes. It was early September and the shops were full of autumn wools and winter furs. Anything summery was hugely expensive, presumably on the principle that you had to be rich to go anywhere hot, and she was committed to thrift since extravagance only increased her guilt feelings. In the end she bought a linen trouser suit in pale blue, to travel in, with a white blouse which she could change for a skimpy navy tee shirt before they landed. It looked cool and casual, yet sophisticated. For the rest, her English summer wardrobe would have to do, and anything else she needed must be bought in Zimbabwe. Browsing round the shops would be a useful way of passing the time, since apart from visiting Susie there would be little to do. She packed one evening dress, a strapless white silk sheath that set off her unusual colouring of dark hair and deep blue eyes. It would probably never see the light of day, but one never knew. The very first tingle of excitement ran through her and she shut the lid of the case, whispering, 'Oh! I can't wait to go!'

Emma appeared in the doorway. She looked from the case to her mother's flushed face and her eyes filled with tears. 'You won't come back,' she wailed. Sarah ran to her, at once flooded with guilt. Surely it wasn't so bad to want to go? Motherhood didn't mean that you could never leave them. Not even for a day. Did it? Only Emma's sobs answered her and distractedly she promised treats, sweets, enormous presents if only the child would stop making her feel so bad.

In a bid to re-establish his authority Douglas took command of the arrangements. It pleased him to be seen as the much-travelled businessman taking good care of his shy and innocent wife. He showered Sarah with guide-books, addresses, insurance certificates and itineraries, as well as essentials such as tickets and a passport. If she had let him he would have put her in charge of the stewardess, thought Sarah, like a boarding school child flying to see its parents during the holidays. But secretly she was relieved. To have to deal with the complexities of travel when she felt so muddled inside herself would have been too much.

They took the children with them to the airport, and chatted cheerfully all the way. The plane left shortly before six and would arrive in Harare in the early hours of the morning.

'They're only two hours ahead of us, so there won't be much jet lag,' said Douglas knowledgeably and Sarah nodded, feeling a total innocent in comparison with her much-travelled husband.

As always Douglas guided her carefully round the airport routine. She began to feel like an invalid about to be deprived of the nurse. Sudden panic engulfed her.

'I don't think this is such a good idea,' she squeaked, clutching Douglas's lapel with trembling fingers.

'Don't be silly, darling,' he said firmly. 'They're calling your flight now, off you go.'

'But I don't want to! Oh, Douglas don't make me go by myself.'

'Go on, darling, you'll be all right. Have a lovely time. Remember – I love you. Always. Come back safe.'

'I love you too. 'Bye darlings. Give Mummy a kiss. I'll be back soon, I promise. I love you –'

She remembered them like that for a very long time. A stocky, dark-haired man, not very tall, wearing glasses, with a little girl on either side, waving, waving, waving, until she was out of sight.

Chapter 2

Sarah stared at herself in the tiny mirror. She looked pale and nervous, and her insides felt like jelly. If she went back he would start again, that flabby, half-drunk man in the next seat, rubbing his leg against hers and whispering suggestively. He was horrible, but she felt incapable of defence. Nonetheless the alternative was to take up residence in the loo, and the other passengers might have something to say about that. She would have to go back and face him. With sudden anger at her cowardice she marched back down the aisle, pushed past her neighbour and sat down.

'Glad to see you back,' he murmured, and again pressed his leg against hers.

'Please stop that,' said Sarah in ringing tones, 'or I shall complain to the cabin staff.'

The man blinked, went pale and huddled in the farthest corner of his seat while Sarah picked up a magazine and leafed through it with assumed calm.

For the first time since she left home she felt a slight lessening of the tension that was making even her jaw ache. These problems were only little ones and if she tackled each as it came, like a batsman facing the bowling, she might manage to get to Harare safely. The mistake was to spend precious mental energy running through possible scenarios without doing anything. That man would never have been a nuisance if she had choked him off at once. For a wild moment she thought about apologising, but ordered a drink instead. It wasn't her fault he was a lecher. That drink was followed by another, and gradually she began to relax. When the curtains were drawn and the lights dimmed she actually began to doze.

The announcement took them all by surprise. In her sleepy state Sarah hardly took it in and almost consulted her neighbour before she remembered the situation. Then the radio crackle came again.

'This is the captain speaking. I have been informed that due to circumstances beyond our control we are unable to fly directly to Harare, Zimbabwe, and will be landing at Nairobi in approximately thirty minutes. You will then be informed of arrangements to enable you to complete your journey. We apologise for any inconvenience.'

A babble of voices broke out. Sarah looked round in bewilderment and met her neighbour's gaze. 'What does it mean?' she burst out. 'Why can't we go on?'

He looked at her with blank, cold eyes. 'Don't ask me, lady. You can sort your bloody self out.'

Sarah stiffened and lifted her chin. 'I can assure you that's exactly what I intend to do,' she said clearly, and began to gather her things.

The lights of the airport appeared beneath the wing, brilliant and unmistakable. The unpleasant thought that there might really be something wrong with the aircraft popped into her head: perhaps an engine had fallen off or something. Still, there was nothing she could do about it and when all was said and done it would solve a great many problems if they crashed. Survival seemed infinitely more complicated. But the plane banked, turned and swept in to land with a gentle bump on the tarmac. When she rose to leave, her neighbour trod on her foot.

It was not as hot as she had expected, in fact the night

air chilled her skin. But the smell was the thing she noticed, trees and flowers and engine oil, just a brief taste of Africa before she was bundled into an airport bus and taken to the featureless uniformity of the lounge. Like airport lounges the world over, it was not a place of comfort. Huge windows looked on to the blackness of an alien night, punctuated with lights like eyes, whilst within all was neon brilliance. In the harsh light the faces around her looked strained and unhappy; no-one smiled. Somewhere in the throng a child began to cry and Sarah's thoughts turned at once to her children. Oh, to be back with them. Such a short time away and she wanted to go home. A man in some uniform or other began to speak and gradually they all turned to listen.

'We are sorry for this interruption to your flight,' he began. 'As you probably know, there have been recent disturbances in Mandoto, and following an incident in Mandotan air space a few hours ago it has been decided to suspend flights for the time being. We hope to have further information for you in the morning, but at present I must ask you to make yourselves as comfortable as possible here for the rest of the night. We do regret the inconvenience and I can assure you that we are doing everything to enable you to complete your journey.'

A roar of noise, questions, complaints, accusations, met him as he finished. He was engulfed in a wall of people and could be heard vainly trying to soothe them. Sarah picked up her flight bag and went to sit on a plastic-covered bench. It was most uncomfortable, hard and unreceptive, with a camber designed to tip you to the floor if you tried to relax on it. What was she doing here, looking at an unreal world through eyes gritty with weariness? It might almost be a dream, the sort you have when near to waking. Little knots of people were gathering everywhere, discussing the situation, but she felt strangely calm. There was nothing she could do. In the morning she would talk to people but now she would rest. She pillowed her head on her bag, swung her feet up and tried to sleep.

It was half past six when she decided she could stand the ache in her back no longer. She stood up, collected her things and went to wash. The passengers had settled at last, lying wherever they could find a space, only the odd restless figure still moving. She picked her way over bodies to the washroom. Outside the sun was already high, a clear white light over the endless tarmac. The temperature inside was governed by the air conditioning but all the same Sarah took off her bra and changed into her skimpy sleeveless top. Then she cleaned her teeth, an action which always renewed her spiritually for some reason. Perhaps it invoked faith in tomorrow. Much refreshed, she set off in search of an official.

A man in a scruffy, khaki uniform was skulking near the baggage section.

'Excuse me,' said Sarah. The man looked hunted and tried to scuttle through a door. Sarah slipped in front of him and smiled. After a second's hesitation he took a good look at her, straightened, pulled at his tunic and smiled hopefully back. 'I was wondering,' said Sarah gently, 'if you could tell me what I ought to do.'

The man was very short but began to puff up visibly. He smoothed his hair. 'What seems to be the trouble?'

Sarah allowed her mouth to droop. 'My sister is ill in Harare. I simply have to get to her, but what can I do? Aren't there any planes at all?'

He shook his head decisively. 'None at all. They're shooting at anything and although they're bloody – excuse me – very bad shots we can't take the risk. Only cargo planes at the moment. Now, may I suggest I contact an hotel –'

'Cargo planes? Couldn't I go in one of those? There's only me and one suitcase, wherever that is.'

'Probably here.' He waved a hand at the mountain of baggage behind him.

Every shape and size of suitcase was heaped in a higgledy-piggledy pile. Sarah gazed up at it. And there was her case sitting right in the middle. It was an omen. 'That's mine,' she said happily and waited while he tugged it free, starting a mini avalanche in the process. He set it on the floor in front of her, a study in reluctance. He had no wish to spoil his comfortable routine for her, although she was as pretty as an antelope, long, long legs and a face of delicate bones. Sarah felt his eyes on her and smiled in genuine gratitude. 'Now, where do I find this cargo plane?'

In the end it was money that persuaded him, twenty pounds to find a plane and a further twenty if the pilot would take her. This decided, he picked up her case and led the way out into the sunshine. Even at this early hour the air was deliciously warm and small birds fluttered to and fro, pecking at invisible insects. Sarah struggled to keep up, her flight bag bumping against her legs. To her left, huge airliners stood in rows on the tarmac, but her guide turned away from them, marching off into the distance with dogged purpose. Their destination seemed to be a few small planes huddled in the farthest corner of the airfield and by the time they reached them sweat was running in a steady trickle down Sarah's back. There was a spreading wet stain between her guide's shoulders and she feared that she had one just like it. If it was like this now it would be unbearable by midday.

'We'll try Cottar,' said the little baggage clerk. 'He's

always a sucker for a pretty face – begging your pardon, ma'am.'

Sarah only hoped she was pretty enough. Her hair was sticking to her head and the crisp lines of her suit, which had withstood everything up to now, were wilting. They stopped beside a small, almost windowless plane. It had propellers on both wings, the leading edges of which were chipped and indented, as if from the attentions of a breed of aerial mice. Sarah would not have been surprised to find a notice stating that it was a relic of the last war, but in fact three men were peering intently under an engine cover. Two were black, one white.

'Mr Cottar?' called the baggage clerk. The white man lifted his head.

'Who wants him?' The voice was heavily Afrikaans. Cottar was a thickset man with a neck like a bull, the face above it solid, deeply tanned, humorous. It gave Sarah confidence.

'I do,' she said. 'My name is Sarah Hamilton and I have to get to Harare. I'm hoping you can take me. For a suitable fee, of course.'

Cottar looked at her, put down his spanner and wiped his hands on an oily rag. He saw a tall, elegant woman, her skin English fair and already flushed with the sun. She was dishevelled but it suited her, the dark hair in tangled curls, the spindly sandals dust-covered. 'Well,' he said, 'and you are a sight for sore eyes and no mistake.'

'I have to get to Harare,' repeated Sarah. 'My sister is ill and I can't hang about here.'

'Don't you know that there are nasty little black men shooting at the planes?' asked Cottar.

'They tell me they're not very good shots. Besides, I don't suppose you want to get killed any more than I do, Mr Cottar.'

He laughed. 'Very true, very true. Now, what about the price. You own a diamond mine, I hope?'

'Just a husband in Wimbledon, England,' said Sarah with a grin. She moved into the shade of the wing and they settled down to serious haggling. It took what seemed a very long time, for Cottar enjoyed looking at her and Sarah was new to the game. Every now and then she thought of what Douglas would say if he could see her, and almost lost the thread of discussion, but in the end they were both happy. Sarah had paid ten pounds less than she had anticipated and Cottar received ten pounds more than he had hoped.

'Now, when do we fly?' she asked.

'Two hours, maybe three. You had breakfast?' She shook her head. 'Well, there's the restaurant back where you came from, or perhaps you'd like a few bits and pieces from the bag inside there.' He indicated an oil-stained canvas holdall just inside the big cargo door. Sarah looked at the vast expanse of boiling tarmac between her and the terminal building and opted for the bag. She settled herself inside the door and ate greasy cheese sandwiches washed down with warm coca-cola.

Cottar went back to his engine. Men from the other planes came up from time to time to talk to him and each one sauntered past to have a look at her. She ignored them and settled herself in the open doorway with a book, legs dangling, one shoe balanced on a toe.

'Hey, Cottar!' The shout made her jump. Her shoe fell from her foot to the ground. A tall, dust-covered figure was walking towards the plane, dressed in crumpled khaki trousers and a stained bush jacket that might once have been green. A rucksack was slung over one shoulder and a long, black rifle was stuck through the top straps. Sarah sat up.

. Cottar appeared round the wing. 'Hey, Joe! Good to see you, man! Heard you were up at Okavango, hunting.' He grasped the stranger's hand and pumped it vigorously.

'I was for a bit. Got sick of pratting about with bloody tourists. The way they're banging away there'll be nothing left to shoot in a year or two.'

'Ah, the same story. You want to hitch a ride?'

'Sure do. What are you carrying?' He lounged against the side of the plane.

Cottar put a finger to the side of his nose. 'What do you think, eh? But you'll have to share a packing case with Mrs Hamilton, if you can bear it. Mrs Hamilton, Joe Langeveldt.'

Sarah's dark-blue gaze met Langeveldt's tawny-brown one. Neither of them smiled. She was suddenly conscious of her bare foot and she slowly crossed her long legs. 'How do you do, Mr Langeveldt,' she said stiffly. 'You startled me and I dropped my shoe. I wonder if you would be so kind –?'

He looked from her shoe to her face and back again. 'Pick it up yourself,' he said flatly.

Sarah's mouth popped open in astonishment but before she could speak Cottar was scrabbling for her sandal in the dust. 'We're giving Mrs Hamilton a ride to Harare, Joe,' he explained hastily. 'She has a sick sister, you know how it is –'

'Oh yes. I know how it is. The bloody tourists get everywhere. I've wet-nursed enough of them in my time and God knows, they need nursing. Thomas Cook has a lot to answer for.'

'I am not a tourist,' said Sarah, her voice slightly shrill.

'So. The lady is not a tourist.' Langeveldt swung his rucksack into the plane, missing Sarah by a fraction of an inch, and against her will she flinched.

'She comes from Wimbledon, England,' broke in Cottar, trying to fit the errant shoe back on Sarah's unresisting foot.

'Ah. Wimbledon. Come to tell us not to be horrid to the natives or nasty to the animals. I bet she's got a pretty picture of a panda on a sticker on her car.'

'Come on, Joe, Mrs Hamilton's not doing any harm. I'm only giving her a lift. How about a beer? We'll be leaving in an hour.'

'Sounds like a good idea.' Langeveldt sauntered off with Cottar to the engine. Sarah could hear cans being opened and the murmur of voices, punctuated by raucous bursts of laughter. She hoped they weren't talking about her.

Time passed slowly. The hour that Cottar had promised came and went. It grew steadily hotter. Flies gathered in clusters, settling on Sarah's mouth and nostrils whenever she ceased fanning her hand. At last she went to ask Cottar what was happening.

'Ah, Mrs Hamilton, you getting restless?' He was sitting in the shade of some packing cases, empty beer cans all around.

Sarah looked at him and sighed. 'I had hoped to leave today,' she said mildly.

A long figure rolled out from behind some machinery castings. Langeveldt.

'You know how the tourists like their timetables, Eric,' he murmured. Sarah thought of Douglas's itinerary and blushed inwardly. She stared at the floor and sneaked covert glances at this strange, dislikeable man. He wasn't at all good-looking, except in the way that anything strong and healthy is good-looking. His hair was a dusty, sand colour, bleached almost white in parts. His skin bore similar marks of the sun in its deep tan and the creases round his strange, tawny eyes. But the main feature of his face was the nose, jutting like a beak. He looked like a hawk and behaved like one, thought Sarah. Aggressive and dangerous. He made her desperately uncomfortable.

'You want my fingerprints too?' asked Langeveldt.

Sarah blushed scarlet. 'I want only to go to Harare,' she said, and her voice shook.

'We ought to go, Joe,' said Cottar apologetically, and after a moment Langeveldt heaved himself to his feet. Sarah swallowed. She felt still more threatened when he stood up for he towered over her, his shoulder on a level with the top of her head. When he strode to the aircraft she had to jump aside, for he was clearly not prepared to walk round her. And she had to spend hours in a plane with him.

'Oh, Douglas, you were right,' she murmured to herself.

At the last moment they almost left her behind. Fright brought on a sudden desire to answer the call of nature and she had to trudge to a smelly little hut far away in the haze. The engines started as she was walking back and she had to hare across the tarmac to arrive gasping and covered in sweat just as they were about to close the door.

'Mr Cottar, how could you?' she asked accusingly.

He looked apologetic but said nothing and she knew it was Langeveldt's doing. She slumped into a corner as far away from him as possible and opened one of the cans of beer. She hated beer, but the coca-cola was gone.

There were only two seats in the whole plane, one for Cottar and the other beside him, which Langeveldt appropriated. She was left to wedge herself in the back between a packing case and an oil drum, wondering as she did so if it was too late to develop a phobia about flying. The whole plane was shuddering and she thought

46

anxiously of the rust spots that surrounded every rivet all the way along the fuselage. The roar from the engines became deafening and Sarah noted with detached interest that her knuckles had turned white as they gripped one of the ribs on the floor. At least if she ever survived this she would have something to talk about when she got home. The plane lurched alarmingly, lifted, touched again, lifted and was away. Sarah swallowed and reached for another can of beer. Perhaps Cottar was better at landings.

The engines subsided to a drone and Sarah began to feel bored, and then sleepy. Apparently Langeveldt felt the same because he left his seat, rearranged some cargo and stretched out with his head on the rucksack. The black length of the rifle lay close beside him. Sarah moved up to sit beside Cottar.

'That man, Langeveldt,' she asked under cover of the engine noise. 'Who is he?'

Cottar grinned. 'I don't suppose you've heard of him in Wimbledon.'

'Not exactly, no.'

'Ah, he's done everything. White hunter for a time, good at it too, the clients got their trophies and none of them got killed. But Joe, he says what he thinks. If they shot lousy, he said so. If they got drunk and had a hangover he wouldn't pretend it was fever, oh no. "Pissed again, Wilfred?" he'd say. But what finished him was the guy who shot a rhino when he should have been resting. He damn nigh strangled the fool; his boys had to drag him off. Protected species, you know. Happens to all of them in the end, I suppose – they get to like the animals more than the clients.

'So then he was a game warden. Drank too much, screwed too much, but that was no matter. It was what he did to the poachers. Tied one up in a giraffe snare and left him. I ask you! Didn't do much for race relations, believe me.' The plane bucked a little in the hot air and he turned little black handles in the roof to adjust the trim.

'Then came the elephant cropping. Hairy job that is and no mistake. Now, don't look so shocked, it has to be done. You ever see what a herd of elephants does to a place and you'd understand. It's a desert, nothing can live. So, they crop 'em. Two men and two rifles go in on foot and take every one. And the elephants don't like it. I saw it once, elephants screaming, charging, antelope bounding away. The smell of blood, cordite, elephant shit. So much dust you can hardly see. And then it goes quiet. There's nothing. Grey mounds, small till you get up to them. And Joe. He'd come out of it like a man leaving hell. And then he'd hit the bottle, drunk for days. Even a man his size can't take that for long.'

'Why did he do it?'

Cottar shrugged. 'God knows. Things happen, I don't know. The pay's good. But I reckon he'd be dead now if it wasn't for Aunt Daisy.'

'Who's she?'

'She isn't any more. Run over by a truck after too much gin, and it wasn't the truck driver who was drunk, I can tell you. But she tried to look after Joe. She used to make me laugh, big flowery hats, even in the rains. Had two ideas only, Dettol and birth control. If she wasn't on about one then it was the other. Taught all her servants a song about Durex, made them sing it every Sunday. You see it was a religion with her – any girl got pregnant they had to pretend it was a puncture.'

Sarah choked on a giggle. 'She sounds dreadful. But she must have sent him to school, surely?'

'Yes, off and on. Not even Daisy could manage him half the time and that uncle of his, Bob, wasn't any damned use. Funny guy, Joe. Sometimes you'd think he hated people, you know?'

'You surprise me,' said Sarah sardonically.

Cottar ignored the interruption. 'You don't cross Langeveldt these days, not if you want to live. He's only really happy alone in the bush, but, well, Africa's getting smaller, not so many places a man can be alone. I suppose he'll go the same way as loony old Bob and it'll be a damned shame.'

'What happened to Bob?' asked Sarah, not sure that she wanted to know.

'Got dead drunk on native beer, went to sleep on his verandah and got eaten by a lion. And he wasn't too drunk to notice.'

'You're not serious!' She looked at him with incredulous awe.

Cottar gave a short laugh. 'Don't tell the tourists but lions take quite a few juicy people of a dark night, especially these days when everyone thinks they're fireside pussies. But you needn't worry, Mrs Hamilton, you'll be quite safe in Harare.'

'Thank God my name's not Albert,' she murmured, but Cottar looked puzzled. She stared down at the earth far below and made a mental note to remember to tell Douglas. They could share the joke.

The late afternoon sun was turning the lumbering plane into an oven. Sarah started to remove her jacket and then caught sight of her sweat-soaked top. Her breasts were clearly outlined against the thin fabric: she could hardly reveal more if she were naked. She pushed her arms quickly back into the jacket, hoping that Langeveldt was still asleep. He wasn't.

'So, it's a modest little tourist we have. What did you

put it on for if not to make us look at you?'

Sarah blushed scarlet and threw a furious glance at him, lying propped on one elbow amongst the crates. 'If I'd known you were going to be around I'd have worn a suit of armour,' she said lightly, exercising massive self-control. 'But I'm not used to being attacked for no good reason.'

'Most creatures attack when they're hungry,' said Langeveldt. For a moment she failed to understand him, but then something in the way he was lying there . . . He ran his tongue slowly over his lips. And looked at her.

Again her face flamed, she gave a strangled gasp and spun round to look fixedly out of the window. Lange-veldt's laughter erupted like the howls of a tribe of monkeys and Sarah felt hot tears pricking her eyelids. To her eternal shame a few drops fell on to her clenched fists. Cottar saw them. 'Leave her alone, Joe,' he called. 'You're making her cry.'

'Crying now, is it? The silly bitch'll have the vapours next. Oh Christ, how I hate these fragile ladies. What this one needs is a good –'

Sarah threw the can of beer with vicious intent. It slammed into the side of the plane and exploded in froth, causing Cottar to let go of the controls to see what on earth was happening. The plane hit an air pocket and lurched sideways, a crate shifted, Langeveldt swore horribly and Sarah fell in a heap on top of Langeveldt's rifle as it rolled across the floor. Iron fingers dug into her shoulders and threw her aside.

'You stupid, bloody tourist!' he bellowed. 'You could have broken it!'

'I wish I had, you mindless peasant,' screeched Sarah.

'That – is – enough!' roared Cottar. 'I am trying to fly a plane! Mrs Hamilton, you come and sit by the window and look at the scenery. Joe, please, as you value your life, keep your tongue between your teeth, sit on that crate and drink some whisky. So help me, this is the last time I carry anything that moves.'

'Silly cow's bent the forward sight,' said Langeveldt, anxiously studying his gun.

'Hurrah!' said Sarah.

'QUIET!'

An uneasy peace descended. Langeveldt started on the whisky and Sarah stared down at the ground. They were flying quite low over earth parched by the sun. At this distance there seemed only to be dust interspersed with tired trees and the occasional patch of greyish scrub. Nothing moved except a few birds, and Sarah thought this odd, reared as she had been on the idea of Africa as a large zoo with lions and elephants round every corner. This bit seemed to have shut up shop.

The gleam of sunlight on metal caught her eye. She leaned forward and peered at the ground. It was a truck of some sort with tiny figures scurrying around it.

'Mr Cottar, what do you think −?' She got no further. There was no noise, or perhaps there was so much that it failed to register. It was as if a giant hand had tweaked the aeroplane's tail, lifting it high and then letting it go so that the little metal box fell with sickening force.

Sarah was flung on to the floor, ricocheting from crates and walls like a ping pong ball until desperate fingers found something to cling to. Even in the midst of her terror she was annoyed that it should be Langeveldt's foot. A broken bottle, the smell of whisky. Cottar's face, how scared he looked, lips drawn back from his teeth in a soundless snarl. Douglas, my children, I am so very, very sorry. Crashing, bouncing, lurching, but hang on, just hang on.

Silence. Was it over? Someone was sobbing; she wished they would stop. It was her. She couldn't stop.

'Will you let go my bloody foot?'

With difficulty Sarah released her death grip on Langeveldt's desert boot. Her fingers left indentations in the leather and presumably in the flesh beneath. She tried to sit up, but her muscles refused to do as they were told and she lay shuddering on the floor for long minutes.

Langeveldt was on the move. A hole had appeared in the side of the plane and he cautiously eased his head through it and looked slowly and carefully around. He came back to Sarah.

'On your feet. We've go to get out, fast.'

'I can't – I can't –'

A hand seized the waistband of her trousers and pulled her upright. 'Get moving. And find something else to wear.'

'What?' She couldn't understand him. 'Where's Mr Cottar?'

Langeveldt did not trouble to reply. He had dragged her suitcase on to a broken packing crate and was rummaging inside. He held up her white evening dress. 'Is this silk?'

She nodded wordlessly and Langeveldt screwed it into a ball and thrust it into his rucksack. Then he turned back to her case, finally flinging some clothes at her. A cream blouse, some fawn trousers, a pair of canvas shoes and a brown jacket. 'You can wear Cottar's hat,' he said flatly.

'But – I don't want to change. And where is Mr Cottar? He may be hurt.'

With her first voluntary action since the crash she climbed over the twisted wreckage at the front of the plane. Cottar was sprawled sideways in his seat, blood oozing from his nose and ears.

'Leave him alone,' said Langeveldt calmly.

'But he's not dead! Look, his eyes are open.' As she bent over him, Cottar's mouth tried to move. She cast a look of hope at Langeveldt. 'Quickly, help me, he's all right!'

'His back's broken. Now get changed and let's get out of here. This thing could go up in flames at any moment.'

'Then we must get him out at once. I know it's a risk if it's his back, but we can't leave him here, it might take days to get help. Come on, help me lift him.' She put her arms under Cottar's shoulders and heaved. He moved perhaps an inch. She tried again, giving everything she had, and a groan escaped Cottar's purple lips.

'Please, Langeveldt, help me. He's your friend.'

Still Langeveldt stood and looked at her. His face was calm and smooth, the gaze of the tawny eyes detached and objective. 'Leave him to die in peace,' he said. 'It's all you can do. And I told you to get changed.'

He took hold of her arm and dragged her back down the plane. In her state of shock Sarah hardly resisted, standing like a child even when he began to undress her.

'We can't leave him,' she whispered. 'We must wait for help.'

Langeveldt pulled her top over her head. 'The only people who are going to find us will be delighted to make full use of these.' He grabbed a handful of pale, pink-tipped breast and squeezed. Sarah yelped and pulled away. He threw the cream blouse at her. 'Now, put on some clothes that won't show up in the bush and let's leave before the people who shot us down come to see what they've bagged. With any luck they won't even know we were on board.'

As she struggled into the clothes, Langeveldt swiftly collected the things he intended to take. It was little enough, just the remaining cans of beer, a small water carrier, two cups and the last of Cottar's food. Sarah took out her three small photographs of Douglas and the children and put them in too.

'I'm not leaving them,' she said warningly, and Langeveldt just shrugged.

Sarah went back to Cottar. Only a thin slit of blue showed beneath his eyelids and the trickle of blood from his ear had dried.

'Please, Langeveldt,' pleaded Sarah. 'Couldn't we at least lift him away from the plane? They might help him, you don't know they won't. Not everybody's like you.'

'If we move him they'll know we were here.' Langeveldt bent over Cottar's crumpled form, feeling in his pockets. He took his knife, his wallet, his cigarette case and his watch.

'You can't – rob him!' gasped Sarah.

'I think his family might like these back, don't you? Get out of the plane, woman, you're a pain in the arse.'

Sarah swung herself down to the brown tussocky grass. Cottar had done a good job: half the plane's tail was missing and yet he had picked his way between trees and ant hills to make a clear landing. At the last moment they had tipped into a small gully, smashing the plane's nose and probably Cottar's back at one and the same time.

Langeveldt jumped easily from the plane and pulled his rucksack and rifle after him. He handed them to Sarah, pointing to a tree some fifty yards away. 'Over there.' His face was bleak. She opened her mouth to question him, then closed it again and struggled over to the tree. They could never carry this load more than half a mile, they would have to leave something. She turned to see Langeveldt tossing some burning paper into the open side of the plane before sprinting away. For long seconds nothing happened, and then with a roar like a train in a tunnel the structure erupted. Gouts of flame and oily smoke shot into the burning air.

'No! No! No!' Sarah pressed her hands over her eyes like a child trying to hide. Not even Langeveldt could have done this thing. There was a man inside there! And Cottar had been his friend, he had actually liked Langeveldt.

The pilot's stained canvas hat plopped on to her head. 'Move it.' Picking up rucksack and rifle Langeveldt hustled her before him into the empty land.

On and on. Nothing to guide her but the insistent prodding of Langeveldt's hand on her spine. So thirsty. So tired. When she stumbled and fell he hooked a hand in her collar and heaved, and put a toe against her bottom and kicked.

'Brute! Beast!' she hissed, longing to retaliate and unable to do more than stagger on. Flies swarmed about their heads, feeding on their sweat. When they crawled on her face she was too weary even to raise a hand to brush them away. And it was so hot. Even through Cottar's hat she could feel the throbbing heat but then with a startling suddenness the sun set and it was night. But it seemed no cooler.

'I can't go on,' she said then. 'I can't see.'

'I can.' Again the prodding hand.

Her mind began to play tricks on her. Was that a witch in the shadows? No witches in Africa, just lions, lions that ate people whether you liked it or not. But she wouldn't be eaten by a lion, Douglas wouldn't allow it. Where was Douglas, oh there, right behind –

'Douglas?' She looked up into Langeveldt's impassive face.

'Keep walking.'

What a terrible backache she had. When Emma was born it had been like that and they kept telling her to lie down, as if you could when it hurt so much. Now she'd give anything to lie down – so it couldn't be the same. Douglas had been so proud. Had he wanted a boy? He would never say.

These horrible mosquitoes. Her mother had a thing about flies; she was probably destroying the ozone layer single-handed with all the sprays she used. Oh, for a drink. Lemonade. Cider. Good, honest water.

She plodded on and on, stumbling into holes, thorns cruelly lacerating exposed flesh. But she was past feeling and soon even her thoughts lapsed. When Langeveldt told her to stop she hardly heard him but when he caught her shoulders she collapsed like a puppet without strings. The moon was almost full and in the silvery light he made a little camp in the shelter of some bushes. He spread his jacket over a bush and rolled Sarah underneath it. Then he drank half a cup of water, pouring the other half carefully down Sarah's unconscious throat. Finally he checked his rifle and keeping it close beside him lay down against her back, letting himself fall into oblivion without so much as a sigh.

Sarah awoke to heat. Dry mouth, sweat running down her back, flies. No Langeveldt. Panic rose in her. To be here at all was bad enough, but to be here alone – even Langeveldt was better than that. She struggled into the open.

'Langeveldt!' she croaked. It was hardly more than a whisper. 'Langeveldt!'

She scanned the horizons of this new and hostile place. He wasn't there. On every side stretched brown tufts of grass surrounding the hummocks of giant ant hills and the occasional twisted tree. Her own cluster of dry-leaved bushes was repeated again and again on every side. Had he gone away and got lost? Had he abandoned her? The rucksack was still there but not the rifle. Oh God, let him come back.

'Langeveldt!' This time it was a shrill scream, piercing the heat haze. A cluster of small birds rose from the bushes and she knew she should have stayed silent. If Langeveldt heard so might others. She shrank into the shelter of the bushes and reached for Cottar's leather handled knife, listening for the sounds of an approach. Still he surprised her. One moment nothing, the next a figure standing over her. She stifled a scream. Thank God. It was Langeveldt.

'Don't you know enough to be quiet?'

'I was frightened. I thought you'd gone.'

'And leave you to tell them all about me? That would make life interesting.'

'But who are they? Where are we?'

'My dear Mrs Hamilton, I'm so sorry. I didn't realise it had to be spelled out in words of one syllable. We are in the middle of Mandoto, I guess five hundred miles from anywhere friendly. I don't really know who's chasing us, but lately various types in odd uniforms have been carving up all the whites, most of the Asians and anybody else they come across. Now, we could stop and say hello but personally I don't think it would be healthy. That was a very sophisticated weapon that knocked us out of the sky.'

She looked thoughtfully at him. 'All right, I'll buy that. It ties in with what I've heard elsewhere. So why aren't we going anywhere? It's almost midday.'

Langeveldt lowered himself to the ground beside her, raising an eyebrow at the knife in her hand. Then he opened a can of beer and poured it carefully into the two cups, making sure they were exactly equal. Sarah tried to drink as slowly as possible, but it was gone almost before she realised. It left a still greater thirst in its wake.

'You see,' began Langeveldt conversationally, 'we are very close to being dead. We have very little water and almost no food. Do you notice how little life there is around here? Everything's gone. There's been a drought for maybe years, and what hasn't gone elsewhere has been eaten by people. Now they've gone too. The place is a wasteland. So we get one shot and one shot only at getting out of here. We have to choose a direction that leads straight to water, which will mean food as well. But we don't want to meet anybody there. We'll have to go perhaps a hundred miles and if we go by day we'll be dead by tomorrow. We have to travel late afternoon and night. In the day we sleep. And we might get out. Or we might not. We shall have to see.'

His bluntness was oddly comforting. Sarah realised that she had feared there was no hope at all. 'Have you decided which way we should go?' she asked, poking her tongue at the very last drop of beer in her cup.

Langeveldt shot her a look of surprise. 'I think so,' he said slowly. 'We'll head west; it's further into Mandoto but there's a big river complex that way. I used to hunt there one time. Swamp land, soda lakes, flies, no people. Then we head south – carefully – and hope to make the border.'

She lay back in the scant shade of the bush and closed her eyes against the sun. 'Why did you do that to Cottar?' she asked suddenly. 'There was no need.'

Langeveldt drew a sharp, annoyed breath. 'Of course there was a need. Was I to leave a plane full of artillery parts for them to get their hands on? It had to be burned.'

'But he was still alive!'

He looked away from her over the barren earth. 'That

he was not,' he said quietly. 'I made sure of it.'

Sarah lay quite still. Then she turned her head and retched dryly on to the sand. Langeveldt took no notice at all.

At last she fell into a miserable, troubled sleep. When he tried to wake her she mumbled and groaned and tried to push still further into the hot earth.

'You're going to have to face it some time,' he said, closing his hand in her hair and jerking her head upright.

Sarah shrieked in pain, but when he saw that she was fully awake he let her go. 'What was that for?' asked Sarah, her voice trembling.

His calm eyes studied her as if she were an odd sort of beetle. 'I left you as long as I could. From now on you do as I say and you do it fast. No questions, no complaints, just do it.'

'Go to hell.'

His hand shot out so quickly that she had no time even to flinch, nor the breath to do more than gasp as he wrenched again at her hair, pulling her head relentlessly towards him. When her face was an inch from his own he spoke with soft fury. 'I don't want you here. It would suit me very well to slit your throat and leave you. But I suppose you want to live, get back to that civilised little husband of yours. So you do it on my terms. Now, you want to argue?'

'No.' It was no more than a croak. Langeveldt let her go. She sat shaking, rubbing her head, amazed that her hair was still attached. Oh God, how to cope with this man?

'Why are you so cruel?' she asked.

He looked at her with bleak detachment. 'Cruelty is something you don't begin to understand,' he said calmly. 'Now, eat this.' He indicated a little pile of food. A cheese sandwich, half an orange and two ginger biscuits. Sarah opened her mouth to speak but caught his eye. 'I tell you once,' he said. Obediently she began to eat.

The first mouthful had to be forced down, but suddenly hunger was alive in her and even the dried-up cheese sandwich tasted ambrosial. She wolfed it all down, and when it was gone picked up the orange peel and ate that. Langeveldt watched. He always watched.

'So much for civilisation,' he murmured. Sarah got up, suddenly embarrassed, and marched purposefully off to some bushes. When she returned she waited for the ribald comment but none was forthcoming. Instead he uncoiled a long length of twisted grass rope.

'What's that for?'

'You.' Before she could move he looped it around her waist.

'I'm hardly going to run away!'

'I should be so lucky. No, this way I lead and you follow. And I don't have to keep looking round to make sure you haven't fallen down a hole.'

'I think I might mention it if I did,' she said incredulously.

'Lady, the time is going to come when you won't have the strength to blink, let alone speak.' He looped the rope through his thick leather belt, shouldered rucksack and gun and began to walk. Sarah fell into step behind him.

'You're going too fast,' she protested when they had gone no more than a hundred yards. 'I have to keep running.'

The pace slackened fractionally and she was forced to take strides an uncomfortable two inches longer than normal, but she dared not complain. She would have to get used to it.

Cottar's hat was too big so she turned the brim back the

better to look around. This was an empty world. The great blue dome of sky held them on the parched plain like ants under a saucer. Everything was in shades of brown, from the dust underfoot to the leafless trees. Nothing to catch the eye, nothing to take attention from the heat and the endless walking. How much further to go? No use thinking of it. Heat. Flies. She pulled her hat down and glared moodily from under it at Langeveldt's back. He walked as if he could go on for ever, those enormous legs swinging to and fro in unbroken rhythm. There wasn't an ounce of fat on the man, only flat smooth muscle outlined against his clothes as he moved. A hard man. No softness at all. Look at what he had done to poor Cottar – but she preferred not to think of how it had been. Langeveldt bending over him. Flames. Helpless flesh. The cheese sandwich rose in her throat and she forced herself to swallow. Think of something else, quick.

Home. Her garden. Green as this place could never be, gentle as this land was harsh. Why had she ever left it, what would they all be thinking, now? That she was dead, it could only be that. And who knows, in a little time perhaps they would be right.

The brief tropic twilight merged into the night, black as pitch until the moon came up. Langeveldt did not slacken pace and Sarah was grateful for the rope that united them. His dimly seen bulk was all that stood between her and disaster and she stumbled along in terror lest he leave her behind. She had always been afraid of the dark. When he tripped and fell her heart stopped and her surge of relief when he walked on took her quite by surprise. Odd how circumstances changed your point of view.

Langeveldt seemed to be navigating by the stars. Every so often he would stop and stare up at the spangled velvet of the night sky and Sarah would sink to the ground and draw shuddering, weary breaths. He was going too fast, there was no way she could keep up for much longer, but she dared not tell him so. Without her he could move far more quickly. Again and again she felt on the verge of collapse, legs leaden, heart pounding, a dull fire in her throat, but each time she forced herself to take just a few more strides. And strangely, in that short space, the feeling receded, for the time being at least. She staggered on, half-conscious.

At last he stopped. 'Here. Drink.' He held water to her lips, cradling her drooping head. It was warm and tainted with the age of the carrier, but it was life. Sarah slumped down and he settled beside her. 'Ten minutes, then we go on. It'll be daylight in two hours.' She looked at him through half-closed eyes. It was impossible to tell if he was tired, the thin, fleshless face with its prow of a nose was as smooth and still as that of an icon. Smiles, frowns, the convulsions of pain, none of these seemed to have touched him. Without knowing what she did Sarah reached out and placed a hand on his arm.

'Thank you,' she whispered, unsure of why she was thanking him, her lips stiff. Perhaps it was simply to acknowledge the care of an uncaring man. Probably because she owed it to her family to try to stay alive. Certainly because of her great loneliness. For a brief second their eyes met and then he was hurrying to his feet.

'Come on. Let's go,' he said gruffly, turned his back and began to march. Sarah tottered along behind, cursing herself. He had started off five minutes early.

Chapter 3

Dawn found them in the deep shade of some thick mopane scrub, but sleep was slow in coming. Exhausted muscles twitched and cramped long after the need to move was gone. Sarah gazed through the leaves at the slowly deepening blue of the sky and then sat up in excitement.

'Look, clouds! It's going to rain!' Huge thunderheads were boiling on the far horizon, like purple mountains topped with a foaming crest of snow.

Langeveldt hardly stirred. 'It won't rain,' he said shortly.

'But the clouds are there, enormous ones, it must rain. You don't realise, we're saved!' She gripped his arm in excitement and shook it joyfully.

He jerked back as if her touch was red-hot. 'For God's sake, woman, calm down. It's weeks till the rains start and then there may be none here. This place has been dry for years. Sure there are clouds, there always are, they mean nothing. It won't rain.'

She stared at him, the joy draining from her face. Then it crumpled into tears and she turned away. Great shuddering sobs racked her and she fought vainly to suppress them.

Suddenly Langeveldt yelled, 'Will you stop that noise! If I've got to stay here with you at least you can spare me that.'

Sarah tried, clenching her fists and holding her breath but then breaking again into a storm of weeping.

Langeveldt tore at his hair. 'What are you crying for, woman?' he asked in anguished tones.

'Because I don't want to die! I'm frightened, and I'm thirsty and I'm hungry and I want Douglas and my babies. I don't want you.'

'Well, I'm all you've got, sweetheart.'

'Then that's why I'm crying.' But she wasn't any more. The words had taken the need away. She scrubbed dirty hands over her face and lay down again. 'Don't you mind dying?' she asked.

He looked bewildered by the sudden change. 'Don't know really. No, I don't suppose I do.'

'But you must! Everyone does, unless they have an absolutely horrible life.'

'Not necessarily. I was brought up to think of death as something arranged by fate. You do your best but in the end if it's going to get you then you stay got. No use moaning. Uncle Bob was a reincarnation nut, swore one of his friends had come back as a hyena. Harry ran into a hippo one time, hunting crocs at night. They found his hat and a few bits of boat. He only had two fingers on one hand and when Bob saw this hyena staring at him as he was having his nightly bottle of scotch, only two toes on one foot, he knew it was Harry. Left meat out for it every night, but then one day it fell in the cess pool and drowned. Bob said that proved it was Harry, still just as much of a bloody fool. I helped him bury the body. We put lilies on the grave. Water, you know. He's probably a frog this time round.' He grinned at the memory, and to Sarah it seemed macabre in the extreme.

'You won't be so flippant when it really is your turn,' she snapped. 'You'll struggle as hard as anyone to stay alive.'

He nodded. 'You're right. But what would the world be

like if I died tomorrow? Any different? Any smaller, bigger, more happy or more sad? Of course not. And the same goes for you but you're too soaked in sentiment to admit it.'

'My husband would be very sad,' said Sarah. 'And my little girls would be without a mother. I hate to think what they're going through now, what they'll be thinking. To them I'm dead already.' She sat up and hunched her knees, resting her chin on them. Then she turned and looked at him. 'Won't anyone at all be sorry about you, Langeveldt?'

'No-one will even notice.'

'Poor, poor Langeveldt.'

There was a small poignant silence and then he burst out, 'Will you stop being so damned pitying! It's the way I want it and the way I like it to be. I'm no lost soul and you're no earth mother, so leave me be.'

'It's obviously something you feel very sensitive about,' retorted Sarah. 'I'm not surprised you have difficulty in making relationships, you're far too aggressive.'

'Now you're going to psychoanalyse me! I knew you were trouble from the moment I saw you. If I believed in God, I'd think he was playing a practical joke. Why couldn't some other poor sod be stuck in the bush with you – nine out of ten would think they were in heaven.' He sighed, pulled his hat over his eyes and tried to feign sleep. Sarah was not deceived.

'Why don't *you* then?'

'Shut up, I'm trying to sleep.'

'No you're not, your teeth are clenched. Don't you like women at all, Langeveldt?'

The hat lifted and he stared at her. Then he began to laugh. 'Oh my God, she thinks I'm queer. The bloody woman thinks I'm a nancy boy. Look, Mrs Hamilton, let me explain it to you. I like Africa. I love the peace, the beauty, even the brutality of it. I'm at home out here, I belong, it doesn't bother me. If I die it will be the way it should be, in the bush, not in some stinking city hospital with a tube up every hole. Bring a woman here and what happens? She talks, she cries, she tries to understand. I've tried it and I know. Women are fantastic in bed and a bloody nuisance everywhere else and you, Mrs Hamilton, are proving it.'

'So you're not queer.'

'I only wish I was.' He pulled his hat fiercely over his face and lay still.

The day wore on. There was very little water left and they were rationed to two mouthfuls every few hours. Sarah lay and longed for those mouthfuls, she could think of nothing else. It occurred to her that she should be doing a mental stocktake of her life, since it seemed to be drawing so rapidly to its close, but try as she would her thoughts were of liquid. Jugs of lemonade. Great foaming pitchers of cider. Perhaps Langeveldt was right, she was of little worth.

He crawled out of their patch of shade to look, he said, for food. The rifle was slung over his shoulder and Sarah did not believe him. Was he leaving her? In panic she scrabbled out into the open and ran after him. He watched her stumbling progress with mild interest. 'Well?'

She hung her head. 'I don't want you to go.' She looked pleadingly up through her lashes.

'Is that supposed to turn me to jelly?'

Sarah's head snapped back as if he had struck her. 'I don't know what you mean.'

'Oh yes, you do. Go back and sit in the bushes. If I wanted to leave you I'd certainly take the water.'

Sarah stalked back with as much dignity as she could

muster. He was the most horrible man, rude, selfish and – she grinned suddenly – not easy to manipulate. Oh well, it had been worth a try.

He brought back an assortment of horrors: some white fleshy strands of root, a few withered berries and what looked like a dead rat. She looked at the rat, then at him, then back at the rat. 'Oh God.'

'Fantastic luck, getting that,' he said. 'I almost fell over it, then hit it with a stick. It should be all right, roasted.'

'Don't you think it might have been ill?' said Sarah cautiously. 'For you to catch it so easily I mean. Perhaps we ought not –'

'Now, now, Mrs Hamilton, do I detect a certain lack of enthusiasm? If you'd rather eat the roots, you can. Bushmen thrive on these things.' He began busily to dissect the furry body with his large knife.

Sarah picked up one of the roots and began to chew. It was foul. She put it down and sighed. 'Oh well, I'll be able to lecture to the Women's Institute on how to cook a rat, I suppose. I hope you've got some matches.'

They built the fire in a sandy hollow and surrounded it with stones. The rat was impaled on a stick and suspended over the flames, and Sarah turned it from time to time. 'It doesn't look so bad without the head and feet,' she commented. 'You can pretend it's something else, though I don't know what.'

'Suckling pig,' offered Langeveldt, but she grimaced.

'That sounds almost as horrid. Oh, I don't care about food I just want a drink. Any drink.'

Langeveldt swallowed visibly. 'Don't think about it. There should be some moisture in the rat. It looks about done.'

To her amazement all revulsion disappeared after the first heroic mouthful. It was hot, running with juice, and it was food. Almost before she was aware she was sucking the thin, brittle bones. Langeveldt had already finished and was licking his fingers. Sarah studied his long, angular frame. It would take more than half a rat to satisfy him.

It was time to go. They packed up their meagre belongings and set off towards the cloudy horizon. She felt almost cheerful. They were rested, they had eaten after a fashion, and although they had little water those clouds did look very encouraging despite what Langeveldt said. They would make it yet.

Within two hours she was in despair. Stumbling, falling, fighting for breath, she could hardly walk fifty yards without incident. Eventually Langeveldt hitched an arm round her waist and half-carried her along.

'I'm sorry,' she murmured 'I don't know – I'm sorry.'

Again and again they stopped to rest. At last she said, 'It's no good, Langeveldt. You go on. I'll be all right.'

He said nothing for a long moment. 'You mean – you want me to leave you?'

Sarah nodded. 'You'll get out, you know you will. Just tell my family please. Tell them – well, you know.'

He snorted. 'No, I won't. "How do you do? Douglas, I presume? Just to tell you I abandoned your wife in the bush. She said to give you her love." I wonder if he'll offer me a drink? Well, you'd better have one anyway.' He upturned the water carrier over a cup. When it was brimful he handed it to Sarah. 'Drink. It's only dehydration: you'll be fine if you drink. Now hurry up, we've got to get on.'

'But that's all the water we have.'

'Like you said, it might rain. Do as I tell you, woman.'

Obediently Sarah drank. When they began to walk although her head still swam and her legs were leaden she no longer fell.

* * *

Daybreak. This time their shelter was a thorn tree in the midst of grey shale. They lay like the dead and indeed two vultures flapped their ghastly black feathers only fifty yards away. Undertakers come too early. 'Can't you shoot them?' she croaked. He shook his head. He had been so long without water that he could hardly speak. From time to time they sucked stones, but now even that gave no relief.

No-one they knew would have recognised them. Dust covered their clothes, their hair, their skin. Only their eyes still showed points of light and occasionally a stiff tongue would lick uselessly at cracked and blistered lips. Even Sarah now accepted that the surging clouds coming ever nearer were bringing nothing more than false hope. This was hell, the very centre of it, the heart of a godless land. Nothing lived but things that crawled and now they themselves were crawling, brought down from their pride by the devil himself. They would both die. Sarah had no strength to feel more than vague regret.

They were still there when night fell. At last he's given up, she thought. But even as she accepted the end he dragged himself to his feet. With weary anger Sarah forced herself to do likewise. They would have to go on.

They blundered into thorn bushes and fell into holes. Clouds scudded across the moon and a hot wind blew sand like a whiplash into their exposed faces. Sarah forgot why they were walking, she only remembered that they had to go on and on, like a dream with no waking. Langeveldt fell. Instead of rising he lay still.

'Please get up,' moaned Sarah. 'Langeveldt. Please.'

He did not stir. She sank to the ground beside him and eased his arms from the rucksack. Then she cradled his unconscious head in her lap. They were still there just before dawn, when the rain began to fall.

It was like nothing Sarah had ever experienced. A few drops at first, blessedly cool on parched skin, then larger and heavier until it was like standing under a waterfall, the onslaught of water almost painful. Lightning began to flash high in the sky, the thunder so loud it could have orchestrated the Day of Judgment. Langeveldt lay frighteningly still, his sandy bed now a sea of mud. Sarah heaved, pulled and pummelled to turn him over. The rain made little rivers in the dust on his face. He groaned and stirred. Sarah's heart thudded with relief as the tawny eyes flickered open.

'It's raining,' she laughed, shaking him still further into consciousness. 'You can't die now, it's raining.' She flung herself flat on her back in the mud and opened her mouth to the life-giving drops, content with just that small trickle of liquid.

Near death only moments before, Langeveldt was rummaging in the rucksack. He pulled out a square of polythene folded small.

'Quick, help me,' he urged and obediently she took a corner. Langeveldt spread it between the spindly bushes, put a stone in the middle to make it slope, pierced a hole and put the water carrier underneath. Within minutes they could drink water by the cupful.

'Drink as much as you can,' said Langeveldt. 'We can't carry much and it won't rain like this for long.'

Sarah, who had longed for water, was soon bloated with the stuff. And still he urged her to drink. 'I can't. I simply can't,' she said at last. They were almost shouting above the roar of the wind and the drumming of the rain.

He shrugged, turned away and began to strip off his

clothes. Sarah stared in amazement. When quite naked, he threw his shirt and trousers over a bush and stood without embarrassment scrubbing at the dirt on his body. 'You should do the same,' he called. Water glistened on the covering of soft brown hair on his chest and thighs and she could not look away. Their days of near starvation had stripped the flesh from bone and muscle until every sinew could be seen like a rope under the skin. Huge, gleaming in the half-light, he was every inch a man. He turned fully towards her and her mouth dried. With a stifled cry she leapt to her feet and fled into the scrub. Only when she was sure he could not see her did she stop. Her heart was thudding, her limbs shaking and cold. She wondered if she were about to faint, but after a little the feeling went away.

In the privacy of the bushes she took off her clothes and washed. She too was thinner, her stomach flat and her hips narrow as a boy's. When she felt her face it was no longer rounded but seemed gaunt and hollowed. She must look a hag, she thought. But her breasts seemed if anything to have improved. They were every bit as high and firm as before she had the children. She cupped water in her hands and scrubbed at her body, then squeezed and pummelled the tangled mass of her hair, longing for shampoo.

The thunderstorm stopped as suddenly as it had begun. Early morning sunlight shone on a sea of puddles and mud. Reluctantly, Sarah pulled on her soaking pants, trousers and shirt and began to walk back to Langeveldt. But where was he? Which way had she come?

'Langeveldt!' she shrieked. 'Langeveldt, where are you? Langeveldt!' She began to run, this way and that, her fear as cold as the clothes she wore. Hands caught at her shoulders and she screamed.

'It's all right, it's only me,' he said. 'Where were you going? That's back the way we've come.'

'I couldn't find you. I was lost.' She was almost sobbing.

'That's impossible, you'd only gone twenty yards. Running like a nun in a men's lavatory.'

Now that they were both clothed Sarah felt stupid. 'I never did have any sense of direction,' she babbled. 'Douglas never lets me navigate in the car any more, we always go up roads the wrong way and things. Oh God, I don't feel well.' She sat down abruptly on a lump of rotting timber.

Langeveldt jerked her to her feet. 'Don't sit there!'

She looked blank. 'But – why not?'

'Snakes,' he said shortly. 'That's exactly the sort of place they like. Boy I knew, Masai, sat on a log like that just once. I watched him die. Look.' Picking up a long stick he poked the log and pushed it gently over. With a movement so swift as to be almost invisible a short, heavily patterned snake flashed into the undergrowth. It was like seeing an Argyle sock on the move.

'Puff adder,' commented Langeveldt laconically. 'It's the season. From now on we'll have to be careful.'

'Now I feel really ill,' whispered Sarah and pressed her hands to her paperwhite cheeks.

Langeveldt looked sharply at her and sighed. 'You're worse than a bloody baby. You get too excited, it's bound to have a reaction, especially on an empty stomach. Pull yourself together, we're walking today.'

'Of course I was excited,' muttered Sarah. 'We'd just been saved from death.' But he wasn't listening. He tossed Cottar's hat, now caked in mud, towards her and prepared to move on.

In the two days it took to reach the river, Sarah saw the

country in gentle mood. Where all had been burned black now there was green; trees put out leaves and rich flowers appeared on bushes that had seemed dead. Great flocks of birds swept across the plain in shimmering clouds of colour and then were gone.

Rodents of all kinds abounded and Sarah became adept at roasting them to an exact degree of crispness, neither raw and bloody nor dry and without juice. It was an education watching Langeveldt catch them, studying a patch of scrub for minutes on end then leaping forward, stick in hand, like a giant grasshopper. When he missed and had to chase the little creature, flailing wildly, Sarah was reduced to helpless mirth, lying gasping on the ground like a landed fish.

'Glad madam finds it so amusing,' snapped Langeveldt, returning with his catch of three small mice. She forced herself to stop giggling, since he was becoming very touchy these days. It was probably hunger, she thought. Such a very big man must find it hard to fill up on mice.

Although the skies were sometimes cloudy, no more rain fell. It was as if God had deliberately sent the storm to save them, thought Sarah, her belief in the Almighty miraculously restored by their piece of good luck.

They began to see animals moving in the distance, some kind of antelope, so far away that they seemed but one creature, many-legged and many-horned, black against a purple sea of grass. And at night, in the sooty dark, they heard lions roaring, a sound to turn the strongest heart to ice. Langeveldt took his rifle apart and cleaned it, to Sarah's fury using an inch torn off the bottom of her silk dress.

'You can't do that,' she complained bitterly. 'That dress cost a fortune, and anyway, I like it.'

'So do I: cleans the gun a treat.'

'I notice you don't use anything of yours,' she went on, aware that she was being ridiculous but unable to stop. 'That's you all over, Langeveldt: take what you want and to hell with the rest of us. I pity the woman that marries you, I really do; in fact you should carry a government health warning, it would only be fair.'

'What on earth are you babbling about, woman? It's only a dress and it's not as if there are many functions you can attend right now. And we need the gun.' He began pulling a length of fabric through the barrel.

'That's not the point!' shrieked Sarah, becoming more and more furious with every scrap of material he appropriated. Without warning Langeveldt's worn boot shot out and hit her in the back. She sprawled, face down in the dust, and lay there.

'Now will you be quiet!' he said calmly. 'And don't give me the histrionics – you asked for it.'

She lay ominously still. He waited and waited but she lay like the dead. Cautiously he got to his feet and went over to her, expecting her to leap up and hit him at any moment. Her eyes were closed and her face milk white. She had fainted.

When she finally came round she was tearful and shivery. 'I don't know what's the matter,' she apologised, Langeveldt's kick seemingly unremembered. 'I feel ill all the time.'

'Half a day and we make the river,' said Langeveldt. 'So stop moaning, get on your feet and move.'

For once too ill to fight, Sarah obeyed. She walked in front and he behind, repeating the pattern of the first hours after the crash.

Without knowing that she did so she began to babble,

talking to Douglas, her children, her mother, even old Mr Braithwaite. Vague images of hands holding, guiding, offering water, swam on the edges of her mind but they seemed far less real than the problem of the scratch on the car. Someone was telling her that she could lie down now, lie down and go to sleep, and she argued, saying no, she really must get to the garage, but then he said he'd go for her. Still with a feeling of unspecified disquiet she finally released her hold on consciousness and fell into a well of sleep.

Soup. Hot, delicious, meaty soup. A pity someone had forgotten the bread; she must remind them. Opening her eyes for the first time in thirty-six hours, Sarah looked up at Langeveldt.

'So. The lady has taken her time. Drink the soup, it's cream of bushbuck and I had the devil's own job shooting the damn thing, let alone finding something to cook it in.'

Sarah peered under his outstretched arm at the stone-circled fire a few feet away. A rusty can was precariously balanced on top of it. Her appetite turned tail and ran. 'No more. Thank you, but – no.'

'Drink it.' His hand clasped her head in an unyielding grip while the cup nudged at her lips. She opened her mouth to protest and in went the soup; she coughed, spluttered, almost drowned and gulped down a scalding mouthful.

'All right, all right, I'll drink it!' she promised, gasping, and he slowly let her go. Too weak to sit upright she leaned against him for support as she sipped. When it was all gone he laid her firmly back down on the sand.

'I'm sorry to be so much trouble,' she said feebly, the

easy tears of illness threatening to course down her cheeks. He did not reply, busying himself with washing the cup and tidying their few belongings. Sarah looked around. They were in a small clearing in the midst of tall grass and scrub, as neatly walled as if it were a room. Narrow paths like doorways snaked away into the surrounding thickets and from all around came the rustle of leaves in the wind, the voices of a thousand ghosts. An insecure little house this, with its mud floor and roof of blue sky.

'Didn't we get to the river?' she asked.

'What? Oh sure, it's about a quarter of a mile away. We're better off here, the water's thick with crocodile and there's a herd of elephant hanging around somewhere. Besides, I never like a room looking on to the street.'

She was asleep before he finished speaking.

The next morning she was awake before him. He lay close beside her, the rifle next to his hand, and for once she could study him without those savage eyes watching when they seemed not to do so. Even in sleep he looked strong, the tight contours of his face owing too much to bone and muscle to relax into softness; even the curly growth of beard followed the harsh line of his jaw. A fly landed on his forehead and she raised a hand to flick it away. At once his strange eyes opened. There was no period of half-sleep, no yawning delay.

'What's the matter?'

Sarah sat up, embarrassed by their closeness. 'Just a fly. I brushed a fly, that's all.'

He said nothing, but got to his feet and began to make a fire. Nothing to eat but meat, and meat that was rapidly spoiling in the fierce heat of the day. Nothing to drink but water tainted with the gravel of the river bed.

'Best I can do,' explained Langeveldt as Sarah closed her teeth on grit, grimaced and spat. 'The main river's alive with bilharzia but I think the stream I got this from is probably safe. Not crystal clear, though.'

Sarah did not bother to reply. When Langeveldt went off to find something fresh for dinner she busied herself with a square torn from her silk dress and set about straining their little store of water. When she had finished she shook the grit from the cloth and sponged her face with the tiny scrap of material. Oh, how she longed for a bath. Her whole body was encrusted with sand and sweat and her clothes were stiff with filth. The smell must be appalling, she thought, although it enthralled the flies. Big fat ones, red-brown in colour, that didn't seem to bite; thinner, blacker ones with delicate wings that raised little lumps that itched; huge leggy things with a bite like an enraged shark, and always the singing hordes of mosquitoes. They hung round her in droning clouds, however hard she flailed and swiped at them, and eventually she gave up and lay down in the shade, her arms over her head.

Time passed, she had no idea how long. At last Langeveldt stepped from the tall grass into the clearing, his shirt black with sweat. A large dead bird hung from his hand, eyes sightless, tongue protuding in the spasm of death. Sarah rose and took it from him, settling herself on the other side of the clearing and starting to pluck. He poured some water and drank, then crouched on his heels watching her.

'You've done that before.'

She nodded. 'Lots of times. Did you have trouble shooting it?'

He shrugged. 'Depends on how you look at it. You fit? I want to move tomorrow.'

'All right.' She stopped plucking and flung feathery hands in the air. 'But I must have a bath! I can't stand being filthy any longer. I simply have to wash.'

He looked slightly amused by her vehemence. 'Don't see why not. After we've eaten. Hurry up, I'll gut that when you've finished.'

'I'm going as fast as I can. Why don't you count flies or something? I don't like being watched.'

But even when her head was bent over her task still she could feel his eyes on her. When she looked up and caught him staring he did not look away and again Sarah had the feeling that she was in a formal, mannered dance with someone who didn't know the steps, and what's more, didn't care. Her fingers flew over the bird until at last it was finished, plump skin pinkly exposed. Langeveldt took it from her and their fingers touched.

'You surprise me,' he said softly.

Sarah flushed and turned away.

By the time they had eaten all they could of the bird it was nearly evening. 'Come on if you want your bath,' urged Langeveldt. 'If we're not careful we'll have company.'

'What sort of company?' asked Sarah fearfully.

Again that shrug. 'Elephant. Lion, perhaps. They all come to drink in the evening.'

'I don't mind waiting till tomorrow,' she said quickly, turning to go back, but he caught her shoulder.

'Tomorrow we walk.'

They were treading a narrow trail through high grass waving in a gentle breeze. With Langeveldt ahead and the grass either side Sarah had no view at all until suddenly she was standing on the flat mud of the river bank. She had imagined a gurgling stream, but this wide, slow water, with its bordering grass and slimy banks, was no such thing. It was an eerie place. Looking upriver she could see that other channels cut through the grass to join the main stream. The feeling of menace deepened. Anything could be lurking in the concealing wall of waving grass. A sudden rattle of noise and Sarah spun round, but it was only a heron, flapping heavily off upstream.

They walked quickly along the river bank, their footprints a jumble in the mud: Langeveldt's huge and firm, Sarah's so much smaller and more frequent as she hurried along behind him. They came to a deep cut, at right angles to the main stream and filled with dark, clouded water.

'This will do,' said Langeveldt, and handed her the gun. 'I'll go first. Watch for crocs.'

He stepped easily out of his clothes and jumped into the water. When he surfaced, hair and beard drifting like waterweed around his head, Sarah shrieked, 'What do I do if I see one?'

'Mention it,' said Langeveldt calmly.

'But – don't you want me to shoot it? What do I press?' She turned the gun round in her hands, peering at its mysterious knobs and levers.

'Don't touch the gun!' roared Langeveldt. 'For God's sake, woman, it's loaded!'

'I should hope it is,' said Sarah. 'Just tell me what to press. Is this the safety catch?' The barrel swung towards the river and Langeveldt disappeared below the surface like a submarine with a destroyer bearing down. When he reappeared, awash with fury, it was to find Sarah speechless with mirth.

He climbed from the river and marched towards her, water running from his body and drawing the hairs into neat, sculptured lines. Sarah put the rifle down and backed away, a deep blush suffusing her skin. He picked up the gun. When he spoke his voice shook with the effort of control. 'Do you realise,' he said slowly, 'that when I was ten years old a friend of mine shot me through the leg. He swore the safety catch was on. When I was twenty, I saw a man killed by a gun that wasn't loaded. And two years ago a guy I knew, a good man with a gun, blew himself up when he loaded a shotgun twice. And you want to play games. Get in the water, you stupid bitch.'

He was in no mood for argument. Sarah obediently turned her back and began to unbutton her shirt. Then she realised that he had not turned away, nor was he making any move to get dressed.

'You can't watch me,' she said indignantly.

'Yes, I can.'

'Then I won't go in.'

To her amazement there was a neat, metallic click from the rifle. The safety catch was off.

'You can't make me,' she said, her voice shrill.

In answer he raised the rifle to his hip. She looked from his still face to the equally still rifle, turned and began to wriggle out of her clothes. When she was naked she bundled them into a ball and leaped into the river with them. The water was freezing. Never once lifting her eyes to Langeveldt she scrubbed first her clothing and then herself. The cold forced her out, the bundle of wet clothes clutched in front of her. Without looking at the naked man who stood impassively staring she struggled into her soaking clothes. Only then did Langeveldt dress.

They walked back to the camp in total silence, although Sarah's thoughts were so loud and furious that by rights he should have heard. The stifling day was drifting towards the brief tropic twilight and there was nothing to do but prepare for sleep. Suddenly she could bear it no longer.

'How could you!' she burst out. 'It was only a joke. You had no right to watch me, no right at all!' She drummed her fist on the unforgiving earth and he swung round to look at her. The heat and fury in his eyes made her quail.

'Do you think it's the first time I've seen your body? Do you? When you were ill, burning, sweating, who do you think it was sponged every inch of your so precious flesh, cleaned you, held you, fed you? I can save your life, that's allowed, but I'm not even permitted to look!'

The thought of those huge, long-fingered hands moving over her naked flesh as she lay helpless filled Sarah with the deepest embarrassment. 'It was different,' she said feebly. 'I didn't know.'

He stood over her as she sat helpless on the ground and he raged. 'What is it you want, woman? An emasculated lapdog like that husband of yours to take care of you? Would you? Well, what you've got is me, and I will look as much as I like. I bet you ration it to dear Douglas, once a week with the lights out. You'll bounce your breasts at a man to make him do what you want, but when it comes to touching –' he shot out a hand and grabbed at the front of her shirt, forcing her to kneel in front of him – 'then it's oh, please don't, I'm a lady. But I'm no gentleman.' He released her and for a brief moment Sarah thought she was saved, but then his shirt hit the earth beside her. She began to crawl away, limbs stiff with fear. His breathing was as harsh and laboured as if he had been running. She heard the chink of his belt buckle as his trousers fell to the ground and turned to see him tall, naked and erect.

'Take your clothes off.' His voice was thick with desire.

'Please, I don't want –'

He stepped forward and wrenched at her shirt, bursting the buttons. She bit back a scream. He stared at her body, white against the dark earth, her pink-tipped breasts rising and falling with every breath.

'Take your clothes off,' he said again, 'or I'll do it for you.'

There was no escape. She undressed with trembling fingers and when she was naked she lay down as she was told, as rigid as the ground on which she rested. He stood over her, feasting his eyes on her long white legs crowned at their apex with a little triangle of black hair. With a groan, he fell on her.

To Sarah it seemed to go on for ever. His mouth sucked at her neck, her shoulders, her breasts, his hands clutched at her hair, and when she screamed it was as if she made no sound at all for he was past hearing. The smell of him, river water, sweat, desire, filled her nostrils. She repeatedly dug her nails into his back and her teeth into his arm but it seemed only to spur him on. When finally he forced himself into her she lay limp and unresponding. But she could not lie still for long. So violent were his thrusts that she was soon writhing under him, arching herself against him in a vain attempt to lessen the pain. When at last he rolled away from her to lie panting by her side a thin trickle of blood flowed from her body. She dragged her knees up to cradle her aching stomach and lay there, more wretched than ever before in her life.

Animals coming to the river to drink filled the night air with their cries; the harsh, proud roar of the lion; the sudden manic cackle of a hyena. Sarah hardly cared. She lay naked and without defence, wanting only for something to happen to take the nightmare away.

Why had he done it? It was not the act itself which so

affronted her but the aggression, almost hatred which it represented. She had thought him a man without softness; in truth he was without heart. Going back and back in her mind over the days since the crash she could see nothing to warrant his attack, except that she was there at all. Was he then some kind of beast? Before she could fumble her way to an answer she felt his hands, draping her shirt gently across her shoulders.

'You must dress. You can't lie like this all night.'

She lay without moving and he went away. The muscles of her stomach unwound themselves a little from their harsh knot, but then he was back. His touch made her shudder. For a terrible moment she thought he was going to do it again, but then she felt the water. Gently, oh so gently, he bathed her face, her arms, her breast – and then he washed away the blood. Tremors racked her muscles, so tense they were like rocks under the skin: she shivered as if with ague. He lifted her stiff body and tried to guide her arms into the shirt, and suddenly the shivers were sobs, the tension dissolving in a river of tears. And amazingly he was holding her, rocking her, trying to help.

'You – you hurt me!' she gulped, clinging to him in the merciful dark.

'I know. I'm sorry. But you made me so angry –'

'I hadn't done anything! Nothing at all!' She hammered on his shoulder with her fist, determined that he should realise, but he said no more, rocking her to and fro, to and fro, until she was calm. Then he laid her gently down, pillowed her head on the small remains of the silk dress, covered her with his shirt and left her. But neither of them could sleep. Thoughts buzzed in Sarah's head like the flies that tormented her during the day until at last she burst out, 'I didn't do anything! You shouldn't have!' Her voice was shrill, almost hysterical, and some part of her mind that was still functioning normally noted it with surprise.

Langeveldt sighed. 'Does it matter?' he said wearily. 'When all's said and done you're a married woman, you've got two kids; it can't have been that much of a shock.'

Sarah almost choked on the rush of words. 'You don't know what you're saying. My husband and I, we kiss, we touch, we hold, we talk to each other, goddammit! With us it's making love, with you it's war, the ultimate weapon, look what I can do to you, not even your body's your own. You didn't want the sex. You wanted to humiliate me.'

'That's not true.' She heard him sit up, but his face was no more than a blur. 'I did want the sex. I wanted you, God, how I wanted you. When I first saw you at the plane, all long legs and white skin, frightened to death but trying to hide it, I could have done it there and then. And what did you do, you swung your legs, tossed your hair, let your jacket fall open, dropped your shoe, and watched the poor fools tie themselves in knots for you. You got what you deserved.'

Sarah took a deep breath. 'I'm sorry. I should go around in a veil, it seems. Would that control your manly passion?'

He chuckled. 'It's not your face that bothers me.'

'Then what is it? Because whatever you say, there was more hate than sex in that – that – rape!'

There was a long silence. When he spoke it was thoughtfully, without heat. 'I don't like women much as a rule,' he said. 'Weak, squealing babies, the lot of them. I despise myself for needing them so much, their bodies that is, you can keep the minds. But you, I could like you. And somehow, I don't know why, you bring me close to murder a dozen times a day. One minute I'm thinking

God, she's got courage, and the next I want to strangle you. Tonight I lost control. I'm sorry – look, what is your name?'

'Don't you know?' Sarah noted with interest that the even timbre of her voice had miraculously returned.

'Only that you're Mrs Hamilton.'

'And that is about as familiar as I intend to get,' she said stonily. Within minutes she was in dreamless, drugging sleep.

Chapter 4

In the light of day they could not look at each other. It seemed impossible for them to spend another hour together, let alone the days and possibly weeks that lay ahead. Not a word was exchanged as they ate the remains of the bird for breakfast, brushing the flies away at each mouthful, packed up their meagre belongings and prepared to move on. Sarah longed to ask him which way they were going and why, but as the minutes passed without either of them speaking it became increasingly difficult to break the silence, even when Langeveldt's long stride forced her to hop and skip to keep up. The semi-desert of days past now gave way to lusher pasture, sometimes part bog and criss-crossed by streams. It was impossible to take a straight course and they meandered through tall grass and reeds, under mopane as high as a cathedral and through thorn as thick as a blanket. The world had come to life, birds cackled and whooped as they passed and there were rustlings in the far bush, but everything was wary. It was a reminder that this lonely place had not always been this way. There had been people once.

Snakes filled Sarah's thoughts. She peered at the ground constantly, sure that she would see some enormous reptile waiting to sink its fangs into her flesh, and her feet cringed inside her worn and now holey canvas shoes. Strangely it seemed a good thing to think about, requiring as it did almost all her concentration. No room to think of the ache in her stomach, impossible even to look at Langeveldt's uncaring back; all her attention was devoted to watching for snakes.

Suddenly he stopped and held out an arm behind him, silently urging her to stay back. She halted unwillingly and looked nervously around at the tussocks of grass, any one of which could be hiding a snake. Slowly, Langeveldt stepped back, moving so quietly and carefully that Sarah was filled with immediate, real alarm. She forgot all about snakes and peered desperately round him. There was nothing there. She let out her breath in a relieved sigh that stopped almost before it had begun. Part of the dusty bush some twenty yards in front of them had moved, was moving now. Standing sleepily, oblivious to their presence, was a large, wrinkled elephant. They were so close that the brown- and yellow-stained tusks were clearly visible, one quite long, the other broken with a jagged end. The little eye under the sunken dome of forehead was quite closed, the ear flapped lazily. Sarah and Langeveldt crept stealthily away.

They stopped only when they were in the open, far from any elephant hiding place. Sarah sat weakly down on the thin grass. 'That was awful,' she said, and swallowed. 'Would it have minded if it had noticed us?'

'Want me to go back and ask?' said Langeveldt, and then took pity on her. 'It depends. Here, it's not so used to people; it might have charged, might not. And it might or might not have meant it. At that distance it would have been interesting. I must be losing my grip, getting so close. If it's come from further north then it's used to poachers and would quite probably have minced us.'

'What super fun,' said Sarah weakly, noting that he looked strained. His lapse had upset him. 'Would you have shot it? If it attacked, I mean?'

Langeveldt looked at her. 'You're not serious are you?' he said in an amazed voice.

'Well – yes. Isn't that what you've got the gun for?'

'My dear girl, this is a Browning .270 that I've had since I was a tiny little boy, when even you would have been fond of me. Uncle Bob gave it to me when I was seven, bullets and all. I shot the dog. It's a very nice little gun, an absolute whiz at potting the odd bird, not to mention an antelope here and there. But as for shooting elephants, I might just as well fight King Kong with a toothpick!'

'Oh. So what do you shoot elephants with, then?'

'A sort of handheld cannon stuffed full to bursting with the sporting equivalent of the dumdum bullet. And even then the elephant sometimes wins.'

Sarah reached for the water carrier and poured herself a drink. 'I don't think I should like to shoot an elephant.'

Langeveldt snorted. 'I bet you really *have* got a panda sticker on your car.'

They walked almost all day, with only occasional stops to drink or for Langeveldt to study the horizon. Whenever they came across a clear, fast-running stream, they filled the water carrier and towards evening Langeveldt started to hunt. Waving Sarah to a seat under a thorn tree where she resumed her search for snakes, he moved slowly and cautiously towards an area of thick scrub. Rifle at the ready, he slipped to his knees and crawled into the tangle of undergrowth. Sarah held her breath. There could be another elephant in there, he could be killed, and there she would be, lost and helpless. Damn Langeveldt.

The shot split the afternoon like a thunderclap. Birds flew shrieking into the air, Sarah's heart beat a tattoo and a slim, black and yellow shape, beautiful in its symmetry, slipped from the patch of scrub and ran easily away across the plain. Then Langeveldt appeared, dragging the carcase of some sort of deer behind him. A round, plum-like body with trailing sticks for legs.

'I saw a leopard – I did, I saw a leopard!' shrieked Sarah, running towards him. 'When you shot, it ran out. Over there, it was beautiful, I saw it, it was a leopard.'

'OK, OK, you saw a leopard,' said Langeveldt and prepared to cut a haunch from his prize.

He was an insensitive brute. She turned angrily away and stared at the thin line where earth and trees met hot blue sky. Langeveldt glanced at her rigid back.

'Er – lovely animals, leopards,' he said awkwardly, but she did not look at him. Thoughtfully he resumed hacking at the deer.

That night lions began to roar in earnest. Again and again the booming noise rang out, first from this side, then from that, then two or three together. Sarah had settled to sleep six feet from Langeveldt but as each fresh burst of roaring broke out she tried to roll imperceptibly closer. Eventually he got up and walked over to her, lying down some twelve inches away. 'I can't bear to watch you trying to do it by osmosis,' he said ironically, and settled the rifle between them.

'Are they as close as they sound?' asked Sarah.

'No. But too bloody close, just the same. Tomorrow night we light a fire.'

'If we live that long. Was your uncle eaten by a lion?'

'Who told you that?' Langeveldt sounded incredulous.

'Cottar. I thought he was making it up.'

He gave a crackle of laughter. 'He wasn't. I don't think Uncle Bob believed it himself until he was halfway down, and by then it was too late. Always remember, if you get drunk in Africa, do it in town.'

'You don't sound very sorry.'

'Long time ago. And he's better dead: he wouldn't have liked it the way it is now. Bwana Bob wasn't about to step down for anyone.'

A fresh burst of roaring began, so loud that when it stopped the air seemed still to vibrate with sound. It was so alien a sound that a wave of longing swelled in Sarah, rose and broke over her. 'Oh, how I want to be home,' she sighed, and hugged herself for the little comfort it provided. Langeveldt's hand rested briefly on her shoulder. With a gasp Sarah wrenched away, putting several feet of space between them.

'I'd rather have the lions,' she muttered and lay down to await the morning.

Throughout the night the heat hung over the land, building to welcome a heat-hazed dawn. Even the flies were affected by the humid, sticky air, clinging to the skin until almost plucked free. Sarah dragged herself to her feet, relieved that it was morning even if it was proving so unpleasant. Langeveldt still lay on the ground, but Sarah ignored him, first retreating behind a bush to relieve herself and then rinsing her hands and face in water from the carrier. Still he had not moved.

'Langeveldt? Aren't you getting up this morning?'

An arm moved jerkily. He struggled to sit up. 'Getting up? Sure. Must get up.' But he only managed to prop himself weakly on an elbow. She moved cautiously to look at him. Who knew what trick he might be playing? But there was no mistaking the flush of fever on the normally sallow skin, or the flickering tawny gaze, always so steady before. He was ill. She sat back on her heels and stared at him.

Conflicting emotions raged within her. How she would

love to leave him to stew. All right, he had nursed her, but in the end he had found a torture more effective than any physical pain. He did not deserve her care. But then again, if she would not shoot an elephant could she in fact let a man die? And that is what it would be. He needed shade, water and food, none of which he could provide for himself. And if he died it would be the end of her, so it was really no choice. She must do all she could, and willingly, for when all is said and done there is no profit in hate.

There was a little group of leafy trees about a quarter of a mile away, and to Sarah's eyes they seemed an ideal place to camp. She moved the remains of the deer first, then the rucksack and gun, and lastly the precious water, and only then did she try to coax Langeveldt to his feet. He lay with glazed eyes, flies crawling in nose and mouth as his breath came in harsh, shallow gasps. He looked at her without recognition.

'Langeveldt,' she urged. 'Come along, you have to move. Up you get. Look, I'll help you.' She tugged vigorously at his arm, and to her relief he staggered to his feet.

'Got to see to the boys,' he muttered, and started off in direct opposition to Sarah's frantic tugging.

'Not that way – come here – oh stop it, you stupid man, you must come this way.'

He turned and gazed blearily at her, moving his head in an attempt to get her into focus. 'Aunt Daisy,' he said wonderingly. 'Thought you were dead. You needn't worry, he's sending me away to school. Damn his black heart.'

Sarah realised it was going to take cunning to lure him to her selected camp. 'Come and take a walk with me, Joe,' she purred. 'I haven't seen you for such a long time.'

'And you owe me twenty rand,' he said accusingly, and stopped dead.

'Er – yes. My purse is over here. Do come and see, there's a good boy.'

Bit by bit she edged him along. Twice he tried to lie down but each time she pushed, pummelled and coaxed him towards her goal. At last they reached the trees, and then he would not lie down at all. He blundered round, muttering worriedly, while Sarah hung weakly on to his arm. His eventual, swaying collapse took her by surprise.

The sweltering day passed slowly. She took fallen branches and built a flimsy barrier and in front she built a fire, copying exactly the stone-circled structure Langeveldt had shown her. Then she made soup, just as he had, and tried to make him drink it, but most went down his chin. There was no doubt that he was very ill, his skin burned her fingers, and there was so little that she could do. She sat and fanned the flies from his face and at intervals held water to his lips. Sometimes he drank like one possessed, at others he turned his head fretfully away and babbled.

The babbling became louder as his fever mounted, and Sarah realised that she would have to cool him. In spite of his delirium she blushed as she undressed him, forcing her hands to be swift and firm. His shoulder still bore the marks of her teeth in a series of purple, infected punctures and she felt a stab of guilt. It was soon replaced by irritation that he could make her feel so, when it was all his own fault. She vigorously soaked yet another square of white silk with water and began to bathe his chest. Steam rose into the afternoon air, and again and again she soaked the cloth and washed him until gradually he burned less fiercely. Scars of many kinds marked his flesh. One arm bore a series of long slashes, white against the tan, and a purple, raised welt lay across his shoulder. His legs were a mass of lesser stripes and one calf bore a deep, round indentation. With so many marks of conflict it seemed incredible that he had survived until now.

It was almost evening. The pile of firewood was as high as nervous forays around the camp could make it, and Sarah had eaten yet more of the meat, now too strong for all but the most determined hunger. For tomorrow there was just the soup, and Langeveldt would need that. If he was still alive. He lay as still as death, and when night fell Sarah thought he had faded with the day. She built the fire higher, feeling a chill that was not of the body, and she watched him. Shudders began to rack his long, brown frame and in a moment sweat rose in beads on his skin. Sarah hurried to cover him, and to build the fire still higher, but the violence of his shivering terrified her. Just a blanket would make a difference, she thought wildly, draping her little jacket over him. Pools of fluid soaked in the dry earth and she tried to drag him closer to the fire. She began to mutter to herself. 'Oh God, please tell me what to do. Please don't let him die, I don't want to be alone here. Please God!'

'I don't think God cares about malaria,' whispered Langeveldt between chattering teeth. Sarah gasped. She had not realised how terrible the day had been without him until he came back to her, and tears of relief pricked her eyes.

'Tell me what to do,' she pleaded. 'What can I do?'

He shook his head. 'Nothing. It goes away. So cold. Just so cold.'

The fire blazed but it made no difference. Towards midnight he slept, briefly, fitfully, before his temperature again began to climb. It was then that the lions began, reducing Sarah to a shivering bundle of terror despite piling the fire so high that sparks flew up into the trees that sheltered them. Her only comfort was the clasp of Langeveldt's unconscious hand and she clung to it, praying for the dawn.

Daylight brought the return of heat, flies and the smell of rotting meat. Sarah dragged the remains of the carcase well away from the camp and left it, then wandered wearily about looking for firewood. She had used almost everything within range last night, and she feared to go too far away from camp, although there was little enough security in those few branches of thorn and her unconscious charge. The cycle of burn and sweat, burn and sweat had been repeated so often that she had lost count, and all she could do was fan, sponge and offer water. Her arm ached with the incessant regular motion, and her head nodded with weariness. A crackle of sound brought her to wakefulness.

Loping across the plain towards the rotting carcase of the deer was a shaggy, spotted animal, huge of head but its hindquarters oddly crouched. Hyena. It began to tear at the meat, crunching bone with ghastly ease. Sarah began to whimper and groped for the rifle. Where was the blasted safety catch? Was it even loaded? If Langeveldt ever recovered, if they ever survived this day, he would have to show her how to use it. The animal's head swung towards her as it ate. Although it was too far to see, she could have sworn it was fixing its yellow eyes on her and her mouth dried with the thought of what it might do. If she fired the rifle would it go away? Movement at the edge of her vision made her turn. It was another of them, hobbling with a cringing gait to share the feast. The two animals squabbled and scrapped, whooping and snarling, while Sarah watched, stiff with terror.

At last it was finished. With a final sideways stare they loped away into the scrub. Sarah collapsed in a weary, shivering heap. Then she began to laugh. Langeveldt was right about women and Africa: they did not mix, if they were English ladies from sheltered homes, that is. She doubted that the country would change, so she must, learning to live with discomfort, danger, dirt and illness. To be reduced to this jellylike state every time something unexpected happened was not only foolish, it was exhausting. From now on she would stamp on her fear. After all, she thought, Africa was full of people happily studying the very animals that frightened her to death. From the safety of tents and Land Rovers, admittedly, and with rather more than popguns to defend themselves, but there was no reason why she should not copy their objectivity. Time enough to worry about being eaten when it happened. She settled firmly back against the thin thorn barrier, allowing herself only one brief glance over the top in case a hyena was lurking there, about to pounce.

It was difficult to hold her resolution during the long, lion-filled night. Once she thought she saw green eyes across the fire and her heart beat furiously, but then they were gone and that was worse. It could be anywhere. Langeveldt stirred and muttered and Sarah prayed as never before for him to be well again, strong, sure of what they should do. She would not let herself think of what he had done to her. Back in the real world, where there was room for things other than meat and water and staying alive, there she could let it matter. As it was, like Cottar's death, it had happened, it was past, there was nothing you could do. And after all, it had been Langeveldt.

She felt a strange softness for him now that he was ill, as if in caring for him she was reaching out in love and tenderness to her children, far away without her. She knew each harsh line of his body as well as its soft folds and curves, and when she bathed him or held water to his lips she felt a lessening of her worry and loss. But still she wanted him well. Towards morning he lay without moving, his skin cold and slightly damp, his breathing shallow. Was this death? She watched the spreading magic of an orange dawn and was very afraid.

'Is there anything to eat?'

She spun round and met his steady, gold-flecked gaze. 'You're better! I thought you were about to die.'

'I will if I don't eat something. God, I've never been so hungry.'

She gave him the last of the soup and then some berries she had found the day before. Her own stomach was groaning but she said nothing.

'How long have I been ill?' He was struggling to sit up but he was still very weak.

'I don't know – two days, I think. Look, you've got to show me how to use the gun. Anything could have happened and I couldn't do a thing. It's only sensible.'

'No.'

Any feelings of warmth towards him evaporated instantly. 'But – why not?' she asked incredulously.

'I never trust women with guns.'

'Oh, I get it. You think they might up and shoot you. Well, I can see your point, but as I've just made every effort to save your life I think you can consider yourself safe for the time being.'

'Don't get in such a temper. It would be a waste of good bullets: women are always lousy shots.'

'I do all right at the fair. I once won three teddy bears and a china pig and the man begged me to go away. Come on, Langeveldt, show me.'

He closed his eyes wearily. Sarah had chosen her moment well; it was easier for him to give in than to argue. Propping himself on one elbow he told her what to do.

'First empty it – put your fingers in that hole behind the trigger and work the lever up and down. It only has four rounds.' Four large round bullets popped out and on to the ground. Sarah picked them up with interest. 'Right,' said Langeveldt. 'Poke them back into the hole at the side. No, not like that, you idiot! Sort of – sideways.' Under his critical gaze she fumbled and dropped them and at last slid them neatly into the magazine. 'OK, you've done it. The man at the fair would have been proud of you. Now, keeping it firmly pointed away from me, pull back the hammer, just like the cowboys, and shoot something.'

Sarah peered worriedly at the gun. 'Oh. What?'

'Try that tree over there.' He pointed to an inoffensive thorn some two hundred yards away. Obediently Sarah cradled the gun against her shoulder, squinted along the barrel and fired. The gun bucked, but to her surprise the tree still stood. 'Did I hit it?'

'Damned if I know. Go and have a look.'

She trudged off to peer at the bark, but if she had hit it the tree was hiding it well. Back again to have another try.

Six shots and a lot of walking later there was at last a shower of splinters and a deep score in the gnarled trunk of the tree. Sarah collapsed in the shade, exhausted and triumphant.

'There you are, I told you I could do it.'

'Good for you. Now, off you pop and shoot us some lunch.'

'Very funny. Don't talk about food, it bothers me.'

Langeveldt did not reply. He was gazing intently across the grassland.

'Quick, hand me the gun!' he said quietly. Sarah did as she was told.

Pulling himself up to kneel on one knee, he put the rifle to his shoulder, aimed and fired. 'There you are,' he said. 'Lunch.'

'I don't see anything,' said Sarah doubtfully.

'Well, it's there. Dash off and get it before something else does. About a quarter of a mile away, over there, quick.'

Quite sure that he was deceiving her Sarah trudged off in the vague direction in which he pointed. And there, lying in the grass was a large dead bird, something like a small turkey. Considerably humbled, she carried it back to the camp and set about plucking it without so much as a word to Langeveldt.

'Never mind,' he said kindly. 'I might need you to shoot a barn door some day.'

Sarah sniffed coldly and kept on plucking.

They stayed in the camp for two days while Langeveldt steadily regained his strength. Sarah used the time to take stock of her clothes, if they could be called that any longer. She was dressed in a collection of rags. Her trousers were so torn and frayed that she cut them off just below the knee. They had a hole in the seat also, but there was nothing she could do about that. It was her shirt that was the real problem, with only one button left and numerous holes. She knotted it below her breasts and tried not to lean over too often, but she often looked up to find Langeveldt watching her. Tension began to build between them.

On the evening of the second day Langeveldt prowled around, restless and irritable. They had hung small strips of meat to dry in the shade and he inspected them again and again until Sarah snapped, 'It won't dry any faster for being stared at! Why can't you go to sleep or something.' She too was fretful, for the rains were about to start in earnest and the weather was hot and sticky, encouraging flies to furious assaults on exposed skin. Langeveldt flung himself down behind their little shelter.

'Thank God we walk tomorrow,' he muttered. 'Here, let me see your shoes.' Sarah handed the tattered things over, relieved that at last he had found something useful to do. Her shoes had been worrying her, for while his desert boots were still serviceable her canvas sneakers were not. He set about cutting some thick, thorny leaves from which he scraped the prickles before inserting them into the soles of her shoes.

'Best I can do,' he said. 'Try them on.'

She sat down and held out dusty bare feet. Dancer's feet, Douglas had once called them, long and narrow with straight pink toes. She reached out for the shoe but Langeveldt knelt in front of her, cupping her heel in his large hand. He looked at her slender ankle and slim, tanned leg disappearing into the frayed end of her trouser. His thumb began to caress the hollow beneath her ankle bone and Sarah felt every hair on her body rise up. Yet for long seconds she could not pull away. A wave of nameless feeling swept through her and she gasped. Langeveldt lifted his eyes to meet hers and it was as if a shutter had been raised inside his head. He was on fire for her, the tawny eyes wide and hungry. Then she did pull away, scrambling to her feet and running. She stopped only twenty yards away, bare feet complaining at the stones, and turned to look at him. Still he stared, desire in every line of his long, lean body. Sarah began to shake. Panic, that was what it was, she told herself and ran a hand distractedly through her hair. Langeveldt slowly got to his feet and walked towards her. Sarah clutched a tree for protection, peering from behind it at the approaching man.

'I'm not going to chase you round half Africa,' he said softly, stopping two yards from the tree. She could hear his short, harsh breathing.

'What *are* you going to do?' Even to her own ears she sounded scared.

'I'm going to say "please". Will that do?'

'What if I say no?'

'I'm trying to be nice, for God's sake. I don't want it to be like last time.'

'That really is awfully good of you,' she said with icy sarcasm. 'Non-violent rape is so much more socially acceptable, don't you think?'

He took two strides to her tree and stood only inches from her, taking care not to touch. She hid her face against the rough bark and would not look at him. Gentle fingers lifted the hair from the nape of her neck and caressed the warm skin beneath. Against her will, Sarah's muscles, iron-hard with tension, began to relax, but still she kept her face hidden, safe in the anonymous dark. Then he began to kiss, soft as a moth's breath at first but then more harshly until he was catching the flesh of her shoulders in his teeth. Sarah half-turned to protest, but her words were never spoken. His mouth was on hers, hot, urgent, and his hands were dragging at the tattered remains of her blouse. There was a tearing noise and for a brief moment her breasts swung free. Then he was cupping them in his hands, teasing the nipples between finger and thumb until she groaned beneath his kisses. Her hands were moving with a life of their own, tangling in his hair, kneading the muscles of his wide back.

And then he pulled away from her, only to tear at his own clothes, his hands fumbling in their urgency. Never taking her eyes from him, refusing to think, Sarah slipped her arms from her blouse and then unfastened her trousers. When she stepped from them it was into his waiting embrace.

Too desperate for gentleness, Langeveldt was almost as violent as before, but this time pleasure took the place of pain for Sarah. Every thrust drove her further towards her goal and she clung to him and begged him to go on. He needed no such urging and when at last a high thin cry broke from Sarah's lips and she fell back, gasping, he was only seconds behind. For long moments they lay entwined, their bodies shiny with moisture.

She was the first to pull away. Grabbing a handful of coarse grass she scrubbed angrily at all traces of their lovemaking and then wriggled quickly back into her clothes. It was almost night and she busied herself piling wood for the fire. Then she lay down with her face to the thorn barricade and pretended to be asleep.

It was quite dark when he joined her. Stretching easily within inches of her stiff back, he sighed with contentment. 'Mrs Hamilton, you were bloody fantastic,' he said happily. Her shoulders quivered and he chuckled. 'You can't pretend you were begging me to stop. Wherever did you learn those words? A lady like you moaning –'

'If you say it, I'll kill you!' Sarah sat up furiously, fist held ready to strike, dark hair in a cloud round her face. Langeveldt's teasing smile faded.

He reached out and caught her fist, gently bringing it to his lips for a kiss. 'Beautiful, beautiful lady,' he whispered. 'I shouldn't tease you. You were just so – wonderful.' He released her hand, reached up and ran his fingers over the curve of her cheek.

Sudden tears started to Sarah's eyes. 'I was terrible,' she said miserbly. 'Wicked! I'm married, I love my husband, I don't want anyone else, especially not you! But I said those things, begged you –' She rubbed fiercely at her eyes, refusing to give in and let the tears fall. Langeveldt sat up and reached for more firewood. His rare mood of peace had vanished.

'What's wrong with wanting sex?' he asked suddenly. 'Male or female, every animal in this damned country wants it, why should you be different? It's a need, every bit as much as hunger or thirst.'

'But we're not animals! I'm quite sure if Douglas was stuck here with some strange woman he wouldn't be doing this sort of thing. He'd behave impeccably, whatever he felt.'

'And I'm not Douglas,' said Langeveldt, almost spitting the words. 'What's he like in bed, anyway? Do you beg him for more? Or is he such a superman you don't have to worry he might blow up and spoil it all?'

'It's none of your business,' said Sarah, drawing her knees up to her chest and folding her arms round them. 'He's not like – he doesn't – Douglas is very gentle.'

'Ohhhh,' said Langeveldt scornfully, and then fell silent. He stared across the fire into the night. 'Do you like it like that?' he asked suddenly.

She shrugged. 'Sometimes,' she replied, her voice small.

'Better than – it was?'

She buried her face in her arms, wanting to lie but somehow knowing she could not. 'No,' she said softly. 'Tonight was best.'

This time, when he took her, there was no restraint. Sure of their power to please they lingered on the way and when at last they reached twin plateaus of contentment it was with nothing to wish for but sleep. For once they did not stir when the lions began to roar.

Still they did not look at each other when they woke in the morning. Sarah was awash with guilt, and the wreck of her one and only blouse did nothing to improve her temper. The last button had gone and a long rip over her left breast made it resemble the naughty underwear that arrives in a plain brown wrapper. Langeveldt chuckled dirtily when he saw her, which immediately sent her rummaging for the remains of her white silk dress. Fortunately, although most of the skirt had been torn up the bodice was intact, and when she had trimmed the bottom edge with Langeveldt's knife she had a strapless white silk top.

'The latest in safari gear,' she commented, struggling to appear light-hearted.

'You can come on my safari any time,' he murmured, and pinched her bottom through the hole in her trousers. She yelped and sprang away from him.

'Now, look,' she said severely. 'You needn't think this is going to be one long orgy. I want to go home, to my husband and family and if I've got to – well – then all right. Sometimes. But you haven't any rights at all, Langeveldt, and I want you to realise that.'

He flung down the rucksack he had been about to shoulder. 'Lady, if you want to fight about who's boss of this outfit may I remind you that I usually win? I say what goes around here and if I want it I get it and that's that.'

Sarah stood speechless, then leaped for a large stone. As she brought back her arm to throw it she met his stare. 'You dare,' he warned. She did not dare. Turning she threw it as hard as she could at a distant tree and was rewarded with a dull thud. 'Good shot,' he congratulated, picked up his rifle and began to walk. After a minute of tearful fury Sarah fell into step behind him.

The sky, flawless blue for so many days past, was rapidly clouding.

'Rain coming,' said Langeveldt tersely and kept on walking. There was no vestige of shelter and when the storm struck in all its tropical violence they simply plodded on through it, their hair plastered to their faces and their clothes heavy with water. A large bird sat sullen on a tree, head hunched into its shoulders. Pools appeared where before there had been dry earth, leaves glistened with water, and when the rain stopped exactly as if someone had turned off a tap, the steam began at once to rise in clouds around them. It was mystical and unreal, like the approach to the gates of heaven, or even hell. A weird country, thought Sarah, a land of contrasts, beauty with harshness, softness allied with death. She pulled Cottar's hat down over her eyes to combat the glare of the sun on the pools and let her thoughts drift. A small movement to the left of them brought her head sharply up. Cold fear turned her heart to ice.

'Langeveldt!' she squeaked. 'Quick! Do something!'

'Thought you'd never see them,' he said calmly. 'Keep walking, they're not hungry.'

Mechanically her legs continued to move but her eyes remained riveted on the lions peacefully lazing some fifty yards away. Females mostly, with some half-grown cubs, but there was one huge male, his mane heavy, his gaze calm and untroubled. Somehow he looked oddly familiar.

'He looks just like you,' she said suddenly. 'No wonder you like it out here, you're half brother to a lion. Look at him, lazy as anything, conceited as hell and the women doing all the work. It's you to a tee.'

'And he bites when upset,' commented Langeveldt.

'It doesn't surprise me,' said Sarah. 'Anyone can see he's a wife-beater.'

The big male rose smoothly to his feet and walked a few strides towards them. There were little brown tufts of hair at the top of his front legs. Sarah reached out and clutched Langeveldt's shirt, but he disentangled her fingers saying, 'If you're going to be so foul-tempered you can't expect me to save you. Me and him, we like our women docile.' She thought for a moment and then fell back to walk behind him.

'I will not crawl,' she muttered grimly and forced herself to walk without so much as a glance at the diners so close to the edge of the table.

They walked for a week, during which it rained every day, during the night twice. That was the worst, when there was nowhere dry to lie and they sat huddled in the mud waiting for it to stop. During the day the sun dried them within minutes but at night their clothes clung damply for hours and by morning they were stiff with cold. Neither complained, there was no point. In the morning streams appeared where there had been none before, harbouring thousands of frogs, come from God knows where, to fill the night with sonorous croaking and the day with leaping movement. Frogs' legs became a tedious part of their diet, when Sarah would have given anything for a potato, or even a single brussel sprout. But at least they could be clean, washing off thick layers of mud each day. Sarah began to be troubled by a thick, racking cough.

Although they were generally following the line of the river, Langeveldt kept well away from its banks, where the crocodiles lay in deceptive indolence. He told tales of people dragged screaming into the water but Sarah thought he was merely trying to frighten her. He might see himself as the ultimate bushman but she was a very unwilling disciple, and she was beginning to doubt if the dangers he so frequently pointed out were real. One evening she learned better.

Langeveldt was scouting for a dry camp site and Sarah sat waiting a hundred yards from the river bank. It was very warm and peaceful, if you discounted the flies, and she was becoming inured to them. A small, elegant antelope crept from the tall grass bordering the river and stepped shyly down to the water's edge. Sarah too crept forward, watching enthralled as the little creature sniffed the air and fastidiously bent its head to drink. Horns like twin spires jutted from its head and black tearmarks ran from the corner of each eye. She could imagine nothing more perfect. One moment the perfect stillness, the next, one single, shrill scream. The water was a thrashing, blood-soaked maelstrom but within seconds even the legs, now kicking feebly, disappeared beneath the surface. The flock of tiny birds that had risen in alarm returned to feed at the water's edge. All was as it had been, but the antelope was gone. When Sarah rose to greet Langeveldt, she was white-faced and shaking.

'A crocodile,' she explained. 'It caught an antelope, right there! It was ghastly.'

'What were you doing close enough to see?'

'I saw the antelope – I wanted to watch it. I won't again.'

'I bet you won't. This place is crawling with crocs, no-one's hunted them in years. I told you what could happen, why the devil can't you take my word for it? But you, you have to see for yourself and now look at you, shaking like a leaf.'

She turned away, too weary to fight, and began to cough, her shoulders trembling with the violence of the spasm.

'Anyway we're leaving the river tomorrow,' said Lange-veldt suddenly. 'I'm going to head east – there may be people that way.'

'I thought you said that was dangerous.' She wiped her clammy brow with the back of her hand.

'It is. But you can't go on like this. Not in the rains.'

'I'm all right. It's only a cough.'

'Don't be so bloody brave, woman, it annoys me.'

Everything she did seemed to annoy him. He was only ever completely calm when they had just made love, and even then he was sombre. He was such a difficult man. Sarah did not begin to understand him.

Now they walked where it was not so easy to find food. Trees and swamps gave way to grassy plains and now, in the rains, the grass stood feet high. The game was wary, easily frightened, and often they went to sleep with only a few strips of dried meat to sustain them. The problem was that you could not hunt and walk at the same time and Langeveldt would not stop walking. Sometimes, if the moon was full, he would shake Sarah from her fitful sleep and make her plod after him through the night. She hated him for it, but she had no breath to argue. The pain in her chest was constant now and although her face always felt hot her fingers and toes were oddly cold. She no longer thought of home and family, except in a vague, dreamlike way, as if remembering something she had read. There seemed no reality but walking, the pain in her chest and, of course, Langeveldt. It must always have been like this, it would continue to be so – endless, pointless march.

One day he shot a warthog and the air was filled with the scent of roasting pork but she could not eat it. He raged at her and she tried, but it was no use. That night again he pushed and pummelled her to walk, when all she wanted to do was lie down and die. The next morning it was raining, steady, endless rain, and they walked on.

After some hours Langeveldt stopped by a tree, dropped the rucksack to the floor and swung the rifle from his shoulder. 'Stay here,' he said softly. 'Keep quiet. I'm going to see what's what.' He checked his gun, unhooking the strap and handing it to her. Then he drifted into the grass, leaving Sarah alone and puzzled. She moved cautiously forward to peer round the tree.

She was on the edge of a clearing. A small white building stood in the centre, dwarfed by three huge fever trees, their yellow stems almost luminous in the rain-filled air. To one side stood a little wooden bell tower, but it was blackened by fire and the bell lay broken upon the ground. Perhaps this was some kind of mission. There was no sign of life.

A flock of parakeets erupted from the trees, their shrieks startling Sarah into a moment's heart-stopping panic. The birds were so deep a blue that it seemed unnatural and she watched them for seconds before she thought to look for what had disturbed them. Langeveldt was crossing the clearing, caution in every stride. The blank windows of the mission gaped like sightless eyes, rain streamed from the iron roof like curtains of the thinnest silk and when Langeveldt's boot hit the rough planks of the door the sound came back to them in a long echo. He stepped inside. It was an age before he reappeared, time enough for the world to end or so it seemed to Sarah. Then he called to her. 'Come on. There's no-one here.'

She obeyed, dragging the rucksack behind her until he came and took it. She mounted the rough steps to the door and peered into the gloom. It was indeed a mission. A small altar at one end, bare except for a rough wooden cross, with half a dozen chairs standing before it. There had been others, as a pile of smashed, scorched timber in the corner testified. The walls, once white, were brown-stained. There was no glass in the windows and at one end of the room a door had been torn from its hinges. Sarah went to look through the opening.

Two little, bare rooms. An iron bedstead, no mattress, and a little prie-dieu, again bearing the marks of fire. In the next room just some shelves, a rough table and a chair. Nothing else. Langeveldt came to stand beside her.

'What happened?' asked Sarah, spreading her hands wide.

He shrugged. 'Attacked. But someone's been here since. However long ago it was there should be bodies, mess, the lot. Someone put out the fire, someone tidied up. So where are they?'

'Perhaps someone came and went away again.'

'Then why bother?'

She did not reply. It was eerie, standing in this strange building and wondering if the owner might return at any moment. Besides, it was so long since she had been in a house that she felt as if the roof was pressing down on her head, the rough mud walls moving steadily inward whenever she turned her back. But at least they were out of the rain. She sank wearily on to the little wooden chair, but it held no comfort. After a moment she moved to the floor instead.

'Look,' she said suddenly. 'There's a trap door under the table.'

He was by her side in an instant. 'Quick. Help me move the table.'

'You don't think –?' She looked at him in disbelief but he wasn't about to explain. Silently they lifted the little table to one side. Underneath, almost hidden by dust and the grain of the floorboards, was a small trap door, no handle, just a square cut into the floor. Carefully, rifle in hand, Langeveldt inserted the blade of his knife into the crack and lifted until he had a large enough gap for his fingers.

'Listen!' hissed Sarah. 'Someone's praying.'

From the opening in the floor came a low, distinctive murmur, rising and falling, with hardly a pause for breath. Langeveldt yanked the trap door fully open. Light flooded into the well beneath and they peered cautiously over the edge.

The voice, now clearly heard, did not stop.

'Confiteor Deo Omnipotentum –'

Sarah looked at the bent head, the thinning hair and the trembling upheld hands and was moved almost to tears. 'You can stop now, Father,' she said gently. 'We're not going to hurt you.'

The voice slowed, but he did not look up. *'In nomine patris et filii et spiritu sancto,'* he murmured, making the sign of the cross.

'Amen,' concluded Sarah.

There was a little, embarrassed silence. Then the priest coughed and rose awkwardly to his feet, brushing the dry dust from his knees.

'How do you do?' he said diffidently. 'I am – er – Father Duffy. Bernard Duffy. I wonder if you could help me out?'

Chapter 5

Duffy had been happy down his hole; it was warm and safe and dark and no-one could get at him. Hours had passed in the comforting ritual of prayer, and sometimes he could almost persuade himself that he was back in the seminary. Why had he ever left? He had been such a success. What was hard for others was easy for him, and when his time there was at an end he had accepted the hardest task with unassuming confidence. How could he have known it would come to this? Why did no-one warn him?

Nothing was the same in Mandoto; the most stupid of his fellows could have done better. The people here were in no need of doctrine: what they needed was food, medicine, some basic teaching in hygiene, and he could not even speak the language! It still had the power to anger him, all those months learning Kiswahili only to go to a region where it was as much use as Greek. No wonder people laughed at him during those first blushful days when he made so many mistakes. The interpreter was neither use nor ornament, and not above the odd sly joke at the expense of the earnest priest. Often Duffy's little congregation, lured by the medicine and flour that he doled out after the service, would collapse in giggles when he least expected it. Father Duffy would look accusingly at his interpreter and the man would look innocently back. Had he told them of the Blessed Virgin or had he made some unsavoury jest instead? There was no way of knowing.

But he had made progress, they would have to admit that in spite of everything. What a world these people lived in, terrorised by demons, spells and curses, as if reality wasn't enough to be afraid of. Death was commonplace, his only regular duty lowering the small coffins of children into the ground. You could tell which would be next: they were like berries on a diseased tree, small, wizened, dropping at the first breeze. If only he could help! It sickened him to see the women fingering maize porridge into the mouths of babes who needed meat, milk, and that stand-by of his own childhood, orange juice.

He started a baby clinic, and the women came, at first warily but then with increasing confidence. Bernard Duffy, aesthete, man of letters, became a fanatic about worms. Every child was dosed and every rear end peered at; he drew charts showing what horrible things the creatures did to people's insides. And when he was sure that there wasn't a wriggle left in a single infant intestine he sent away for half a ton of soya flour and set about building people who, if not Christian, were at least healthy. Yes, it was progress of a kind, and in time he would have built a school and a bigger church and he would have been a success. And then the soldiers came.

He would not think of it now, there was no use thinking of it at all. But he could think of nothing else. The straight path, the path to God, so plain before him and he had turned aside. All the years of training and hope and at the first trial he had failed, failed his people and failed his God. Small wonder he could not look at this strange couple who had appeared from nowhere. Much better that he should have stayed down his hole.

'Are you all right? You're not hurt, are you?' The woman was holding his arm. She was beautiful, and she

114

was wearing embarrassingly few clothes. Dark hair tumbled about smooth brown shoulders and her cheeks bore two high spots of colour. Fever. Father Duffy cleared his throat.

'I am quite well, thank you,' he said politely. 'Perhaps I can offer you some tea? If I may say so you seem a little under the weather yourself.'

'I don't believe this,' muttered Langeveldt. 'He's probably got a plate of cucumber sandwiches down there. Look, mister, what we need is penicillin, fast.'

Duffy glanced nervously up at the tall, assured figure and as quickly looked away. 'I do have some antibiotics,' he agreed. 'Is it for the young lady? I'm sorry, I don't know your name –'

'Sarah Hamilton,' she replied promptly and then bit her lip. Langeveldt shot her a look of triumph.

'Joe Langeveldt,' he offered on his own behalf. 'We're making for the border but we'll have to lie up here for a day or so, she's well on the way to pneumonia. When did they hit you?'

There was a small silence. 'Food!' exclaimed the priest. 'You must have food. Come this way both of you, I have some tins, and you are welcome to a sack of flour –' He made for the door of the church, almost running. They began to follow but Sarah was seized with a fit of coughing and subsided again on the floor. Langeveldt cursed softly and went after the priest.

All the food was kept in the cookhouse, a tin-roofed shack to the rear of the church, concealed by bushes with thick, silver-grey leaves. Someone had trained a creeper round the doors and long racemes of white, scented flowers brushed Langeveldt's arm as he entered. Duffy was scrabbling in the sand on the floor. It was another trap door.

'I keep everything down here,' he said brightly. 'I find it so much easier –'

'You must be second cousin to a mole!' Langeveldt was sour. 'Look, what I need is blankets, medicine, a fire. That girl could die.'

Duffy looked vaguely up at him. 'We have had many deaths,' he said sadly.

Langeveldt squatted beside the hole. 'I know. The usual thing, I suppose – that church has bloodstains as wall paintings. Now come on, little man, pull yourself together. There's work to do.'

Within half an hour Sarah was tucked up in bed, on a makeshift mattress it was true, but cocooned in rough woollen blankets before a blazing fire. The rain drummed on the roof but for the very first time since she left home she felt warm and sleepy and safe. Langeveldt was boarding the window, his rifle propped in a corner.

'It really isn't necessary,' said Father Duffy, hovering round him. 'If anyone comes we can just go under the floor. They never suspect.'

Langeveldt looked blankly at him. 'We found you. And if staying alive means crawling in holes then I don't think I'll bother. If anyone comes then she goes down the hole and I take to my trusty pop-gun. You can do as you like, of course.'

'You're not putting me down that hole,' objected Sarah, close to sleep.

'You'll do as you're told.'

Father Duffy bobbed nervously from one foot to the other. 'There must be no more murder under this roof,' he said at last. 'I insist.'

'Fine,' said Langeveldt. 'You just nip out and tell the chap who's shooting at us that he's in a neutral zone. I'm

sure he'll listen. You have such wonderful faith, Father.'
His voice held bored contempt.

The priest met his gaze for almost the first time, and to
Langeveldt's amazement the big, limpid eyes were brim-
ming with tears. 'Look, Father Duffy,' he said awkwardly.
'It's probably been a bit of a strain. Why don't you sit
down and have a cup of tea or something? You're quite
safe. No-one's going to come.'

'That is rather the trouble,' said the little man wearily.
'What good is a church to which no-one comes? But I
really am very tired.' He slumped on to a blanket in front
of the fire and within minutes was asleep.

Sarah looked enquiringly at Langeveldt. 'What do you
think happened?'

He shrugged. 'Terrorist attack. You don't want to hear
about it and I don't think I do either. If they come you go
under the floor. No arguments.'

Sarah grunted non-committally. It was strange that she
could lie there and talk of attacks and yet feel so safe. It
was Langeveldt, of course. Somehow it was impossible to
imagine him losing.

All night it rained, drumming on the roof to the exclusion
of all other sounds. Sarah and Duffy slept, secure in the
knowledge that Langeveldt kept watch. He could not
match their confidence. The mission was an obvious target
and it would be so until there was barely a stone standing.
It was only a matter of time until the soldiers of one side
or the other returned, and then they had better be gone.
The whites had done much in Africa, some of it good,
much of it less so, and always they had the upper hand.
They could pretend that they were welcomed, accepted,
even loved, but in the end they were the oppressors.
When the time came for vengeance it was as well to

remember that, and for himself he found it hard to forget. How he longed for the tranquillity of a place without people, the mindless preoccupation of a job that needed doing. That had been elephant cropping for him, filthy, dangerous, but all-absorbing. He should have stayed there. But a man can't use his life and his wits dispensing death, not if he values his soul.

He longed for a drink. How many other nights had been like this, staring out into the dark, waiting for them to come. Sometimes you were almost glad when they did, until you saw it in the morning. They reserved their worst horrors for the dogs. You could hate them then, and go on hating until that was all there was, but it was no use. The country never changed: sunshine and explosions of life, darkness and violent death. Only fools and tourists pretended that it was otherwise. Even that pathetic little priest acknowledged it, you could see the fear in his eyes. Amazing that the place could still fascinate. Langeveldt's head drooped and he jerked himself awake.

Towards morning he rested a hand on Sarah's forehead. Still a slight fever. Gently, taking care not to wake her, he drew her hair back from her face and studied her in sleep. Despite its tan her skin was smooth as porcelain, her lashes dark crescents on pale cheeks. No-one who lived a long time in Africa would ever have skin like that, he thought, and pulled her hair still further back to look at the untouched whiteness of her temple. Sarah. The name suited her. Gentle English summers. Suddenly the lashes lifted and he was gazing into her eyes, the pupils so wide that they seemed as black as her hair.

'You look like a witch,' muttered Langeveldt and hurriedly withdrew his hand. Sarah pulled herself up in bed. If she was not mistaken he was blushing.

'Has anything happened?' she asked.

Langeveldt moved back to his post by the window, almost tripping over Duffy in his haste. That in itself was odd, he was the least clumsy man Sarah had ever known, almost catlike in spite of his size. She thought of what he had done to Cottar. Had it been like that? Cottar, barely conscious. The tall figure, leaning over, perhaps with a knife – she gave a convulsive shudder and sat up.

'Is it morning?' she asked abruptly. 'I'll make some tea, it tasted so wonderful when – oh!' No sooner had she put her feet to the floor than the room began to sway alarmingly.

'Get back into bed,' said Langeveldt, all trace of discomfiture gone. 'I don't want you collapsing all over the place, we move in a day or so.'

'I don't understand it,' muttered Sarah, her voice trembling. 'I was walking around yesterday –'

'If you can call it that. Like a drunk at New Year. Stay in bed, woman, for God's sake.'

Sarah complied, watching from the comfort of the blankets as Langeveldt boiled water and mixed up a weird kind of bread with flour and salt.

Duffy slept through it all, and when it was ready Langeveldt had to shake him awake. The priest blinked vaguely at them, obviously struggling to remember who they were and where they had come from. The dark stubble on his chin was an incongruous symbol of masculinity for someone so determinedly sexless. It seemed entirely proper for him to hurry to shave it off before he sat down to eat.

Sarah could eat almost nothing, and at once Langeveldt began to bully her. Duffy watched in growing distress.

'I am sure if Miss Hamilton doesn't want to eat –' he began.

'*Mrs* Hamilton,' interrupted Langeveldt. 'The lady is

most respectable, as she keeps telling me.'

'Oh. Well, Mrs Hamilton, then. There can be no need to force her to swallow what she does not want.'

'So I should just let her fade away, is that it? Real Christian example to us all you are, Father.'

The priest looked at him for an agonized moment, then sank his head into his hands and sobbed. Langeveldt and Sarah stared at each other, then at him. 'It doesn't matter, Father Duffy,' said Sarah. 'I'm quite used to him and he's right, I should eat. Please don't get so upset.'

The priest raised streaming eyes and cried, *'Eli, Eli, lamma sabacthani!'*

'What's got into him now?' asked Langeveldt in amazement. 'He's gone bonkers.'

'Shut up, Joe, he's really upset,' said Sarah. She pulled a blanket round her shoulders and crawled down the bed until she could slide off on to the floor next to Father Duffy. 'There, there, Bernard,' she soothed, putting her arms round him. 'Tell Sarah what's the matter, there's a good boy. Did something nasty happen?'

'If you ask me somebody pinched his marbles,' said Langeveldt.

'Will you shut up!' snarled Sarah. 'Now, Bernard, tell Sarah what happened.'

Father Duffy gave a last shuddering sob and then the words began to pour out of him. 'It's a punishment for my pride,' he began. 'I was sure I could do so much. I was going to return in triumph! I paid the merest lip-service to the word humility, I had pride, such pride! That is the reason for it, I see that now. God wanted me to understand how weak and frail I am, how little is my faith. It was a judgement.'

'But what happened, Bernard?' persisted Sarah. 'You must tell me, please.'

The priest nodded urgently, his words tumbling over themselves in his haste to rid himself of them. 'Yes, yes, I will tell you, I have to, it's only right that you should know.'

There was a groan and Sarah glanced up to see Langeveldt leaning up against the wall, his face turned to the rough plaster. She felt a vague surprise, but now Duffy was speaking in earnest.

'Such a lovely day,' he began. 'Warm. But then they always are, here. I was feeding the birds – you may have noticed the parakeets. So pretty. One of the women had left her baby in my care – they often did that, you know, when they went into the forest to collect wood; it pleased me so much. A whole party of them had gone, I could hear them laughing, singing. The sound of the heart of Africa. When the screaming began, I thought at once it was an accident – those knives, you know – and I ran to get my medicine chest. I was coming out of the door when they broke from the trees. The women, some with children on their backs. And the soldiers.' He put his head in his hands again, clutching at his thin hair. 'There was nothing I could do, you see,' he went on. 'Already they were slashing – everyone was screaming, the children crying. A woman fell. She had a baby, it was hard for her to run. I saw what they were doing and I honestly wanted to go to her, try to stop them, but – before I realised it I was under the floor. God knows I wanted to help, but there I was. Crouching in the dark, listening.' He drew a deep, sobbing breath. 'They killed them with pangas. I could smell the blood. Like a butcher's shop. It took – forever!'

There was no more crying. Sarah said bleakly, 'What happened to the baby? The one you were looking after.'

Langeveldt's voice was no more than a vicious whisper.

121

'I should think it was chopped into cubes while our hero hid in the dark. Wasn't that it, Bernard? Wasn't that what happened?'

'Yes. Yes. Yes.' His misery was too great even for tears.

Sarah wrapped her arms around him and held him close.

'You foul little man,' said Langeveldt, and went out into the rain.

Later, when Duffy was calm, Sarah wrapped the blanket round her shoulders and went in search of Langeveldt. At first he was nowhere to be seen; she wandered in the fine drizzle listening to the hiss of rain on the leaves and felt far, far away from it all. Even the mud beneath her feet seemed to belong to another world and when she saw Langeveldt watching from the door of the cookhouse, squatting on his heels in a frame of white flowers, he too seemed strange.

'You look like a gnome climbed up from the under-world,' she said. Her hair was streaked tight against her head and water trickled down her face. 'How can you sit like that?'

Langeveldt blinked at her, his thoughts clearly else-where. When he spoke it was as if he were waking from a dream. 'Born to it, I suppose. My father's friend, Baragu, used to take me to his village, right from when I was tiny. I learned to be like his own sons.'

'This Baragu – he was a native?'

'Yes. Shocking, isn't it? I bet you don't have any black friends in Wimbledon though they're jolly useful on the buses, I'm sure.'

Sarah moved under the sheltering canopy of flowers. Her head was spinning and sounds came from very far away. 'I don't know how you can talk, I thought men like you used blacks as sort of glorified slaves. Carrying guns, doing the cooking, that sort of thing. Not friends. I thought it wasn't done.' The outdated expression caused Langeveldt to grin.

'It isn't "done",' he said. 'But I owe my life to my father being friends with a black man.'

'Tell me,' urged Sarah, but he shook his head and rose to his feet.

'Go back to the church. You look like death yourself.'

'Come with me, I know you didn't mean what you said to Father Duffy. He's so unhappy, I want you to try and make it right. Please, Joe.' She took his arm and gazed up at him, too ill to play at coquetry. Rain spattered her skin and tension and illness had drawn the flesh tight on the bones. Her face could have been a carving brought up from the waves, thought Langeveldt suddenly, and looked quickly away.

'I meant what I said,' he snapped. 'He is foul. Do you realise that he believes God murdered all those people just to teach Bernard Duffy a lesson? As if Bernard Duffy, twit extraordinary, is worth the lives of dozens of black women and children. He behaves like the coward and the fool he is and then says a thing like that. And you cuddle him! I'd rather get into bed with Hitler, myself.'

'I always knew there was something funny about you,' said Sarah dryly. 'He didn't mean it, you know. He feels so guilty and ashamed, somehow he's managed to persuade himself that the whole thing was his fault. He's only been here a year he says, but he seems to think he should have produced an entire nation of converts all capable of singing psalms in four-part harmony. Poor man.'

Langeveldt was striding round the little cookhouse with such speed that Sarah's fevered brain saw him as a figure on a roundabout. She began to hum in time with his steps. 'I wish you'd save your sympathy,' he was saying. 'Out he comes, no knowledge of the country, no knowledge of the customs, and presumes to tell everyone how they should live. What do you think they made of him? At the very least they must have thought he was some kind of nut. What the hell are you doing, woman?'

Sarah was conducting an invisible band with her finger. She stared owlishly. 'Oh. You've stopped. But he did start a baby clinic.'

'For that he came all this way? The power of the man.' But Langeveldt was again in control of himself. Sarah wondered at him. Sometimes he seemed a man of stone, but when something pierced the armour underneath there was a strange mixture of fire and ice. And very little love. Nonetheless, she leaned on him as he trod a wavering path back through the rain.

That night Sarah's breath came hot and painfully, she tossed restlessly with frequent shallow coughs. Langeveldt bent over her constantly, offering water and bathing her dry, heat-filled skin, while Duffy slumped by the fire, apparently oblivious to anything except the tumult inside his head. At last Langeveldt turned and shouted at him. 'Is there nothing you can do except sit there and brood, you useless little man? She's ill, she could be dying, and all you care about is your own miserable soul. A fine priest you are, Father Duffy.'

The balding head lifted. 'You don't understand – how hard it is for me. I am not doing as I should, I know that. A man's torment is such a private thing, there is no way that another can feel as he does.'

Langeveldt turned his head aside. 'I know how much you feel,' he said shortly. 'Believe me, I know. But others have picked up and gone on, when they've lost far more than you can imagine. Blaming yourself is just so much self-indulgence. Look at it this way, perhaps God meant you to survive, perhaps he intends you for great things –' he looked at the crumpled little figure '– though it beats me what. You didn't do anything so very terrible. If you'd acted differently you'd be dead and no use to anyone. Not that you're being much help now. Oh, Father Duffy, why did you ever leave home?'

The little man lifted his head. His squashed, defeated face became tinged with colour, his shadowed eyes flickered with a small, wavering light.

'Because I believed I had something to offer these people which would transform their lives. Because I believed it was my duty to show people the love of God. And despite everything, that is what I still believe.' He rose to his feet and crossed the room with deliberate strides, pausing by the bed to feel Sarah's forehead and pulse. 'Mmmm. More penicillin, I think, and possibly some glucose. Keep her covered until I return.'

Sarah waited until his footsteps faded and then pushed herself weakly on to one elbow. 'Thank you, Joe,' she whispered. 'I knew you could help him.' She slumped back on to the hard pillow.

'Cover yourself up, woman,' said Langeveldt angrily. He thought she was too ill to hear.

It was nearly a week before Sarah was sufficiently recovered to walk more than a few yards without resting, and during that time Langeveldt became increasingly anxious. He was turning night into day, prowling unseen round the buildings in the dark and frightening Sarah and Duffy witless with his silent return. During the day he slept, and there was nothing for the others to do but talk.

Duffy spoke of his home in England, a peaceful manor house in Dorset. His father was dead, his mother a widow. She had not wanted him to come to Africa, but in the end she had given her blessing, and even now would be praying for him. A soft smile touched his lips. She was such a lady, he said.

Sarah pursed her mouth wryly. If she ever had a son she would make very sure that he did not think she was a lady, it would be too great a handicap for the poor child. No wonder Duffy had taken to the priesthood. Only there could he be sure that he need never meet women in anything but the most ladylike situations. Her thoughts turned to her two little girls. It was so long since she had seen them. Would they still miss her, or was she by now just a fond memory revived occasionally by Daddy or her mother? There would be no tractor for Joanne. Emma would be learning to live without their earnest chats about hair-pulling and Kirsty McEwan's funny teeth. Her poor, motherless babes.

A thought struck her. Suppose they weren't actually motherless? Suppose Douglas, the fickle brute, had decided she was well and truly out of the way and had replaced her. Even now there could be someone else on her side of the bed, dropping cigarette ash on her best suede jacket, using up her Christmas bottle of perfume. How could he? If he appeared before her now she would strangle him. Directing a furious stare at a somewhat startled priest she marched to the door. 'I'm going for a walk,' she announced, and flounced out.

Langeveldt was awake when she returned and one glance was enough to tell that he was not happy. 'Where the hell have you been?' he roared the moment she entered.

Sarah took her time in replying. 'I went for a walk,' she said at length. 'Nothing terrible, I can assure you.'

126

'Except that anything could have happened and then it would have been left to me to come racing after you and get my head chopped off. Have you no sense, woman?'

'I do wish you wouldn't call me that,' said Sarah wearily. She had gone too far and was very tired. At one point she had feared she was lost.

'What should I call you? Fool? Half-wit?'

Sighing, Sarah walked over and put her hands on his shoulders. 'Don't get in a state,' she said softly. 'I'm sorry. There,' she popped a little kiss on to his lips '– will that do?'

Langeveldt stared down at her and his hands moved to encircle her waist. Her eyes were huge in her thin face and her hair, blown by the wind, was a dark halo. 'No,' he said huskily. 'It won't do at all.'

Sarah turned her face from his kiss, but as usual he took no notice, contenting himself with her neck and shoulder, moving inexorably towards her breast.

'Stop it, Joe, Father Duffy's here!' She pushed at his shoulders.

'Bugger Father Duffy. He can go take a walk.' Reaching up, he caught her hand and imprisoned both wrists in one fist, not once pausing in his soft and insistent mouthing of her flesh.

'I thought you said it was dangerous.'

'Did I? Oh Sarah, Sarah, a woman never tasted as good as you.' Pushing aside the slight resistance of her bodice he found her nipple. Her gasp of reluctant pleasure was drowned by Father Duffy's shrieking protest.

'This is intolerable!' he howled. 'Get out of here, both of you. This is lust – adultery – I will not countenance it!'

Sarah buried flaming cheeks against Langeveldt's shoulder, but he was unconcerned. 'No-one's asking you to watch,' he snarled. 'Get out, Duffy.'

'I will not! This is a sin, a mortal sin and I will not – cannot –'

Before he had decided what it was he wanted to say Langeveldt had spun him round and thrust him roughly through the door. He found himself facing nothing but the heavy wood panels. 'Stop! Stop! Mrs Hamilton, Sarah, think of your soul!' he cried.

Sarah's voice came faintly to him. 'Please go away, Bernard. Please – please.' She ended on a sob of pleasure, or of pain. Covering his ears with his hands, Duffy ran into the open. The fever trees stood tall in the sunlight, the patches of shade deep and dark at their feet. His throat was tight and hot. Walking as if exhausted he made for his old, familiar resting place, with the parakeets chattering and squabbling in the foliage above his head. Stiffly he knelt, and as always turned to the familiar patterns of prayer, his solace whatever his distress.

Sarah and Langeveldt lay lazily together in the heat of the afternoon.

'I think Douglas has another woman,' she said moodily.

Langeveldt chuckled. 'You must have fantastic radar. Is she sixteen, nubile and rich?'

'It's not funny. He could, you know; he must think I'm dead. I might as well be dead.'

'In that case, long live necrophilia. Oh Sarah, you have a belly as warm and soft as a feather pillow.' He nuzzled her and she tangled her fingers in his hair, watching flies buzz across the stained wood of the ceiling.

'I like you best when we make love,' she mused. 'I can touch you then, I can see behind your eyes. Oh Joe, why are you so difficult?'

'I'm being a real pussycat,' he murmured, 'and I think it's time you began to purr.' His head moved lower and

Sarah's words of protest turned to moans.

It was almost dark when Langeveldt went to find Duffy. He was still kneeling beneath the trees, a motionless figure murmuring prayers in the half-light.

'You can come in now,' said Langeveldt awkwardly. Now that his need was past he could afford to be embarrassed. 'I'm sorry if we made things difficult for you. I suppose it's hard for you to understand –'

Duffy rose stiffly to his feet. 'We priests do have some human feelings. But it is hard for me to see what makes two people – and especially Mrs Hamilton – behave in a way which is contrary to all decent habits and beliefs. She is married with two children. Her behaviour today shows her to be a woman without conscience.'

'It does take two, Father! Next you'll be saying she's some kind of whore!'

'I can see very little difference. Each takes the expedient course: there is no moral consideration.'

Langeveldt was oddly pale. 'And does that make me the innocent dupe of woman the seducer? What a relief – I get to heaven and she has to make do with the fiery furnace. She probably thinks she's there already. But you're in no position to judge, Duffy: your sins may not be of the flesh but they're sins just the same.'

Duffy jerked at the hem of his jacket, pulling it roughly into place on his narrow shoulders. 'It is for you to judge yourselves, I cannot presume to do so. Perhaps I shouldn't have been surprised. Mrs Hamilton's clothes alone, or rather her lack of them, should have shown me what sort of woman she is.'

Langeveldt's hands roughly grabbed the lapels of Duffy's jacket, so recently set in place. 'I ought to beat you to a pulp,' he said with soft menace. 'Sarah is the kindest, most caring woman you could wish to meet. Not one word has she said against you; she even asked me to –' He swallowed and let go of Duffy's coat. 'You don't understand. I made her – insisted – that we become lovers. And as for her clothes, I wonder what you'd look like after what she's been through. I think she'd jump at the offer of your third best dog collar, though I don't suppose you have the wit to think of such things. You're a fool, Duffy.'

It was quite dark now, their faces reduced to the gleam of teeth and the glitter of their eyes. Sarah's voice called to them. 'Are you coming in? Food's ready.'

The two antagonists turned and walked towards her, keeping as far apart as possible and refusing to look at each other, even when they converged on the narrow door. In the end it was Duffy who stepped aside.

In the morning Langeveldt, who had watched throughout the night, fell into a dreamless sleep on the bed. Duffy walked round the clearing, threw some crumbs to the parakeets and finally sat down, ignoring Sarah as best he could.

'Really, Bernard, you are being silly,' she said crossly. 'It is simply none of your business what happens between Joe and me.'

'I don't want to discuss it,' said Duffy and opened his Bible, staring fiercely at the pages of Deuteronomy.

Sarah knew it was a mistake to try and justify herself to him, but his disapproving presence was like seeing her conscience on legs.

'It's not as if we're hurting anyone,' she wheedled. 'And you've no idea how much nicer Joe is when we're – when he's – Joe is very highly sexed,' she finished lamely.

Duffy turned a page of his book. 'I only hope your

husband finds that sufficient excuse,' he said distantly.

Sarah lost her temper. 'You are so pious you revolt me!' she snapped. 'If it hadn't been for us you'd still be shivering down your hole. I don't expect you to be polite to me but Joe at least deserves it, now he has you as well to nanny for. He'd much rather be alone, you know. I think, when you consider that he's not a very caring man, that he's being awfully kind. He would do much better without us.'

Duffy put down his Bible. 'I'm not keeping you here. There's no need to bother about me, you can leave as soon as you like. I shall stay and do what I can for the people when they return. It is my duty.'

'Don't be stupid, you'll only get killed. It might stick in your throat to depend on Joe, but we have no choice, you and me. He's the only one of us with a clue about how to survive in this horrible country.'

'Unlike you I have my faith to support me,' said Duffy pompously, and flushed pink as Sarah erupted into laughter. 'You may laugh, Mrs Hamilton, but there are greater things than food and drink to consider –'

She got to her feet and gave him a brief, embarrassing hug. 'Come off it, Bernard, save the sermons for the unfortunate heathen. Let's play five stones instead.'

And against all his principles Father Duffy sat on the dusty floor and played.

When Langeveldt awoke the atmosphere was almost cordial. The upset had served to turn Duffy's thoughts away from the massacre and now when he remembered it was as if the events had occurred months ago. He was back with the little problems of life and the relief was exquisite. After supper he shyly unearthed his small remaining store of clothes and spread them out on the floor. Sarah fell on a black clerical shirt with relief, thrusting her arms into the sleeves and knotting the tails at her waist. 'Does it look all right?' she asked, peering down at herself. Langeveldt was grinning. 'Divine, darling, just divine. Not so much fun though. Are you sure you want to abandon the natural look?'

'Quite sure. Decency apart it gives the mosquitoes less to work on. I've been a positive banquet for them up to now.'

'Soft young flesh,' said Langeveldt, lifting her wrist and closing his teeth on it in a mock bite. Duffy drew in his breath sharply and Sarah withdrew her hand, exchanging a glance of laughing conspiracy with Joe. It was almost like having a chaperone.

She fished around in the little pile of clothes and found a pair of black trousers. 'How about these, Joe?' she asked. 'Yours are in tatters.'

He held them against himself. The hems reached to just below his knees and the waist would have fitted a girl. Langeveldt zipped them up and swung them to his head like a hat, the legs trailing down his back like collapsed stovepipes. Then he danced, a prancing daddy-long-legs, reducing Sarah to a giggling heap and Duffy to polite chuckles and exclamations of 'I say! Good heavens. Most amusing.'

Suddenly Langeveldt stopped in mid-stride, one leg poised.

'What is it, Joe? What's the matter?'

'Quick, put out the light! Douse the fire.'

Spurred by the urgency in his voice, Sarah ran to turn down the oil lamp, Duffy to put earth on the fire. They crouched in the dark, listening. Faintly, from very far away came the unmistakable drone of an engine.

'What do we do?' breathed Sarah. 'Are they coming here?'

'Only place they could be coming,' said Langeveldt. 'Let's get out of here.'

Sarah had a brief fierce desire to crawl into bed and pretend it wasn't happening, but instead she stuffed things into the rucksack with fingers that felt stiff and cold. They would leave little behind, they had intended to go in the morning anyway and were well prepared.

'They'll know we were here,' said Duffy. 'The fire's still warm.'

'We'll burn the place,' said Langeveldt. 'At least it should keep them guessing.'

'You can't!' Duffy was gazing at him with wide, pained eyes.

'We must. Get him out, Sarah.'

She dragged the reluctant priest towards the door, stopping only to allow him to pick up his Bible. Langeveldt was moving things around behind them. On the threshold of the night Sarah stood and screwed her courage to go out into the dark. Although her mind accepted that to stay was to die, her more primitive soul craved the security of the building. The engine noise was much nearer now, grinding over the rough, unmade road. She started for the trees, dragging a bewildered Duffy behind her. When they reached the first sheltering bushes they turned to wait for Langeveldt. A dull glow lit the mission from within and a tongue of flame licked lazily from a window, leaving little flamelets in its wake, like fairy lights at Christmas. It was almost pretty, the stark lines of the building softened by night, the deep blue of the sky for backdrop.

'Where's Joe? He isn't coming.' The familiar panic almost drove her back into the open, but then he was running towards them, his long legs covering yards with each stride.

'What are you hanging about here for? Get moving, now.' Shouldering the rucksack he began to walk, the other two stumbling in his wake.

Only Duffy looked back, muttering, 'Oh dear God. Oh dear God,' as the flames rose higher into the sky.

Even Langeveldt could not quickly adjust to the gloom of the forest, and after two hundred yards of crashing, awkward progress he signalled to them to stop. 'If we go on they'll hear us. We must wait.'

'Suppose they search?' hissed Sarah. 'What then?'

She could hardly see him but she knew he shrugged. 'We does what we can, lady,' he whined in bad imitation cockney. Sarah reached for his hand. It was comforting to know that he wouldn't pretend, even when the alternative was fear for them all. If there was one thing to rely on in the shifting sands of her life it was Langeveldt's word.

The approaching engine gave a final roar and subsided. Voices floated through the dark towards them, babbling excitedly. The sound was so foreign that Sarah almost whimpered; it seemed dreadful that the enemy, if that was who they were, should not even speak English. Then she grinned at herself – she was the typical Briton abroad: what sort of blighters were they if they couldn't speak the Queen's English, what?

There was a sudden roaring crash, followed by fierce crackling and the unmistakable rattle of gunfire. Duffy squeaked and began to mutter prayers.

'What was that?' whispered Sarah, just as terrified but more reluctant to show it.

'Roof fell in,' replied Langeveldt with maddening calm. 'And they like firing guns; any excuse sets them off. Come on, they won't hear us now.' He set off again into the blackness, the other two hard on his heels in case they were left behind.

Gradually, as the noise from the mission faded, their eyes became accustomed to the depth of shade within the forest. What had seemed to be entirely without light now became a pattern of greys and blacks, but flat, without the depth that daylight would bring. Even so, the walking was treacherous. There was no path and the carpet of leaf mould hid many a hole, each one of which might break an ankle or harbour a snake. Duffy was having the most difficulty although he carried least. Every time he tripped or bumped against a tree he yelped and eventually Langeveldt turned and hissed, 'Will you shut up, Duffy! It's like being pursued by Lassie.'

'I wish we were,' said Sarah dolefully. 'We'd be guaranteed a happy ending.'

'I'm awfully sorry,' apologised Duffy. 'But it's so very dark. Can't we wait for daylight?'

'In daylight our trail will be yards wide,' explained Langeveldt patiently. 'We have to get so far ahead that they get tired of following. But you can sit down and wait if you like; you can practice your pacifism on them.'

'Come on, Bernard,' Sarah encouraged. 'You can hold on to me if you want.'

Langeveldt pinched her bottom. 'Can I hold on too, please, miss? I keep falling down holes in the horrid beastly dark. Please, miss, please?' He gave her breast a sly squeeze and she pushed him away. 'You never miss a chance, do you, Joe? Anyone would think you were enjoying this.'

Langeveldt was enjoying himself. After days cooped up in the mission, waiting, with nothing really to do, he was relishing the action. And, if he was honest, he loved the danger. Life for him was too often bland, tasteless: it took fear to add the salt. Now, leading his little band from almost certain pursuit, he was aware of himself and his surroundings in a way which he never achieved during the normal ebb and flow of life. He felt consciously fit, strong, the muscles in his legs operating in the smoothly flowing rhythm of his walk. The bark on the trees looked rougher, more noticeable, as if a man with short sight had suddenly been given glasses. The very smell of the forest was different: instead of the usual leafy miasma it held the acrid tang of rot, the soft scent of flowers and the pungency of over-ripe fruit, each separately identifiable. It occurred to him that it would be the ideal time to make love. Damn Duffy, he was always in the way.

As dawn approached they made swifter progress, to the tune of the ecstatic birdsong that greets every African sunrise. Despite everything Sarah's heart lifted; they were still alive, it was morning, and for once it did not rain. Now it was her turn to look around and make what sense she could out of the forest. At the mission it had been an encircling green wall, intersected by the road but otherwise featureless. Now they moved amongst trees so tall that the tops intertwined almost out of sight, leaving the forest floor scattered with decaying logs and leaf mould. Creepers hung in clinging coils, huge flowers lifted brilliant heads towards the light. It had something of the quality of nightmare, oversized and irrational. The morning darkened a little for Sarah.

They walked all day with only brief stops for rest and food. Unsurprisingly Duffy was finding the going hard. His shoes rubbed blisters, the flies waged war on his soft flesh and his pack continually became entangled in creepers and hanging branches. Langeveldt's patience soon wore thin and Sarah too was responding to each new call for help with irritation verging on anger. For her the walking was a continuation of all that had gone before, and she slipped easily into the state of mind that expected no end but simply kept on plodding onwards. The luxuries of stopping, resting, going to sleep, were something not to be thought of. Duffy thought of them all the time.

'Good heavens, we must have covered some distance this morning,' he said for at least the third time. 'Shouldn't we have a break, Joe? I'm sure Sarah's tired.' When Langeveldt neither replied nor paused in his long-striding walk he subsided for brief minutes and then struck up again. 'Nearly lunchtime, I dare say. There's the last of the bread and some dried meat, not the greatest feast but jolly welcome all the same. Walking certainly gives you an appetite, doesn't it, Joe?'

Again no response. That was when he played his trump card, giving a yelp of pain and falling to the ground clutching his ankle. Success. Langeveldt stopped and turned to see what had happened. 'I do believe I've twisted my ankle,' said Duffy brightly.

Langeveldt looked at him, one eyebrow raised quizzically. 'You don't say? Well, sorry, old chap, but Sarah and I have to get on. You know how it is. Be seeing you. Give our regards to the soldiers.'

Duffy blinked at him in disbelief as he gestured to Sarah and walked on.

'Goodbye, Bernard. Best of luck,' said Sarah hurriedly and scampered after Langeveldt.

'But – but – Sarah!' said Duffy in amazement, but she was gone, following Langeveldt into the thick leafy undergrowth which closed behind them like a wall. The silence rose up and swallowed him. In truth the forest was full of echoing sound: the close buzzing of flies, the cries of strange birds and the shrieking monkey choruses when a troop moved through the tree tops calling to each other. To Duffy it was silence. He was alone. He rose to his feet and began to follow the others, at first slowly and then with a shambling run. 'Sarah! Joe!' he called. There was no reply. Running with the awkwardness of near panic he crashed through the bushes, blundering into creepers and thick, fleshy flower stems. A sudden burst of laughter stopped him in his tracks. There they were, the two of them, helpless with mirth, clinging to each other for support. Duffy's sweating face, already purple with heat and exertion, turned puce. He stared fiercely at the black earth, plainly wishing that it would open beneath his feet. Sarah stopped laughing.

'Oh, Bernard. I'm sorry,' she gasped. 'But it's your own fault – you drove us to it. You've been moaning all morning.'

'I'm extremely sorry you find me so tiresome,' said Duffy stiffly. 'I only hope your amusement at my discomfiture has made up for it. Now, shall we continue?' He strode off purposefully.

Sarah looked at Langeveldt. 'It seems to have worked,' she said doubtfully.

He gave a chuckle. 'I don't know so much. He's going back the way we came. Hey! Bernard! Stop!'

It was too much for Sarah. This time she laughed so hard she almost choked.

When evening came they were all exhausted. There was no question of lighting a fire and they slumped on the damp ground and chewed on food for which they had little appetite.

'Do you think they're following?' asked Sarah.

Langeveldt shrugged. 'Hard to say. Sometimes they're as tenacious as bulldogs, sometimes they lose interest in half an hour. We can't go any faster so we'll have to hope for the best.'

'Where exactly are we going?' asked Duffy. He had been very quiet since the morning and even now spoke with a distinct frost.

Langeveldt took a bite of dried meat and chewed reflectively. 'Buggered if I know,' he said.

'What?' The others gaped at him, and he had the grace to look uncomfortable. 'I'm not Tarzan, for God's sake! I can't whistle up an elephant and ask for a map. The border must be somewhere in this direction. If we keep walking we have to get there eventually.'

'Joe, you have shattered all my illusions,' complained Sarah, but in fact she was relieved. Joe's infallibility had been unnerving to say the least and she was delighted to find him capable of human weakness.

When they settled down to sleep she snuggled close under the blanket with a feeling of warmth that would have surprised her had she bothered to think about it. Langeveldt threw an arm casually over her shoulders.

'All right?' he asked gently.

'Any reason I shouldn't be?'

He chuckled. 'Lost, pursued, hungry, cold – no, no reason.'

'Go to sleep,' she murmured.

The night was very dark, the tropic moon hidden by the canopy of dripping leaves. Sleep was long in coming to Sarah, and when it did it was full of rustlings and animal shrieks that were not all in her dreams.

Chapter 6

'Duffy, you are a useless, idiot priest!' Langeveldt stared from the mound of spilled flour to Duffy's apologetic face and felt capable of murder.

'I'm so sorry, Joe, it slipped. My hands are so cold.'

'Of course they're cold. We're all cold, the sun isn't up yet. But what were you doing with the flour anyway? We can't cook it!'

'I thought it was something else —' explained Duffy reasonably, but Langeveldt was past reason.

Sarah intervened. 'Look, Joe, why don't you go and shoot something for the pot? Then this evening we can take a chance and light a fire: it's been days now, they can't possibly still be following. I'll scrape up some of the flour while you're away; we won't lose much.' To prove her point she bent to the little white mound and began scooping it up. Already it was full of ants, huge, black and busy. One sank needle-sharp pincers into Sarah's finger and she yelped, letting the flour cascade back on to the ground. 'Oh dear,' she said.

'Oh dear, indeed,' said Langeveldt resignedly. 'God knows what I am going to do with you two, and don't feel obliged to ask Him right now, Bernard. I would much rather you did something useful. Come along, children; if we try really hard we need only throw half our supplies away while we pack.'

Sarah picked up a blanket to fold it and stuck her tongue out at him while he wasn't looking.

141

* * *

Somewhere in the forest monkeys were whooping. 'You know, I think I will go pot something,' said Langeveldt. 'They don't sound too far away.'

'What? The monkeys?' Sarah was shocked.

'Better than rat, I can assure you.'

'I don't care if it's African caviare, I am not eating monkey. It's cannibalism.'

'I must say it does sound a little unappetising,' added Duffy. 'One feels so much empathy with like species, as it were.'

Langeveldt looked from one to the other. 'I don't believe this,' he said helplessly. 'Uncle Bob, you were right, I should have listened. Marie Antoinette and St Francis of Assisi come round again. Don't mind me, I'll just wander off into the forest with my feeble little gun and find something you'd like to eat that won't eat me first. Birds OK, I suppose? I'd hate to stagger back and have you trying to give the thing first-aid.'

'A bird would be fine, Joe,' soothed Sarah. 'But monkeys are out. And snakes,' she added as an after-thought.

Langeveldt gave an exaggerated bow. 'As madam wishes. Your humble servant will just toddle off with a smile and a wave while you do something vital, like plucking your eyebrows. I'll try not to be long in case you get bored.'

'I can't help wondering what you were like as a white hunter,' remarked Sarah. 'Were you as horrid to the clients? Hitting them over the head when they shot badly, that sort of thing.'

Langeveldt snorted. 'I was perfectly charming,' he said with a tiger smile. 'Fat little Americans nearly killed themselves scurrying after me. I quite liked a few of those, they were so thrilled by it all – one mangy lion and they were satisfied. And it paid well, I can say that much for it. Then I got a reputation and it was different. I got the hard core hunters, trophies by the ton, to hell that it's the last one on earth, blast it. They never noticed the sunsets, never watched a giraffe float across the plain. If you couldn't kill it they didn't want to know. I quit.' He met Sarah's thoughtful gaze and coloured. 'But that's long past. Keep quiet, stay out of the open and stay put. I'm off to get us some dinner.' He shouldered his rifle and began to walk away.

'Take care,' called Sarah, but he gave no sign that he had heard.

She and Duffy sat down to wait until he returned. The forest would be a steam oven later but now it was cold and dripping. They moved into a clearing where the sun would soon filter through.

'He does have a very quick temper, doesn't he?' said Duffy.

Sarah grinned. 'I don't think that's quite the right word. He's on a sort of permanent simmer, and he has absolutely no patience. But he can be very kind.'

'He finds me extremely trying, I'm afraid.' Duffy was folding and refolding a grimy handkerchief. 'It's strange, but as a priest people are usually very polite to you, even if they don't believe in your religion. Joe's brand of insult is something quite new to me. Are you a Catholic, Sarah?'

She gave him the stiff, excluding smile that she reserved for Mormons and Jehovah's Witnesses calling at the door. 'Church of England,' she said with apologetic finality. 'But I wouldn't be at all surprised if Joe was brought up a Catholic. Some of his insults have rather too much edge for the occasion, if you see what I mean. Perhaps he's revenging himself on a priest who got him into trouble for swearing when he was ten.'

'Or one of those ferocious nuns that terrify small boys,' agreed Father Duffy. 'I shall never forget Sister Theresa; she spanked me once with a hymn book.'

'Perhaps you only became a priest to get one up on her,' teased Sarah. 'And now you'll realise it's all been a terrible mistake.' But the mistake was hers. Duffy flushed and as quickly paled.

'A-hem,' he coughed. 'I can assure you, Sarah, that just because I am not the outdoor type it does not mean that I have made a mistake as fundamental as you seem to imply. My vocation is sure. Firm. I have no doubts.'

'I'm sorry, Bernard, I didn't mean – I'm sure you're a wonderful priest.' Even to her own ears she sounded insincere. There seemed no way to put things right. They sat without speaking, each with their own thoughts.

There came a crashing in the trees. They looked at each other, speculation tinged with the beginnings of alarm.

'Joe?' said Sarah, 'or an animal? It sounds so –' She half rose to her feet. From the trees around them stepped six or seven men, black, menacing, pointing guns. She reached for Duffy's hand. They wore uniforms of a sort, camouflage jackets swathed with ammunition belts, but round the neck of one was a necklace of bones and when another smiled his teeth were filed to points. Her mouth was painfully dry. She could hear Duffy's breath coming in terrified gasps. Gradually the men approached, step by creeping step. They wore rope sandals on their feet. One held his gun like a spear.

Suddenly Sarah turned to run. A howl broke from the throats of the men and as if released from a spell they leaped forward, imprisoning both Duffy and Sarah with relentless ease. Black hands reached into her shirt, fumbling her breasts; she twisted, trying to bite. A man grabbed her from behind, pressing himself against her and chuckling lewdly. She screamed, a shriek of shrill desperation unlike any sound she had ever made before. Someone struck her. She fell to the spongy earth and lay there, eyes tight shut, fingers clawing, praying that when she looked again they would be gone.

Langeveldt set off into the forest with a feeling that verged on relief. It was good to be alone. Or, more truthfully, it was good to be without Duffy. The little man was infuriating by his very existence and whereas he and Sarah had evolved a peaceful routine of living together, the presence of Duffy disrupted everything. Yet it was hard not to be sorry for him, or to see the qualities that would have helped him excel in so many other spheres. Gentleness. Faith. The capacity for reflection. He should never have come to Africa, this harshest of continents. Langeveldt breathed the morning air and was content.

With the rising of the sun came the rejuvenation of the forest. Flowers spread themselves like an easy woman, a snake came out to bask on a rotting log. There was plenty to shoot, but he did not lift his rifle, treasuring the moment as it was. It had brought it all back to him, talking of his days as a hunter. Terrible days. A paid executioner. Even elephant cropping had not been so bad, so it must have been the waste that offended. Killing without sufficient reason.

A creeper drifted damp fronds across his face. For all its beauty the forest was hostile, too hot and too cold in turn, infested with flies, dripping with water. They must get out soon or Sarah would be ill again. He turned his attention to business, gliding from tree to tree, his head twisting towards the leafy canopy in search of a fat and trusting bird. Then he heard it. Shrill, piercing and unmistakable. The blood froze in his veins, he spun round, began to run – and stopped. Years of training laid invisible chains on his limbs. Whatever the danger, whatever the emergency, remember to think.

They must have been following all this time. Stupid of him to assume otherwise, even though he could have done no more than he had. Would they have posted lookouts? No, they would be too interested in what they were doing. A sob broke from him and he jumped at the unexpected sound. This was no way to behave when she needed him. Automatically checking his rifle he felt the spare bullets in his pocket and blessed the habit that had placed them there. Swift and silent as a hunting cat, he slipped through the undergrowth.

Sarah's head jerked in weariness against the rope and she staggered. They had tied her to Duffy like a slave, hands behind, necks linked together. It was simple but effective: the man who led them had only to tug and they were forced to obey. She had no idea where they were going, she hardly cared so long as she was free of those fumbling hands. They were saving her for later, that much was obvious.

Duffy was a worse case. They had kicked him almost senseless, hard, horny feet thudding into his body with dull, solid sounds. Then they had forced him to walk and his staggering gait tugged continually on Sarah's neck. She was very near despair. Always in her imaginings Sarah had been convinced that were she ever in a tight spot, in a burning building or standing before a firing squad, something would happen to save her. A fireman would appear at the window seconds before the floor collapsed;

a pardon would arrive just as the gunmen took aim. Reality seemed about to let her down. Not even Joe could save them now, one man against so many soldiers all armed with weapons that made Joe's rifle look like the pop-gun he had always declared it to be. And they knew who Duffy was. That was why they had followed and that was what would determine their end. The rope tugged and she thought about falling and refusing to rise. Then they might shoot her and be done with it, for it was not dying that terrified her but the manner of her death. She could not bear it if they raped her, one after the other, on and on, she would kill herself first. No more fear or pain, no guilty apologising for having done the wrong thing, which had been the only thing to do. An end to the whole exhausting mess. There was just the awkward problem of how to go about it. A knife would be best, but she had none. And in any event would she be able to plunge it into her own, cringing flesh? Her stomach tensed at the thought. She was too much a coward, it would hurt so very much. She needed a miracle and there was only Langeveldt. Against all reason her spirits lifted a little. He would not desert her, and he was not a man to fail.

Langeveldt did not share her confidence. When he glimpsed them through the trees, surrounded by soldiers, he felt only a sweeping tide of relief that they were still alive. He was to be given another chance. Fear of stumbling across their mutilated bodies had numbed his mind but now that they were there before him, however weak and stumbling, he could relax and allow his brain to function. Now was not the time to attempt a rescue: they would be dead before he had fired two shots. No, he must wait.

Duffy fell, dragging Sarah down with him. Legs flailed and thin cries rose and died in the thick, humid air. But they were up again, blood bright on Duffy's head. The scene, with variations, was repeated again and again. Still Langeveldt waited.

It was late evening before they reached their destination. The smell of woodsmoke from the cooking fires, the distant chatter of children. For Sarah it was a scene from a nightmare: the mud-walled huts with their shaggy grass roofs seemed full of menace, the curious faces of the women clustering round were the masks of ghouls. They smelled strong, like healthy cows. She blinked in the flickering firelight, hunching her shoulders against the fingers that pinched and prodded her bruised flesh. What would happen now? She was too tired to care. When they pushed her into a hut she fell asleep where she lay, her face resting on the hard mud floor.

The morning sunlight woke her, falling in a stream of gold through the doorway. She tried to stretch and realised that her hands were still tied. She was still there. No rescue, no magical reprieve. Duffy lay slumped against the far wall, emitting an unhealthy snore through a broken nose. Sarah went on her knees to the door and peered round the edge of the woven grass curtain. A man squatted there, face as dark as stagnant water, eyes meeting hers implacably. Hurriedly she ducked back inside. There was no help to be had from him. The women were calling to each other, preparing food, and inexorably she was drawn back to the doorway, peeking through the narrow gap between the wall and the curtain.

She was in a village of some ten huts, all much the same as that in which she rested except for one, which was much larger. A woman knelt on the ground outside it, her hands working in a bowl. She was beautiful, her hair cropped close to her head, her skin like black silk. A pattern was raised on her face in a series of pricks, encircling her eyes and forming whorls on her cheeks, and from each ear hung a heavy copper weight grotesquely stretching the ear lobe. Breasts as heavy as melons swung as she worked and her only clothing was a leather apron in front and behind. Sarah fingered her own arm, thin and bruised. Surely she would be a poor prize in comparison with such as that.

Nobody came. The woman finished what she was doing and went back into the hut. Yawning and stretching from all around came the soldiers. There were some twenty altogether, and they gathered in groups, talking and smoking. One man stood continually on one leg, like a stork, apparently not in the least uncomfortable. Three deep scars were etched into either cheek and Sarah wondered at a people who could inflict such pain merely for decoration. They would think little of torture. And yet when a baby scrambled from its mother's side and clutched at the man's leg he lifted the child into the air with obvious affection. She looked away in bewilderment. There was no understanding these people.

Duffy was waking now. 'What's happening?' he asked thickly. No-one had brought water or food and their lips were dry and cracking.

'Nothing. I think they're waiting for something. Can you feel your hands? Mine are dead.'

'Mine also. I fear it is the least of our problems. Oh well, it will pass, as everything must. Do you mind if we don't talk? I should like to make my peace with God. Unless of course you wish for confession –'

'No thank you!' The thought of admitting her many failings in stark words filled her with horror. Duffy could prepare for death, she would wait for Joe. No-one could despair in the morning, it was too much a time for life and doing. She would never die in the morning.

But the bright dawn faded into the heat-sodden afternoon. The soldiers slept, the children played desultorily in the dust. Sarah strained at her tied hands, but her flesh had swollen around the ropes and they were tighter than ever. James Bond would have a razor blade concealed in his shoe, she thought miserably. Why hadn't Joe thought of that? This was all his fault, and where was he anyway? Didn't he realise what they were going through? If she ever got home she would take to her bed and never, ever leave it again.

A different sound penetrated the buzzing of flies and the murmur of Duffy's prayers. It was an engine and she was not alone in hearing it. Everyone in the village was stirring, the men laughing excitedly and grabbing their guns, the women running to and fro, gathering their children, driving stray chickens out from under their feet. The noise reached a crescendo and a jeep burst into view, revving fiercely, filling the air with dust. The men ran to form a ragged line, standing stiffly to attention. As the dust settled a tall, thickset man stepped from the jeep, swathed in ammunition belts, a cluster of grenades swinging from his waist. A green beret was set smartly over one ear, and sweat glistened on the velvet black skin of his face, so black that it was hard to distinguish his features. He walked stiffly, with conscious dignity. This was the man for whom they waited.

The camp was alive with bustle and excitement. Women ran to bring food, and the one Sarah had noticed that morning knelt before the newcomer and he rested a hand in benediction upon her head. Then, before she could draw back, the grass curtain of Sarah's hut was thrown aside and rough hands dragged her into the open. She stumbled, failed to find her feet, and collapsed in a heap in front of the tall man. Their eyes met. The whites of his were stained yellow. 'How do you do?' he said in stilted English.

'How do you do?' replied Sarah, croaking.

'This priest – are you his woman?'

'Priests do not have women.'

'Ah, but that is not true. Always a priest takes a black woman to his bed. White women also. You are his woman.'

'No.'

The man ignored her. Reaching down he dragged her shirt aside, exposing her pale breasts. A long sigh rose from the watching men and the tall man flicked her nipples with a thick black finger. Sarah wriggled desperately away. This was it. This was the end.

'You are too thin and pale,' said the man. 'My men shall have you. But first let us see your priest.' He waved an authoritative arm and men ran to fetch Duffy. Sarah struggled to her feet and watched in numb misery as they dragged him into the light, his two large eyes blinking and squinting. He stood swaying, thin, slight and pathetic.

'You are a priest?'

Duffy nodded and searched for his voice. He was trembling uncontrollably and even his words shook. 'I am Father Bernard Duffy,' he said finally. 'From the mission at Langata. Of the Roman Catholic Church.'

The man leaned forward until his face was inches from Duffy's. He opened his eyes very wide and hissed, 'You are a cheat. You are a liar. You take my people and you steal their hearts!'

Duffy stared as if mesmerised. Drops of the man's spittle spattered his cheek. 'No,' he said. 'Like you I am a child of a loving God. By His grace and that of the Blessed Virgin we shall all be saved.'

The man threw back his head and laughed. 'Let us see him save you!' he shouted. 'Let us see him send down his chariots to take you up. Look, I strike you, now, and now! Is he coming? Does he send a snake to bite me? Where is your God now, priest?'

The watching men roared with sycophantic laughter. Blood flowed anew from Duffy's nose and stained the dry earth as he struggled to regain his feet. Nothing happened, not even a little shower of rain. No miracle for Duffy, no magic rescue for Sarah.

'My God is not a witch doctor,' quavered Duffy. 'He has no need of signs. I am but His poor servant, you may kill me if you choose. I shall receive my reward –'

'Oh, but I shall not kill you,' said the man, hooking his thumbs in his thick leather belt. He was enjoying himself, parading in front of his men. 'You may go. There is just one little, little thing.' He snapped an order and at once a man ran to the jeep. Lifting the canvas cover behind the cab he removed a large, ornate cross, booty from some mission. The Christ figure was of ivory, the cross itself jewelled. It was heavy, the man carried it with difficulty, but when his superior took it from him and held it aloft he showed no sign of strain.

'This is your cross,' he roared, waving it at his men. 'This is what they made you worship. See what I make him do.' He repeated it again in his own tongue and the men murmured, their eyes rolling. Clearly they were afraid, the white man's god might still strike. The tall man grabbed Duffy's thin hair and pushed his face to within inches of the cross.

'Spit!' he urged. 'Spit and I let you go. You may both go free. I will not harm you. Look, I untie you.' Releasing Duffy he drew a knife and sawed at his bonds, then turned and did the same for Sarah, nicking her swollen flesh. She felt nothing. Her hands hung at the ends of her arms as useless, unfeeling lumps. Nonetheless she did try to draw her shirt around her, all the time watching Duffy. Not for a moment did she believe the man would let them go, but Duffy did, his face was alight with desperate hope. He took a few wavering steps towards the lines of soldiers, staring into the dark faces that understood so little of what was happening. They muttered and looked away, as if they feared the evil eye.

'Come, priest,' said the tall man, feeling the situation slipping from him. 'If you wish to live you know what you must do.' He held the cross in one massive hand and shook it in Duffy's face. 'Spit!'

It was so quiet that Duffy's harsh breathing was like thunder. He stared at the cross, the figure of Christ thin, elongated, the ultimate expression of human anguish. Slowly he shook his head. 'No,' he said and his voice was firm. 'I will not deny my God. He is the one true God and in your heart you know it. Kill me if you must, He will not turn from you. Remember that in the time of your despair. I go to Him with a light heart.' Small, thin, bloodstained as he was, Duffy was a man at peace. At the last he had not failed.

The men were openly turning away, shielding their eyes from Duffy, not daring to look at the cross. With an enormous cry the tall man brought the cross crashing on to Duffy's head. He fell like a stone and lay still. Instantly there was a single shot and the tall man fell also, slowly, crumbling from the knees, an expression of amazement on his face and a small red hole in his forehead. Everyone was running, screaming, and the jeep was coming, filling the air with noise and petrol fumes. At the wheel was Langeveldt. Sarah stood stunned. 'Get in!' he screamed. 'Hurry, woman, hurry!'

She swallowed, moved to obey, then turned. 'Duffy,' she said. 'We must bring Duffy.'

'He's dead, get in!' roared Langeveldt, but she was trying to lift the limp body. Langeveldt leaped from the cab, levelled the rifle at the fleeing men, fired twice and then hauled Duffy into the jeep.

Sarah gathered her wits. 'I'll drive, you shoot,' she said. Langeveldt opened his mouth to argue but already she was wriggling behind the wheel and ramming the vehicle into gear. He hung from the door, barely sighting before each shot. A man fell to the ground clutching his belly, Sarah swerved to avoid another who leaped on the bonnet, scrabbled for a hold and then slid away as she jerked the wheel. Her hands were coming to life, they were on fire with pins and needles but it was of no importance. A machine-gun began to chatter behind them, and the muscles of her back tensed in readiness for the bullets.

Langeveldt was reloading; and there was the track, open, inviting, but deeply rutted. She slammed the jeep down a gear, rammed her foot to the floor and screamed to Joe to hang on. The jeep bucked violently, the wheel twisting in Sarah's hands, but she clung to it, only dimly aware of a man racing alongside. Then he was gone and they were away! They were free!

'Stop by the trees,' yelled Langeveldt. 'Hard up against them.'

What for? They would be caught. But this was not the time to argue. She spun the wheel and stamped on the brake, stopping with Langeveldt's door inches from the green wall of the forest. In a split second he was out, there was the boom of an automatic rifle from the man in the back of the jeep and the lesser crack of Langeveldt's light sporting gun. Then he was in again, Sarah let in the clutch and they were away.

'Blasted hitch-hikers,' said Joe with his usual calm control. He moved his arm stiffly, taking care not to let Sarah see the blood that trickled down, nor, minutes later, the shudders of reaction that racked him.

They stopped when the engine started to boil, sending clouds of steam high into the air. It was almost dark. Sarah rested her head on the wheel and listened to the hiss and splutter of the cooling radiator and wondered if she would ever have the strength to move again.

'What happens now?' she asked, but there was no reply.

Langeveldt's head was thrown back in exhaustion, his eyes closed. 'Joe? Are you all right, Joe?' She squeaked in fright.

The tawny eyes flicked open. For once they were without light, drained. 'I'm all right. It's stopped bleeding, I think.'

'What has? Are you hurt? Let me see.' They climbed from either side of the jeep and met in front of the bonnet. Langeveldt's sleeve was stiff with dried blood and he uttered a stifled cry as she drew it gently back. A bullet had ripped along his inner arm from wrist to elbow, leaving a trail of torn veins and flesh. Pink tatters hung from the edges like pieces of frayed silk and when she prodded with tentative fingers she left marks in the swollen meat. 'You could have bled to death,' she said softly.

'I stopped it at the elbow with my other hand,' he remarked. 'Bloody tiring, though.'

'I suppose that's one way of putting it. Really, Joe, you are quite irresponsible. It's your duty to take better care of yourself: what would I do if you upped and died? At least there doesn't seem to be anything in it. What can we use as a bandage?'

'How about Duffy's shirt?'

Sarah swallowed. The corpse-like figure slumped over the gear lever was something it should have been impossible to ignore, although she had managed it for some hours. She went back to the jeep and climbed in beside him.

Duffy's face was ghost white, at least those parts of it which were not stained with blood from his mashed nose or covered with the thin stubble of his beard. His skull bore a neat indentation, marking the spot where the cross had struck him.

'I'm sorry, Bernard,' muttered Sarah and began to bundle him out of his shirt, moving swiftly to avoid noticing how cold and heavy his limbs felt. There was a low groaning sound. She leapt out of the door as if pursued by devils.

'He's alive! Joe, he's alive!'

'He can't be.' Langeveldt peered in at the door. 'Come on, give me a hand to get him out,' he called.

Together they laid Duffy in the mud and stood looking down at him. He groaned again and his arms twitched, but when they spoke to him he gave no sign of having heard.

'What do we do now?' asked Sarah. Duffy dead was one thing, alive another, but with all the disadvantages of both he was without doubt an appalling problem.

'Trust him to bugger things up,' said Langeveldt. 'He can't even die properly.'

'Be fair, Joe, he was so brave. I was so proud I could have cheered.'

'I didn't think he had it in him. And I suppose it might make that collection of savages think twice before they rape their next nun. But trust Duffy, now I can't even apologise. How does he manage to be so feeble and yet win all the time?'

'I wouldn't call this winning,' objected Sarah.

'He's doing better than me. I've got to haul him around like an oversized baby and I dare not suggest leaving him because you'll scratch my eyes out. Won't you?' It was not a rhetorical question.

'Not that again, Joe, not like Cottar.' She was warning him to go no further along that track.

He sighed. 'I couldn't anyway. I liked Eric, I was doing him a favour as a friend. With this guy I'd have a job convincing myself I wasn't doing it for fun.'

Sarah nodded. Of course it was right to preserve life at all costs, although . . . She went back to the jeep and hunted for something for Joe's arm. The rag she came up with was so oily and grubby that she hesitated to use it, and in the end she bound the wound with soft, fleshy leaves from the forest. 'Don't blame me if you get Dutch elm disease,' she said lightly, and in her heart uttered a fervent prayer for good, quick healing. They were saving Duffy, so God must owe them something.

They lifted Duffy into the back of the jeep. He was still deeply unconscious, but swallowed the water that Sarah dribbled into his mouth. She pulled the tarpaulin over him and climbed into the front. They were going to drive until the petrol ran out, on the principle that wherever they went was bound to be better than where they had come from. Joe dozed uneasily as they bucketed along the road, the headlights making nightmare shadows in the dark. Sarah was aware that she was unbearably hungry, almost to the point of nausea, and yet she was forced to expend all her energy on driving. Even in four-wheel drive the jeep could get stuck in potholes, and it was hard to avoid them in the dark. Suppose they met someone coming the other way? It did not bear thinking of. Joe only had a dozen bullets left.

It was the early hours of the morning and still dark when the engine finally coughed and died. Without a word Sarah lay down across the seat and went to sleep. Langeveldt rested a gentle hand on her hair and slid quietly out. He saw to Duffy and then melted away into the night.

The heat woke Sarah. The jeep was like a greenhouse and sweat was sticking her to the seat. There was no Joe and when she went to look in the back, to all intents and purposes, no Duffy. She shielded his head from the sun and sat down to wait for Joe to come back, and for once she did not doubt that he would. It occurred to her how much worse her plight would be if the children were with her. Wailing with hunger, thirst and fear, doubling her anxieties and slowing her progress. She could at least be thankful that they were safe at home with Douglas. Her husband would not know her now, she was so changed, and not only in looks. She was harder physically and mentally. The timid woman who had feared to go on a plane by herself could never sit here with a man in a coma, without food or water, in danger of her life, and think it not so bad. They would muddle through somehow, she and Joe. When he stepped from the forest with the body of a dik-dik slung around his shoulders she greeted him with a peaceful smile and began to build a fire.

They waited until they had eaten their fill and slaked their thirst from a forest pool before they discussed what they should do. Joe thought they should go east, out of the forest, and hope to come upon friendly villages. The terrorism that swept the land was largely of one tribe and was as much danger to the people in general as it was to the whites. They might find help from comrades in adversity. They would take the gun and some meat and set off, well away from the road.

But there was Duffy. 'We can't take him, Sarah,' said Langeveldt wearily.

She nodded. 'I know. But we can't leave him, either. He might still feel, we don't know that he doesn't. And they might find him.'

Langeveldt nodded and rose to his feet. He took a step towards the back of the jeep and then turned and cried in a desperate voice, 'I can't do it! Oh God, I can't do it! I'd be finishing their job for them, those murdering bastards would crow.' He put his good hand to his head. 'There's only one thing to do: we won't go anywhere at all, we'll wait until they come and pick them off one by one. Then I'll have them. I've waited long enough, God knows.'

Sarah rose and took his arm. He was irrational with loss of blood and fever, but underneath there was something else. You could not spend so long with another person and not become attuned to thoughts that had never been spoken.

'Of course you can't do it,' she soothed. 'Don't worry, we can stay here if you want. Poor Joe, you've been so strong, you've done so well. Rest now. Just for a little.'

They sat together and she put a tender arm round his shoulders, bowed now with weariness. He began to speak in clipped, tight phrases.

'I suppose it had to come. I've been running away from it all these years and now it's like seeing it again, watching it happen. All this time I'd thought I'd forgotten, and there it is, waiting for me.'

'How old were you?'

He took a deep breath. 'Nearly six, I think. We knew there was trouble of course: Mother always carried a gun, Dad went off hunting them every now and then. But we should have been safe; Dad had been born there and we'd done so much for the people, you know, proper schools, health care – a bit better than Duffy's baby clinic, I can tell you. Baragu warned that we should get out, but it was our home. Everybody thinks like that until it happens.

'The night they hit was like being surrounded by screaming dervishes. They carried torches and their eyes gleamed like madmen and some of them wore leopard masks. I've never been so scared in all my life. I'll never be that scared again. Just a few minutes changed so much. My mother hugged me so tight it hurt. She told me to run to Baragu. She lifted me out of the window and told me to go, and quickly. But I never could do as I was told. I ran and hid behind the jacarandas and I watched. It didn't take very long. They chopped a couple of servants and then they dragged my mother out. Two of them – they raped her. I didn't know what they were doing. I'd never seen my mother with no clothes on before. My father was there, he was screaming and howling – and then they killed her. She didn't make any noise at all. I couldn't believe it, I simply couldn't take it in, and then I wanted to do something, anything – but I was so scared. Just like that feeble idiot Duffy. God, how I despise myself.'

There was a silence. He stared at the ground and watched it all happen again, the film running through his head with undimmed clarity. The knuckles of his hands were white. 'I went to Baragu then,' he went on jerkily. 'He took me in and hid me. It was as if none of it had happened, we never referred to it, just pretended I was on an extended visit. He made a spear for me, a short, boy's spear, and he took me to my uncle. We went like warriors, running, and we hunted as we ran. I don't know how long it was, a week, perhaps two. I never thought once of what had happened. I was happy. Baragu was so tall, you know, and he had a lion scar, deep, on his upper arm. When he came to Uncle Bob he walked tall and straight and I walked tall beside him, he with his great long spear and me with my little toothpick. Both of us stark naked. And he said, "I bring you a warrior who is the son of a warrior. A cub now but with a lion's heart." And he saluted me with his spear, like a warrior. And he went. And then I would have cried, God, how I wanted to cry, I thought my heart would burst. But warriors don't cry, not even when they're six.' He drew in the dust with a finger, sketching the long legs of an African, the slim length of a spear.

'What happened to your father?' asked Sarah.

The sketching stopped abruptly and he scrubbed at it with his hand. 'They found him after about a month,' he said shortly. 'He'd been buried alive.'

Sarah gulped. It was no longer Langeveldt's oddness that amazed her, but his sanity. She groped for words to steer him away from it all.

'But your Uncle Bob was kind, wasn't he?' she asked. 'And your Aunt Daisy? You were happy there.'

Langeveldt uttered a clipped laugh. 'They were good to me, yes. But they were past children, they'd had none of their own and they lived a pretty odd life, a sort of halfway house between white and black. Too much drink, food at all hours, bed when you felt like it, guns everywhere. When I was nine I'd nip out and shoot crocs at night without even mentioning I was going. I longed for someone to tell me not to go, but no-one ever did and I was bloody terrified half the time. Then Aunt Daisy decided I ought to go to school and when I got there it was all the things I'd longed for, a steady routine, organisation, people worrying about you. I hated it. Spent seven years running away, trying to run away or being taken back from running away. In the end the school threw me out.' He grinned at the memory.

'What for?' asked Sarah suspiciously.

'Oh, nothing much.' He grinned again, wider this time and she poked him in the ribs with an insistent finger, willing him to go on. While he smiled the stark agony of the child he had been could sink away into the depths of his consciousness. Far better that it should again be forgotten for there was no living with such thoughts.

'What for?' she said again.

'If you must know it was for seducing the housemaster's wife. Well, actually she seduced me, black négligée, come and rub my back, the whole bit. I spent six glorious weeks screwing her here, there and everywhere until we got a bit over-confident.' He started to laugh. 'We were caught in the cricket pavilion, giving a very enthusiastic perform-ance, by the whole first-eleven come to practise at the nets. Things got a bit hectic after that.'

'Joe, you really are disgusting,' complained Sarah. 'Couldn't you at least have locked the door?'

'I think I wanted to be caught, really. God, I was glad to escape from that place. You know, the head talked exactly like Duffy at his most pompous. Gave me the creeps listening to him, it was like being back there. "It's a sin against God, my boy" and that woman sobbing into a tatty lace handkerchief.'

Sarah grimaced. 'What did the housemaster do to her?'

'Nothing much. Took a job in Rhodesia, I think, and pretended it hadn't happened. Well, with the things she knew I suppose he felt it was worth it. That man must have spent his life permanently shagged out.'

Sarah looked out into the far distance. 'What sort of things?'

Langeveldt chuckled. 'You can't expect me to tell you that!'

'Yes I can! It's all very well for you but I've led a virtuous life up to now. Douglas is very gentle and loving but he doesn't – he never – oh, you know what I mean.'

'Do you want me to say you're fantastic in bed? Is that it?' The laugh was still there but both knew they were quite serious.

Sarah took a deep breath. 'No. Yes. I want to be good in bed. Douglas and I can't talk about things like that somehow and it really was all getting very dull. He was too polite to say so of course but he must have thought it. And with you it isn't dull at all. It's all your experience, I suppose. So if you can just give me a few tips on what I should be doing, then when I go home –'

Langeveldt held up a restraining hand. 'Now just hang on a minute. What's OK for a forty-year-old nympho-maniac is not OK for you. What happened to all that stuff you were giving me about love and tenderness? You're turning it into car maintenance.'

'A good mechanic can make any old banger run smoothly,' retorted Sarah and got up. She needed time to sort out the things she had heard, to reassess the man she was with. It was as if she had been in an aeroplane complaining about the funny colour of the ground, only to realise they had been flying upside down. What would he have been like if his parents had lived? Not half the man probably. But it was so unfair, he had been robbed of so much happiness and yet she could see little hope of any in the future. He was an odd-shaped piece in Life's jigsaw puzzle: he had never fitted and he never would. It was all so sad.

With a sigh, she went to look at Duffy, and there at least there was relief. No mistake this time, he was quite, quite dead. There was such stillness and peace about him that she felt tears prick her eyelids. Even his bruises had faded as if a symbol of his release from bodily affliction.

Langeveldt was standing beside her. 'Well. That's that,' he said grimly.

'I think we should say a prayer,' said Sarah.

He shook his head. 'I don't believe.'

'I'm not sure if I do, but he did. It's right, even if it's only a gesture to him. Are you ready?'

'I feel a complete idiot doing this,' muttered Langeveldt and clasped his hands in front of him. She began to speak.

'Dear God, we weren't very kind to Bernard when he was here. We tried but things have been a little difficult just lately. He was a good man. Not perfect, but then neither is this dreadful country, it makes sinners of us all. But he tried, and he always kept faith. So look kindly on him Lord, and give him peace. Amen.'

'Amen,' repeated Langeveldt.

Sarah stood and wondered if Duffy's God knew what she had been going to do and would hold her to account. Surely not so bad a thing, to ease poor Duffy's body out of life with just the gentle pressure of her hands. A necessary duty and a kindness to them all. Even Duffy might have seen the logic of it.

Flies were already crawling over the corpse. Silently they collected the little they had and prepared to go. Finally Langeveldt tossed a match into the jeep and sent the mortal remains of Bernard Duffy up into an African sky.

Chapter 7

The plain stretched before them, shimmering in the heat, a sea of waving grass. Seed pods rattled together in the breeze, which itself carried a faint zoo smell. Elephant. Sarah felt an unexpected tide of happiness rise up and engulf her.

'Look at it, Joe,' she whispered. 'It's wonderful.'

He rested a damp palm on her shoulder and scanned the horizon, trying to imagine how it would look if it was all as new to him as it was to her. He had spent his whole life in Africa and yet through her eyes he was seeing it afresh. She was right, it was wonderful, and to him it was home.

He pointed. 'Cheetah.' A still head momentarily raised above the grass, each eye marked with a coursing black tear. A second later it was gone. Joe gave Sarah a little shake. 'Move along there, lady. We've got things to do, remember?'

'I don't know what,' she replied. 'I don't believe we're ever going to get anywhere. I don't know what day it is, I don't even know what month it is and I don't think I care. Food, water and no immediate danger, that's all I ask.'

Involuntarily Joe reached into his pocket and jiggled the last two bullets. When they were gone things would be truly perilous. Sarah caught his eye and unerringly read what he was thinking. 'Nuts and berries?' she said hopefully.

'I'll stick to mice. But we'll find a village, this is cattle country. Or at least it was.' This was not a game park.

There should have been herds, each accompanied by a single youth whose job it was to protect and shepherd the wealth of the village. Joe led the way across the plain, searching for some evidence of current habitation.

Towards evening they came upon some abandoned huts, surrounded by a broken barrier of thorn. The women had grown maize and sweet potatoes but now the little plantations were weedy and trampled by elephant. They settled to sleep in one of the huts, but the roof seemed to press down upon Sarah. There was a creaking and a rustling in the thatch, of insects, or perhaps snakes. In the early morning she woke from a nightmare and burst out into the open. A soft wind blew. The sky held a million stars.

'What is it? What did you hear?'

'Nothing. I don't like the hut. It's better here.'

He took her in his arms and they began to kiss. Sarah pulled open her shirt to feel the wiry hair of his chest against her breasts. She moved against him, without haste, feeling him stone-hard with desire. With a low murmur she reached for him and felt the urgent motion of his hips.

'This way. Do it this way.' He was pulling her down on top of him, but she twisted free and stood, slowly taking off her clothes. He was in torment, clutching at her long, slim legs. She laughed and pushed him to the ground, murmuring, 'Wait, wait. You shall have it, but wait.' She knelt astride him and teased, stroking him with gossamer fingers, sitting back on her heels in mock revery. It was too much for him. Clutching her buttocks in fierce hands he plunged upwards, bucking and heaving. Sarah cried out, impaled like a fly on a pin, filled with him and with delight. The end was sudden and all consuming. They lay together covered in dust and sweat, panting and content.

'What you need,' puffed Langeveldt into her ear, 'is some lessons.'

She bit his shoulder.

They breakfasted on maize porridge cooked over a fire whose smoke rose invisibly up into the blue. Sarah washed in a stream and it seemed that she was washing her soul, so clean and shining did she feel. Where does happiness come from that it can descend so unexpectedly? Was it the lack of things that made them see how much they still possessed? They were well, unthreatened and whole, Joe's wound no more than a healed stripe along his forearm, one scar amongst many.

Their slow pilgrimage took them past herds of elephant moving purposefully on the skyline, a single body with a forest of moving legs. Once they saw a very tiny baby, running beneath its mother, her trunk continually nudging. Sarah felt for her in her obvious concern. Langeveldt steered her resolutely away.

They met no-one. Every village was deserted, some had been burned. Every now and then they would have the feeling that they were being watched, but whoever it was remained hidden. They were right to be timid, thought Sarah. They passed a clump of trees. 'Giraffe,' said Langeveldt, and laughed at Sarah's disbelief. Yet there they were, tall and gangling, blending into the sun-dappled shade and chewing with bovine reflection. It was a truly miraculous day, and she thought nothing of the heat, and the walking, and the endless biting flies.

Evening brought them to another deserted village, but this time there was the feeling that the people had left only moments before, and would be back. Cooking pots were overturned in doorways, some grain lay spilled upon the ground. Each time they looked into a hut they expected to see someone there, crouching frightened in the gloom, but there was nothing.

'I don't like it here. Please let's go on,' Sarah urged.

Langeveldt looked thoughtful. 'It should be all right. We'll stay.'

'Please, Joe, it's horrible. Someone could come and we'd be trapped.'

'We're staying here,' he said shortly.

'Well, I'm not,' declared Sarah and set off, nose firmly in the air.

Langeveldt grabbed her arm and spun her round. 'Do I have to spell everything out?' he demanded. 'This place is thick with lion, pug marks everywhere. Sleep in the open here and you might just as well pin a notice on your chest with the price per pound.'

She pulled her arm away. 'You could have said.'

'I didn't think I had to.' He sounded hurt and she looked at him quickly. In all their time together she had roused him to anger, exasperation, desire, but never that.

'Joe,' she asked suddenly, 'have you ever been in love?'

He was taken aback. 'What do you – well – hasn't everybody?'

'I don't know. Have you?'

He went pink and his usually steady gaze slid away from her. 'I've had a lot of women,' he said thickly. 'Sometimes I've thought I might care. Before. Not afterwards, then I was always glad to get away, like the male spider making good his escape before she eats him. So I don't suppose I've ever been in love. Satisfied?'

'Is it because of your mother, do you think?'

He stared at her in the half-light and his eyes glittered. 'That's got nothing to do with anything. Nothing to do with you. I should never have told you. Damn it all, I was right, women eat you alive. Why should I love and be slowly pulled apart, like a child tormenting a fly? You know all about that. Isn't that what you do to Douglas, the wonderful, charming Douglas, who loves you?'

'You don't know anything about it,' cried Sarah. 'If you must know it's the other way round – but I don't mean that. He doesn't torment me, he wants only the best for us, me and the children. You don't understand.'

'No,' said Joe and stared at her with sudden curiosity. 'I don't understand at all. Don't you like being married to Douglas? Doesn't he make you happy? I thought he loved you.'

'He does, of course he does, he gives us everything. It's just that – sometimes I think it isn't me at all. There's this woman who does everything properly and dresses well and doesn't make a fuss, who gives perfect dinner parties and charms his friends and – I'm not like that. I'm messy and silly and lazy and noisy and I hate men who come to dinner and talk business and ignore me, but – I do it for Douglas. So I suppose I must love him. And he does everything for me so you see he does love me –' but her voice tailed off, giving her words a lack of conviction. It all seemed so far away, almost a thing of the past. She did love Douglas, of course she did, but Joe stared at her oddly, his strange eyes interested and aware. She turned her back on him and did not speak again. The turmoil of her thoughts pushed her fears aside as they settled down to sleep.

In the dark of the night she heard it, thin and piping. It dragged her out of sleep as if by a rope attached to her heart, and then she lay there, wondering what it was she heard. The hut was so stuffy, the thatch creaking noisily in the breeze. It came again, insistent, wailing, and she strained to hear.

'Joe! Wake up, Joe, there's a noise!'

He woke instantly like the hunter he was, and lay listening. It had stopped.

'There! Do you hear?'

'It's only an animal. Go to sleep.'

'I can't. I must see.' She was up and out of the door before he could stop her and he followed at a run.

'Go back inside! Don't you realise how dangerous this is, blundering round in the dark?'

'I can hear it, over here!'

He ran after her, cursing softly. She gave a low, murmuring gasp.

'Joe!' she breathed. 'Joe, look what I have found.' Standing forlorn amongst the bushes, wailing thinly, was a tiny black child.

Within the safety of the hut they studied their prize. It was a little girl, perhaps two years old, wearing nothing but an anklet of beads. Her arms and legs were thin and stick-like, but her stomach was a distinct pouch.

'Kwashiorkor,' said Langeveldt. 'Disease of malnutrition. And she's got an enlarged spleen – that's malaria.'

'Oh the poor baby,' murmured Sarah and cradled her. The child looked fearful and began to wail. 'What can we give her to eat? Is she still breast-fed do you think?' There was no way of knowing. They had nothing, except some dried meat. In the morning they could mix up some maize porridge, but it was not what the child needed. The first tinge of alarm darkened the corners of Sarah's mind. Yesterday they had been responsible only for themselves. But tomorrow –

'Where do you think her mother is?' she asked abruptly.

Langeveldt shrugged. 'She could have been taken by

lion,' he said doubtfully. 'Perhaps hiding out, waiting for us to go. We'll see in the morning.'

They spent the rest of the night uneasily, the child between them, quiet now but not asleep and smelling of urine and sour milk.

In the morning it was all there to see. While Sarah urged the child to eat Langeveldt pieced the story together. For whatever reason the woman had stayed in the village when the others fled. She had made a little camp for herself and the child in the scrub nearby, and it was there that she retreated when danger threatened. Traces of vomit showed that she had been ill; perhaps that was why she had remained. It was while she lay helpless in the bushes that the leopard struck, ignoring the child and taking the larger prey. The body was nowhere to be seen, there was merely the blood and the paw marks. Poor kid. It would have been better for it to die with its mother thought Langeveldt, and went back to tell Sarah what he had found.

She was feeding the child like a baby bird, popping the sticky porridge in every time the little mouth opened. She listened in silence.

'So,' she said at last, unconsciously mimicking Langeveldt's habit of speech. 'We are left with her. We must give her a name. What shall we call you, sweetheart?'

'Millstone,' said Langeveldt sourly and she shot him an angry look.

'It should be something African. You decide, Joe.'

He thought for a moment. 'Tanu,' he said. 'It's Swahili for five; five huts here, five thorn trees over there.'

'Tanu,' repeated Sarah. 'Not bad. We shall have to make you healthy, Tanu my girl – look, your hair's all brown and bits of it are falling out. Whatever shall we do?'

'Find some village that will take her, and fast,' said

Langeveldt firmly. 'We can't keep her so don't think of it. Let's get up and get moving. I don't want to hang around here longer than necessary.'

He began to search through the huts and reappeared bearing a long length of cloth. He folded it into a triangle, settled Tanu in the middle and then knotted it round his waist, supporting the baby awkwardly on his back as he did so.

'I'll carry her,' offered Sarah. 'The native women manage it so I can too. Please Joe, let me.'

'She's too heavy,' he said flatly, but that was not the reason. There was a softness about Sarah that he had not seen before. When she tended the child she was filled with gentleness and longing and it caught at his heart. So must his mother have been with him, and Sarah with her own children, and he could hardly bear to watch. That was why they could not keep the child, even if they were able to feed it as it should be fed.

For the first time in his life he thought about having a child of his own. Someone totally his, needing him, giving him unstinting love. At once he rejected the idea. Looking at the difficulties posed by this brat now, and their responsibility would soon end. Your own children were always there, your whole life was ruled by the necessities of care. No, he would forego the pain and the pleasure alike. It was better to be alone. So thinking he hoisted the weight of the baby on to his back, held a hand for Sarah to rise and set off with his little cavalcade to search for a village.

In the midst of the plain stood a lone thorn tree, its branches forked, its trunk scored white by claws. Langeveldt looked and looked again. Wedged in the branches was the remains of a body, head hanging, limbs spreadeagled. One leg was missing. Sarah followed his gaze and let out a horrified gasp. 'Don't tell me that thing is – her mother!'

'Must be. That's a leopard larder if ever I saw one. He'll be back tonight for another slice or two. I suppose someone ought to pot him but it won't be me.'

'Shoot it, you mean? You must! You can't let an animal like that go on killing people, it's obscene!'

Langeveldt grinned bleakly. 'I don't see why. He's killing to eat and humanity is not an endangered species after all. If you ask me it was a fair cop; she was ill, in the open and in the dark. No-one else is going to be that stupid.'

'Except us.'

'Well, there is that. Let's hope he has a taste for dark meat only.'

Sarah snorted. 'Then we can offer him Tanu and relieve ourselves of two problems at once. Brilliant idea, Joe. As usual your charity is such as to amaze. Do you mind if we move on now? If I look at that for much longer I shall be sick.' She settled Tanu more comfortably in the makeshift sling. The child was fast asleep, lulled by the rhythm of the walk. As they moved away a lithe tawny shape flowed up into the tree. It rested there for long seconds, watching their retreating backs with glowing eyes. Then it turned its head and began to feed, tearing the wet flesh with nauseous ease.

The child slept too much. Oh, it made life easy but a baby of that age should be full of life and devilment. Tanu spent her days asleep or swinging dull-eyed on Langeveldt's back. Sarah started seriously to worry. The child seemed to be slipping out of life.

Langeveldt was still saving his last two bullets. He had ensnared a guinea fowl with a rope of twisted grass and Sarah had tempted the child with thin slivers of the most tender meat, but the baby chewed listlessly and only sometimes swallowed, more often letting the sodden lump fall from her mouth. They found a marula tree, loaded with plum-like fruit, and the child ate two and was sick. Sarah and Langeveldt ate pounds and paid the penalty with violent stomach cramps and diarrhoea, which they discussed with great interest and total lack of embarrassment. Sarah grinned to herself – it was the same with her periods. She had always told Douglas that she 'wasn't very well' and undressed discreetly in the bathroom, but Joe had been completely baffled by her erratic behaviour until she shyly explained that it was the 'time of the month'. Then he demanded to know what she was being so coy about. She really couldn't say, except that, well, all bets were off, so to speak. Not that he took much notice. She allowed herself an amused chuckle and blessed the day the clinic had fitted her with a coil. At least she was not going to end up pregnant. Dead possibly, but pregnant no.

She resumed the tedious, hopeless business of trying to feed the baby. The meat was dry now and rapidly spoiling. 'If only I could mince it,' she said desperately. Joe looked at her worried face, the blue eyes dark. He took the meat from her and fingered it, then put it into his own mouth and began to chew. When it was quite pulped he spat the mess into his hand and pushed it between the child's bloodless lips. She swallowed. Again and again he did it, until the two large eyes began to droop in sleep. Sarah let out her breath in a relieved sigh and gave Joe's wet hand a squeeze. 'You clever, clever man. Oh, but it takes so long, Joe. When are we ever going to walk?'

He shrugged. 'We weren't going anywhere much. She'll be better in a week, we can dawdle along till then.' She nodded and he remarked, 'You don't look very bothered. I thought you were panting to get back to dear Douglas and his fancy woman.'

'I don't suppose a week will make much difference. England seems like another world. I can't believe that I'll ever go back. Do you know I used to worry about spots on the carpet? I must have been mad.'

'Be back a month and you'd be worrying about them again,' said Joe philosophically. He ran a reflective hand down the barrel of his rifle. 'This is the place to be, where you can worry about real things – life, death –'

'And spots on the barrel of your gun,' interrupted Sarah. 'You give that thing more attention than a newborn babe, and don't tell me it's because our lives depend on it. You're more of a housewife than I am.'

He grinned. It was true, he was fussy. Not for him the squalid camps favoured by some hunters, surrounded by litter and jumbles of equipment, plagued by flies. Once a snake had flashed at electrifying speed through one of his camps and a jaundiced client had remarked that he even had the mambas trained to travel in straight lines. From then on he tried to be something less of a boy scout, but he did loathe mess, in particular the squalor that accompanies civilised living – the wrappers, the used tissues, the empty tins. Blood, excreta, vomit, sweat, none of these revolted him, yet a litter-filled street could rouse him almost to rage. He swung the sleeping Tanu on his back, pulled down his battered bush hat and began to walk, each footfall with its own echo as Sarah followed behind. It was hard to say who had adjusted but these days their steps matched exactly.

Towards midday the sun was burning hot and they were searching for a resting place. Tanu's mouth was crusted with dried foam and she did not sweat. The grass here was waist-high and thick, with stone-like termite mounds sticking up at intervals like castle puddings. Suddenly

Langeveldt stopped, and Sarah followed his gaze, screwing her eyes against the noonday glare. She could see nothing, but he was untying the baby.

'Stay here. Keep quiet, don't move. If I'm not back by evening just keep heading east.'

'But what is it? What do you see?'

'People. A hunting party, four men with spears. I want to talk to them.'

'Joe! Please Joe, don't. We're all right here, we don't need them. Suppose you don't come back? I can't face it alone. Please don't go!'

He bent his head and brushed her lips with his own. 'Bloody tourist,' he murmured. 'We have to do something about this baby, she's dying by inches. Do as you're told and wait; I won't be long.'

Sarah sat and nursed the child and felt hopeless. The child was going to die. At home, in England, life seemed a strong, thick chain on which everyone had tight hold. Only in great age did the grip loosen, and then you allowed it to do so rather than struggle to maintain something that was increasingly meaningless. Oh, the young did die, of course they did, but no-one she knew. Sad paragraphs in newspapers and third-hand tales were the nearest she came to unseasonal ends, but here it was all so different. You killed to eat, confronting the unsavoury facts of existence each and every day. Things tried to eat you, which was a very nasty turn of events, and if they did not succeed there was disease and accident, drought and starvation. And if you evaded all that, then people tried to shoot you. Cottar and Duffy dead, and now Tanu. How long before it was Joe Langeveldt? And then that nice Mrs Hamilton, respected mother of two? Tears of dismay at the awfulness of it all welled in her eyes and plopped on to the thin face of the child.

176

'Make an effort, Tanu, please,' murmured Sarah, and the child mewed and whimpered like a kitten.

It was unbearably hot, even in the shade. Flies clustered in the moist corners of eyes and lips and nose, small sparrow-like birds with red beaks fluttered over the grass, but Joe did not come. Then, close and unmistakable came the low, guttural cough of a lion. She had been too quiet, too still, the thing might fall over her at any moment. She let out an almighty shriek, startling the baby into wails and causing a sudden crashing in the grass a scant two yards away. She stood up and looked desperately round. A yellow back was racing away, tail thrashing, and running towards her came Joe, followed by two blacks with spears. He slowed when he saw her but fright made her babble.

'The damn thing nearly trod on me! What sort of country is this, you can't even sit in the grass and mind your own business without bloody great lions blundering about. If it hadn't coughed we'd have been exchanging dinner invitations. I said you shouldn't leave me. Oh dear.' Her legs gave way and she subsided into the grass.

Joe peered down at her. 'I wish you'd be a bit more careful,' he complained. 'You gave that lion a terrible fright. Wildlife's important, you know – we must do all we can to protect and conserve.'

'Bugger wildlife,' snarled Sarah. 'What about me?'

He chuckled. 'There speaks every poacher in the continent. Come on, ducks, and meet the people.'

She felt foolish. Two long-limbed men stood and stared at her, their hair in thin plaits in front of their ears, wearing nothing but small loincloths. Each was stained a peculiar grey colour, streaked here and there with rivulets of sweat. They carried their spears with a loose familiarity. Sarah forced herself to smile.

'The baby is ill,' she said, holding out the bundle for

them to see, unconsciously appealing to what must surely be a constant amongst humankind, care for the young. Their mouths formed round 'O's of interest and one fingered aside the covers to stare at Tanu. She was awake, but very still. He said something to Langeveldt, accompanying the words with rapid and vigorous signs, a rocking motion of the hand, a fierce shrug, a large sweep of the arm. Langeveldt nodded and replied, also with signs.

'Do you understand?' queried Sarah. 'What do they say?'

'They speak a little of the language of the mines,' said Joe. 'We can get by. Their village is not far from here, a little near, a little far is what he says, which might mean anything. One's going on ahead, the other will stay to guide us. They say there are many bad men, many soldiers, but they are gone now.'

'Thank heavens for that,' Sarah breathed. 'But are you sure they're friendly? It might be a trick.'

'Smile when you say it,' he cautioned. 'I think we should be all right.'

'As the missionary said when he stepped into the pot. Oh well, as usual we have absolutely no choice. Lead on, Macduff.'

One man turned and loped off, a seemingly effortless, ground-covering stride that would have crippled Sarah in yards. The others prepared to walk. 'This time you carry the baby,' said Joe. 'I have my image to think of.' Indeed, he was treating her with lordly disdain. Sarah meekly padded at the rear, weighed down by the child. It was reminiscent of the first days after the plane crash, and although she knew it was an act, nonetheless she felt slightly bereft.

The village was not far, perhaps five miles, but the heat made it exhausting travel. When they were in sight of the thorn fence their guide and Langeveldt set off at a run, making their entrance in style and leaving Sarah to plod on alone. By the time she arrived they were squatting in a circle of men, drinking and talking vigorously. The women surrounded Sarah in a gaggle and she looked desperately for help, but Langeveldt ignored her. She pinned a nervous smile to her face and tried to look confident.

The women were small, bare-breasted, but without a fine sheen of health. They wore kilts of red and blue cloth and the dye was not fast so that in places their skin was stained. Some had copper bracelets, some wore only an anklet of beads. One woman was obviously aged, her skin wrinkled, her breasts flat folds of skin falling limp on her chest, but others might have been quite young, it was hard to say. Underneath their excitement and curiosity, they looked tired and underfed.

They fingered Sarah's hair and the tattered remnants of her clothes, pulling her with gentle but insistent hands away from the men. She felt a rising panic but Joe continued to behave as if she were invisible. The women's own gathering place was a small circle of earth surrounded by huts, each with its cooking equipment in evidence before the door. Like the men they squatted on the ground, but Sarah prudently sat, cradling the baby in her lap. The elderly woman looked hard at Tanu, then took Sarah's arm in bony fingers. She crowed something to her friends and they all giggled behind their hands. They were amazed that the child could be so different from the mother. Sarah shook her head vigorously, but they looked blank. She turned to more immediate matters and motioned to the baby's lips. The women again looked perplexed, and muttered amongst themselves. Finally one, braver than the others, reached out and squeezed

Sarah's breast. She gave an amazed cry, and at once a forest of probing hands disappeared into her shirt. Sarah sat paralysed. When they had all confirmed that indeed she had no milk, they drew back and said 'Eh' and 'Oh' in wondering tones. Sarah felt a terrible shame at being so useless a woman in their eyes, and humbly lifted Tanu in her arms and held her out to a girl whose own strapping infant was tugging vigorously at her nipple. With a shrug she took the child and nonchalantly thrust the other breast into Tanu's mouth. The baby turned her head fretfully away. This put the women on their mettle. After a short discussion one went and fetched a small pot and coated the rejected nipple with the contents. This time Tanu did not turn away but began to suck, and the women clucked and nodded in satisfaction.

Sarah extended a tentative finger to the pot. It was full of honey, sweet and delicious, sending her underused tastebuds into convulsions of delight. Her 'mmmm' of pleasure made the women laugh and slap their legs, and someone pushed a bowl of maize porridge into her hands, gesturing for her to eat it with the honey. She took only a little, guessing that it was precious, and pushed the delicious mixture into her mouth with her fingers. Then she drank thick yellow liquid from a battered tin cup, and the world began to sway. She was bathed in a warm glow and the discomforts of life seemed not to matter any more. It was sitting thus, smiling beatifically at the world, that Joe found her.

'You're drunk,' he accused.

'I know,' she replied smugly. 'It's lovely. Tanu's all right, I'm all right and you're about to be made king. I've got a right to be drunk.'

'Wait till you get the hangover. And don't patronise them, they're not stupid even if they don't speak English.

You know we must do something about these people.'

'But I thought they were supposed to help us.'

'That was the idea. But they're on the verge of starvation. The soldiers ruined their crops, they've no meat and it's damned hard to catch much with a spear, especially when you're weak from lack of food. I don't know what we can do.'

Sarah sighed. Her golden glow was fading and life was beginning again, sinking its horrid little needles into her flesh. 'Go on, then,' she said wearily.

'Go on what?'

'Shoot something for them. Just make sure it's something big so we get a share.'

He grinned. 'Good girl. We can use that hut, by the way. Someone's moved out for us.'

She got up and weaved her way over to it, ducked through the narrow door and collapsed on a bed of grass covered with a reeking grey blanket. Dimly, she thought someone gave her a hug, but the world was spinning and it was hard to tell.

When she awoke it was dark but the village was lit by a dozen fires and laughter and chatter rose noisily into the night. There was a smell of roasting meat. Two whole antelope were suspended on wooden spits, dripping gobbets of hot fat into the fires and causing the anxious cooks to leap away to save their bare legs from burning. Joe squatted in the midst of the men, drinking maize beer and listening indulgently to highly-coloured tales of the hunt. A man, Sarah thought it was their original guide, jumped up and pretended to shoot, rolling his eyes furiously. Then he was the antelope, swift running, but suddenly jerked to a halt to fall quite dead. One leg twitched and lay still. His companions bubbled with laughter: they seemed to think he was a bit of a clown. Sarah's head was pounding and her mouth was dry; the delicious smell was making her feel sick. She went in search of Tanu, and to her surprise when the child saw her she cried and stretched out her arms. It was enough to melt the coldest heart and the woman who had been caring for her smiled and nodded. Sarah took the woman's hand and pressed it in thanks.

The party was beginning. The men were swallowing chunks of meat and soon it would be the turn of the women and children. Every now and then a hunter would toss something to a child, carelessly indulgent. The women had to wait. When at last it was their turn they spoiled Sarah, making sure she had the most succulent pieces, but she would have none of it, taking only enough for Tanu and some of the stringier leg meat for herself. After all, she had been living on meat but these people had not seen such a feast for many a long day.

The beer began to flow and the drums began to play, sending a resonant cry out into the night. So it must have been since the beginning of time, a hunt, the feast, and then the drums. A woman began to sing, a short high question, receiving its answer from a dozen voices. Feet began to beat on the caked mud, the children were swaying in brief extracts from some dance. But their parents were not ready; it was only when the fires were dying that they formed their circles and began. Men danced with men, women with women. Sarah blinked. There was Joe, stamping away, barefooted, not as a white man engaged in amusing imitation but as one of them, knowing the steps as well as they. Casting aside the last remnants of her separateness she deposited the sleeping Tanu in the hut and joined the women.

The circle opened briefly for her and then closed. It was

not difficult, the singing and the drums dragged you into the rhythm whether you wanted to or not. The endless repetition began to drug her mind: there was nothing but the drums and the dancing, and when it changed and became faster, more urgent, Sarah moved with it. The circles opened and became lines, men facing women. The men were in mock hunt, running, throwing a spear; the women continued their stamping chant. There was no denying the sexuality of it all: the women tempted with their swinging breasts, the men challenged with thrusting bodies. A couple broke away and disappeared into the darkness beyond the fire. Joe was facing her now, his face stained with ash but absorbed, mindless. She dipped and swayed, rotating her hips with conscious lechery, avoiding his eyes. He lunged, in the dance, but instead of withdrawing he scooped her up and carried her out of the line, which closed and went on. In the darkness of the hut they made love in desperate, frenzied silence, and at once fell into exhausted sleep.

They stayed for a week, and Sarah's view of the people moved from mistrust, through lofty contempt, to a surprised respect. They were surviving, happily, in conditions which would have reduced her to bad temper, squabbling, and unrestrained snarling at the children. Prosperity was something they had lost, but they spent no time in bemoaning it, the women busy replanting crops and foraging for wild figs, the men hunting and making snares. At night the warrior youths curled up by the fire, wrapped only in a blanket, hence their greyish skin. It was a coating of ash. The scent of woodsmoke was always with them, like an English garden in autumn, and it struck strange chords in Sarah's memory. She had thought them stupid, but this was far from the case. Joe soon explained how they had acquired Tanu and the women struggled to suppress their giggles, striving as always to show the utmost politeness to their guests. They were unsophisticated, but without civilised trappings. Sarah was the more helpless. They were uneducated, but not in the things that directly concerned their lives. On the debit side they were superstitious, and debilitated by recurrent and avoidable disease, dysentery being common, but then they took their water from anywhere. Almost at once Langeveldt began gently urging them to take more care and to Sarah's surprise they seemed to listen. He had a knack with them, fitting in without patronage, talking without condescension. He was never so easy with his own kind, thought Sarah.

It was soon clear that the villagers had no intention of taking the baby off their hands. Good manners did not allow them to refuse, so they pretended not to understand whenever the subject was raised. The head man called for beer, Tanu's foster-mother gave a weaving demonstration. Sarah thought they were deranged until she realised what they were doing.

'I think we're stuck with the brat,' complained Joe wearily.

Sarah took the little girl on to her lap. One of the women had given her a thin strip of cloth, intricately woven with beads, and she was making a necklace for herself and one for Tanu. 'I think you're right,' she agreed, without concern.

Joe looked at her and gave a reluctant grin. 'You mother hen,' he said, and ruffled her hair. The baby watched wide-eyed, a finger in her mouth. 'I thought we'd leave in the morning.'

This time Sarah did take notice. She knew it was time, they were in danger of outstaying their welcome, but the thought of the walking and the sun, and the loss of even the little security they had at the moment made it very hard. She sighed. 'I suppose we must. Have you decided which way?'

Long discussions with the head man had revealed two courses of action: to continue as before and run the almost certain risk of meeting soldiers, or to travel through the swamp, a network of streams and reed beds some twenty miles away. The men knew it well, they had fish traps there, and you could travel the water almost to Zimbabwe they thought. But the tsetse fly, the hippo and the clouds of mosquitoes made it a place to avoid.

'The swamp,' said Langeveldt.

Sarah swallowed. 'Are you sure?'

'As sure as I can be. The worst that can happen is that we get killed. If we go the other way and things go wrong we might not be so lucky. And at least we can fish. Come on, tell me what a wizard you are with a bent pin.'

She shook her head. 'I've never fished. I don't like boats much, actually, even big ones. I mean, look what happened to the Titanic.'

He blinked. 'I think we can rule out icebergs. And I can fish, actually.'

She patted his hand. 'Joe dear, that goes without saying. The world will end on the day I find something you can't do. All right, the swamp it is.'

She thought vaguely that it would be like most things, far less nasty than you feared.

Chapter 8

The smooth, tanned skin of her forearm had become a relief map of the surface of the moon. Except that the moon was cold and peaceful, and her arm was hot and itched continually, pitted with fly bites, some raw from scratching. She hardly knew what she must look like. On the first day, when Joe had seen how bad it was, he had plastered all of them with mud, which at least gave some relief, although when it dried it crumbled into dust and got into Tanu's eyes.

Yet she supposed they were lucky, for they had found a canoe. The head man had given Joe explicit directions which had turned out to be as accurate as those of a Japanese tourist in London, but somehow they had blundered on a canoe, left at the edge of the swamp by some itinerant fisherman. It was simply a hollowed out tree trunk and not too well hollowed out at that for Sarah felt precariously balanced high above the water. It was not paddled but punted. When it ran aground they hauled it from the water and heaved and bullied it to the next open stretch. They were exhausted long before the day was over, all except for Tanu, who was fascinated by the water and seemed determined to try and drown. And the fish they caught were thin and bony and tasted of mud.

They slept that night in the canoe, resting in a bed of reeds. Instead of the lion chorus that had become part of Sarah's nightly expectations, there were now splashes and

187

plops and a horrible slithering sound, repeated time and again.

'Joe!' she whispered at last. 'Are you awake?'

He stirred. 'Yes. God, these mosquitoes.'

'I hate this place. We should never have come this way, it could be weeks before we get out . . . the flies and the wet and the food and – what is that noise? I keep on hearing it.' Again there came the slithering plop.

'Crocodile,' said Joe shortly. 'Go back to sleep. There's no use bleating, we're going this way and that's that.'

Sarah sat up and the canoe rocked violently. 'Damn you, Joe Langeveldt, that is *not* that! I don't have to do as you say; if I want to go the other way then I will!' She ignored for the moment the fact that they only had one canoe and that only Joe knew where they were. Tanu stirred and began to wake, rubbing at her eyes with minute black hands.

'Off you go, then,' said Joe and lay down again, stretching into the space where Sarah's head should lie. He tensed in readiness for the attack he knew would come.

'You pig!' yelled Sarah and aimed a punch at his ear. He caught her fist in a lightning grasp, twisted and had her leaning backwards half out of the boat.

'Ready to leave?' he asked kindly. 'Then you can make an early start. You get the baby, of course.'

Tanu started to wail. 'Let me go,' said Sarah crossly, and he did. They sat side by side in the boat. 'You really are a pig,' repeated Sarah, cuddling the child.

'And you're a cow. What did you expect, the bleeding Serpentine?'

'I don't know. But I loathe this place. The flies never stop and we'll all catch something horrible from the water, unless the crocodiles eat us first. It's ghastly, like something out of a nightmare!'

'Can't say I'm all that thrilled with it,' said Joe, grateful for the dark that hid his face. 'Those crocs. I've shot hundreds in my time and never regretted one, they're such evil, cold-hearted beasts.'

'Do you think they are going to take their revenge?' asked Sarah in sepulchral tones.

Joe shivered. 'It had crossed my mind. God, how I wish I had a decent gun, I feel lost without one. I saw a girl taken once, it's often the women, going to draw water. The brute hauled her in so fast that she hardly had time to scream, just like that oribi you saw, but you could see her thrashing as he killed her. We found an arm later, washed up on the bank, and when we had a hunt we took her anklet from the belly of the biggest croc I'd ever seen. And I saw one today that was bigger.'

Sarah reached for his hand and held it tight. 'It won't be so bad when we get further in,' she said confidently. 'There won't be so many of them.'

'I thought you wanted to go back!'

She chuckled. 'Well, I did until I thought you might agree. On balance I'd rather face the crocs than the soldiers. Oh, do be quiet, Tanu, and stop wriggling! You're like a tadpole, child.' Her voice was sharp.

'Be kind, Sarah,' urged Joe. 'She only wants you to love her. It's not her fault that all you can think of is Douglas and your two pampered brats.'

'If Douglas were here now he'd go on and on about hygiene and bugs and exhausting myself and was I all right, which I'm not. But I couldn't say so because it would upset him, so I'd be awfully nice and sweet until in the end I'd turn and be perfectly foul. No, I'm better off with you, Joe, you ill-mannered swine.'

He was ridiculously flattered. He opened his mouth to say something embarrassingly revealing, but fortunately for him the baby chose that moment to wet all over them. Whatever he had meant to say was lost in the soggy, smelly aftermath.

They struggled on through countless days. The continual lifting and bending turned their arms into corded ropes and lined their bellies with flat muscle. Tanu fell in so often that of necessity she learned to swim and paddled like a puppy with her head held high, regardless of crocodile. They let her because there was nothing else they could do, although Sarah ruefully remembered how she had hovered over Emma as she floated her boat in six inches of water in the pond in the park. All three of them were hard as leather and at night, when the frogs began to call, they slept like the dead.

Then the beds of reeds and stagnant water began to change, there were streams and small rivers, not so many flies, and now they encountered a different hazard. Hippo. They wallowed in their dozens, portly, irascible and dangerous. If they took exception to the canoe it would be no contest and Joe often hauled the boat out and carried it rather than brave them. On one clear, cool morning they made an early start, punting swiftly round a bend straight into a herd of feeding hippo. At once the yawning started, and a big scarred bull began to roar. He was coming for the boat. Sarah gasped and hugged the baby, Langeveldt whipped the pole in and out of the water, but there he was, right beside them, huge pink jaws gaping wide to reveal tusks like powder horns. The canoe lurched, Sarah screamed, and at that moment Joe brought the pole crashing down on the animal's head. It sank from view and in tense silence Joe began again to punt. They each knew what could happen when the hippo surfaced. Many a small boat has been wrecked by an angry hippo and survivors are few and far between. Only when they reached smooth, clear water did they relax, and that night, in a patch of marsh swamp, they heard heavy, low grunting.

'It can't be the same one,' hissed Sarah.

'Perhaps he's the sulky sort. Keep quiet and keep still.'

Sarah needed no urging. She put one arm round the sleeping Tanu and the other round Joe's knee, which was the largest piece of him that she could get hold of. The animal hung around almost until dawn and they left as soon as it was light.

It was a strange, pink-tinged morning. Exhaustion and the aftermath of fear left Sarah with a feeling of detachment. A fish eagle plunged into the water, rising again with a huge fish flapping in its claws, and she thought it hardly worth a comment. A long, pale watersnake undulated past the canoe and she trailed her fingers in its wake and watched the bubbles. Flocks of small birds swept down and away in a flowing cloud of wings. Were they drinking, or perhaps feeding on something invisible to other eyes? Sarah hardly cared.

When they stopped Joe rested while she prepared the food. Today fish, as always, but sometimes they caught a frog and once they had dined on the remains of a swamp-dwelling antelope left by some over-fed crocodile. When they had eaten Joe ran a hard hand down Sarah's arm.

'My compliments to the chef. I've never tasted mud fish with quite that unique hint of waterweed.'

'Takes years of practice,' she remarked. 'I wonder if we'll ever eat real food again? Potatoes. Melon. Bread and butter. I wonder if we'll ever go home.' She watched without seeing as Tanu built stones into a pile. In her mind's eye she saw the table laid for Sunday lunch, with white napkins and the silver gravy boat.

'When we crashed,' said Joe suddenly, 'I was going to Harare to get a job on a farm. I hadn't a bean and this guy wanted me to manage his blacks and grow his crops. Nice chap, he was, needed someone to be polite to his wife and friends and his teenage daughters. God knows why I thought I could do it.'

'I can't see you working for anyone,' commented Sarah. 'You're either the boss or you don't play.'

'I thought I might learn to,' he said wearily. 'I've got to do something with my life. I never saw it before, but I've been bumming around doing nothing for years. I haven't built anything, I haven't made any sort of a mark. When I haven't liked something I've upped and gone elsewhere rather than stay and do something about it. In a way I don't want to get back, because then I'll have to decide what the hell I'm going to do.'

Sarah was thoughtful. 'I think,' she said slowly, 'that if you really wanted you could do great things for Africa. No, no, don't laugh, I mean it. You love the place so, even though you know how terrible it can be. You don't want to turn it into a park with picturesque savages for the tourists to gawp at. You're not appalled when European standards don't apply, you have no European standards. Don't just get a job, Joe. Do something to help.'

He grinned and stretched out in the sunshine. 'Another Albert Schweitzer, that's me. You always see me as bigger than I am, Sarah Hamilton.'

She looked at the length of him, long and strong and virile and remembered how she had thought him so fierce. The prow of a nose was still there but his mouth seemed set less harshly. Whereas before he had seemed incapable of smiling now you could often see the beginnings of a laugh twitching at his face, even in repose. An interesting man, she had always found him so, and now of course she knew him, and he was no less interesting.

'Stop staring at me,' he murmured and she flicked water into his face.

'Get up, you idle oaf, you can't sleep all day.'

'I know what I'd like to do.' He sat up swiftly and pulled her to him, nuzzling her neck. She murmured in pleasure but he soon drew away and they each glanced at Tanu and grinned. The presence of the child moderated their behaviour far more effectively than ever Duffy had.

There is a saying that children bring their love with them, and Tanu seemed to have brought an extra large parcel. She was not demanding or difficult but she had a wistful air of need that was very hard to ignore. She would play quite happily by herself but if Joe or Sarah joined in then she responded with giggles and beaming smiles. She would sleep by herself, but if one or other of them lay down beside her then she would turn and snuggle like a squirrel into a warm embrace. It is easy to give to the child who has never received, and in return she wove gossamer threads of commitment round their hearts. They never spoke of Tanu's future if ever they got out. It was impossible to think that she could exist apart from them, and besides, the future was still only a distant dream. They looked no further than the river bend.

Every day the water grew wider, the islands of reed more widely spaced. Sometimes they paddled through lilies spreading a magic carpet across the pools, sometimes shoals of crocodile slithered hopefully into the water as they passed. A day came when it was not clear which way they should go. There were many channels, some deep and fast, others slower and more shallow.

'If we choose the wrong one we could waste days,' said

Langeveldt. Sarah murmured agreement. She wasn't concerned, they had no way of knowing how far they were from the border and she had long since ceased to count the days. As far as she could see they would stay there for ever and nothing they did would change things. Joe paddled around looking and grunting, until finally he decided upon the swiftest and narrowest channel of all.

'Joe! Are you sure? It looks awfully dangerous.' A shaft of anxiety pierced her comfortable lethargy. The canoe was never stable at the best of times and this channel had bubbling white water on either side.

'At least it should liven things up,' said Joe, and she saw his wolfish grin. He had chosen this channel simply because it was the most dangerous: the rhythm of days that lulled her soul was boring him to death.

There was no time to protest and in any event there would have been no stopping him. He poled the canoe into the mouth of the channel, and from then on they were at the mercy of the current. Joe stood in the stern steering as best he could with the clumsy pole. The water rushed ever more swiftly between banks that were almost sheer, they flashed past rocks sticking blackly through the foam like the backs of seals. Sarah clung to Tanu who in turn clung to her and they were showered with spray as the front of the canoe bounced against something solid, freed itself and then bounced again.

'Joe! Make it stop!' she shrieked and she could have sworn she heard him laugh. There was no end to it. They rounded a bend and they were in some sort of rapid. Water sloshed into the boat and swilled round their feet, soaking Sarah's bottom as she crouched with her knees to her chin. The canoe grated against rocks, a ghastly tearing sound, then swung free and went on. A roaring filled Sarah's ears. She looked up, once, through the spray and it was enough. She hugged the baby, closed her eyes and waited. When they went over the fall it felt as if they were jumping off a cliff.

She seemed to go down for ever into the green water, tumbled in a washing machine until she opened her eyes and saw the light far away above her; she wanted desperately to be up there. Her legs began to kick and her lungs began to hurt and at last her head broke the surface and she could open her mouth and breathe. Tanu lay like a crushed rabbit in her arms; she looked dead. Frantically treading water Sarah shook her until her head rolled, water pouring from the child's mouth and nose. Then she tried to breathe into her but she was too poor a swimmer and they kept sinking. Something solid struck her across the shoulders and she automatically flung out a hand and grabbed it. It was the canoe. Thus anchored she managed to force a few weak breaths into Tanu's lungs. The child gave a sneeze, a mighty cough, and began to breathe. Such was Sarah's relief that she almost let her go.

She looked round for Joe, and could not see him. At first she could hardly believe it. Of course he would be all right, Joe was always all right, but where was he? Complete terror engulfed her. He was dead, he was drowned, he had left her and she was all alone.

'Joe! Joe! Joe!' she wailed, and tears ran salt into her mouth.

There was a splashing on the other side of the upturned canoe. 'It's all right, I'm here,' said Joe. 'Is the brat OK?' He swam round to her side. His hair was plastered to his head and he was smiling. 'Good girl, you hung on to her, I knew you would. Hell of a trip, wasn't it?'

'She nearly drowned,' gasped Sarah, and then he looked at Tanu's lolling head, the eyes heavily lidded.

'Poor kid, she does look a bit past it. Give her to me, I'll take her to shore.' He took the little body in an effortless grasp and paddled to the bank. Beneath the fall, the water formed a deep pool, surrounded by trees and bushes hanging low. Joe laid the child down on a small patch of grey shale and then came back for Sarah and the canoe.

It was a hard business, pushing the great log to shore. Sarah struggled to obey the directions Joe was yelling from the other end. The water was very clear and she could see her pale legs in their tattered knee-length trousers bicycling in slow motion. A familiar slithering sound drew her attention to the far bank, and to the crocodile making his leisurely way towards them. There seemed no point in saying anything. She swam and pushed and waited for it to come and eat her, and she was amazed when the canoe bumped the shore with the crocodile still yards away. He nonchalantly took his ivory smile else-where and Sarah tried to haul the canoe out of the water, her fingers numb with shock.

Joe was seeing to the child, lying her on her front and forcing water from her lungs. She was coughing and being sick, and he was soothing her in soft words. Sarah felt sudden fury.

'This is all your fault,' she cried. 'We didn't need to come this way, I said if was dangerous, but you didn't care. You half kill Tanu, you wreck the boat and are you sorry? No, why should you be, you do as you like and we have to go meekly along. Why should you bother if I get eaten by a crocodile? One was nibbling my toes just now if you're interested! You don't consider anyone but your-self, you're a selfish bastard, Joe Langeveldt!'

He was staring at her in surprise. 'Am I so? Well, you're the grateful lady, aren't you? I feed you, I nurse you, I shoot people to stop you being raped and what thanks do I get?'

'Since you're pretty hot on rape yourself I'm surprised that you feel so strongly about it.'

'Don't give me that, you asked for it.'

'Like hell I did! You don't care, Joe, you just don't care!' She sank to her knees and sobbed.

He was stroking her hair with hands that caught in the tangles. 'Sarah! Oh Sarah, how can you think such things? My beautiful, lovely lady, I love you so much. You are my heart, I never want to hurt you. I didn't know the fall was there, damn it!'

Sarah looked into his eyes and saw something that she should have seen before. 'I thought you were dead, Joe. I couldn't bear it without you. And it was all your fault, but – oh, why do I say such things when what I mean is that I love you. I don't care what happens so long as I've got you and I thought you'd gone away!'

Joe flung his arms around her and hugged her as if he would crush her to death. He was racked with sobs, dragged from him as if he had never cried before, and it was long minutes before he was calm enough to speak.

'Did you mean it?' he said then. 'If not, say so now. I never wanted to love you, I never wanted to love anyone, but you're such a plucky, bitchy woman that I couldn't help it. So don't pretend. You can break me, Sarah.'

She touched his face with gentle fingers, wiping the tears from his cheeks. 'Dear, dear Joe. Of course I love you, you're so kind and so pigheaded and you make me so happy. I don't even mind the swamp so long as you're there, though I do draw the line at waterfalls. And you enjoyed it, you bastard!'

He grinned reflectively. 'It was pretty good. And it wasn't much of a waterfall. Have a look.'

She turned and glanced back at the fall, which was indeed a good deal smaller than it had seemed when they went over it. It was of no interest. Tanu was in an exhausted sleep and she had a great, hot longing to lie with her lover and try a different sort of drowning.

In the days that followed it seemed to Sarah that all the world conspired with her to preserve their fragile bubble of happiness. The river was smooth and kind, the sun shone, as it always did, but with an added glow. Fish came easily to them, large and fat and tasty, and the canoe, little worse for its adventure, punted along bearing them gently downstream. It was incredible that there had been a time when she had never known Joe, when she had never seen him smile. She loved to make him smile, resting her head against his knee as he punted, knowing that when she looked up he would be smiling at her. If in the evening her fish seemed particularly good she would feed him pieces from her fingers, and shiver at the touch of his lips. He was so hungry for her. He could not bear her to be apart from him, even by so much as the length of the canoe; he had to touch, as if in need of continual proof that she truly cared. And she cared so much that it frightened her, much as it had when Emma was born, when she realised that all her happiness and all her peace of mind were centred on the wellbeing of this one tiny scrap of humanity. The nights came as a blessed relief when with Tanu safely sleeping they could cling and plead and sob and bite in an ecstasy of love. The best time, the only really perfect time, was in those few seconds before orgasm when release was certain and yet they possessed each other completely. Afterwards they were apart and the moment was gone.

'I could eat you,' said Joe in weary despair. 'Piece by piece, swallow you down; then I'd have you safe, then you'd never be away from me. Sarah, Sarah, how shall we live? I could die from loving you.'

And she would laugh and press kisses on his dear face and feel him enter her again, and would wonder if he was right. It was all exquisite agony and she longed for it to end and let her rest and knew that if it did she could not bear it. Each day was imprinted on her mind like a leavetaking.

The presence of Tanu both restricted and released them, laying a structure on the days and plucking them from their hot house absorption in each other to be the people they had been before. The child was talking a little: 'no', 'water', 'me'. It reassured Sarah who had wondered if she might be abnormally slow. Her own children had seemed much brighter, but then they were on a golden freeway while Tanu chugged along on a dirt track. Malnutrition, fear, disease, distress, these were this child's birthright. It would be better now, she could transform the world for Tanu. When they got out – but she stopped herself. No use thinking of that. They must enjoy the day, diamond-bright and precious, for which one needed no qualifications.

They knew each other's bodies as well as their own. Sarah traced Joe's many scars. What was this? How had he come by that? One was from an elephant that should have been dead, another from a wounded leopard.

'And this?' The neat round hole in his leg.

'Like I told you, a friend shot me when I was swimming. Fooling with a gun he swore wasn't loaded.'

'Joe! I didn't believe you. Oh Joe, I'm so sorry.'

He rolled over and kissed her. 'Don't be. You paid for it after all. I hurt you and I shouldn't have done, you didn't know. I loved you and I wanted to make you suffer the way I was suffering. Perhaps you should have shot me.'

She giggled. 'You know perfectly well that it would have taken half the night. Take a pot, reload, another pot. You'd have drowned first.'

He grabbed her wrists and shook her in mock fury. 'You're an irreverent bitch. One day I'll teach you to shoot, I promise. And we'll ride together in the morning and go on safari and –'

Sarah gave an exaggerated yawn. 'Such a change from this pampered life we lead. No, please don't tickle me, please Joe, no –' She splashed away across a sandbank, running not quite fast enough.

All the drive and urgency had drained from Langeveldt, he was content to spend the days in slow drifting. The river would have none of it. They were at the mercy of the current and it carried them onwards whether they wished it or not. Sometimes maribou storks flapped heavily past, or stood on the little floating islands, shoulders hunched, watching them pass. Their soft leg feathers fluttered in the breeze, like the stoles of aged dowagers at Brighton. Once or twice they saw a hunter or fisherman staring from the bank, but they always fled when Joe hailed them. Sarah felt her fear revive. It would not be long before they had to face people again.

If she thought at all about a return to home and Douglas it was in a remote way, as something that might happen in the far distant future, like old age. Joe gave no thought to it whatsoever. Sarah was a part of him, as he was of her. He felt complete, and his burning anger against the world was turned to ashes, an occasional remembered taste upon the tongue. He was loved and nothing would ever go wrong again.

The weeks passed, perhaps two or three, they did not care. Then they came upon a mud dam in the heat of the afternoon. There was no-one to be seen. They floated in the man-made lake and spoke in whispers.

'Where are the people?'

'Sleeping, I should think. This dam's in good repair, and look, there's a fishing hut. Let's get the boat out and get round it before anyone appears.'

Sarah hurried to obey, but the log was never light and now it seemed weighted with stones. They had to carry it fifty yards or more which meant at least three stops in which Joe watched the paths with anxious eyes while she gulped air and tried to slow the pounding of her heart. How could it be so easy for Joe and so hard for her? She felt a grim fury at her weakness. They were about to lift for the final time when someone shouted. Sarah's head came up and she dropped her end with a bang.

'Pick it up, damn you!' roared Joe.

People were running towards them. Black men in khaki uniforms.

'Pick it up!' Joe's voice was a lash. She bent to obey, staggering under the weight. They were so close, they were going to get her!

Without consciously meaning to do anything of the kind she let go of the canoe and dropped to the ground beside it, hands over her head, literally gibbering with fright. The running feet were all around. There was silence, with only the little sound of her crying. Gradually she became aware of what she must look like, crouched on the ground like a terrified rabbit. Even Tanu was behaving better, her little black legs stockstill beside Sarah's right ear. Shamed, Sarah uncurled and looked about. Joe was standing between her and the men, the punt pole held like a staff before him. She forced herself to rise and stand beside him, aware of an almost overwhelming desire to pass water. Another man ran up, very black, wearing the same khaki uniform but with a green beret. He rapped an order and then stared at Joe.

'Mr Langeveldt? I can hardly believe my eyes. Do you remember me, sir, Stephen Boekelo? I was one of your rangers in the park service.'

Joe slowly lowered the pole. 'Steve? Good grief, it is. Well, I'm damned. You know, Sarah, I think we've made it. We're here. We're in Zimbabwe.' He slapped the other man on the back and they began to chatter, exchanging information on what they had been doing as casually as if they had met for a beer in a bar.

Sarah sat limply down beside the upturned canoe. She felt ill, weak and shivery, her brain actually hurt inside her skull. There was no thought in her mind but sleep: she would escape into the dark and when she woke she would be able to cope with it all. Tanu was shy of all the people; she curled on Sarah's lap, fingers in her mouth. Sarah gathered her up, closed her eyes and fell fast asleep.

When she awoke Joe was still talking, leaning back in a chair with a glass of beer in his hand. He looked different somehow, and after a moment she realised that it was because he was clean. He wore the same dusty trousers, with a borrowed shirt that would not do up, but his skin bore a sheen of cleanliness that had been absent for many months. His hair curled rakishly about his ears and although it was still sandy in colour it held glints of gold. She lay and thought how good-looking he was, and then laughed at herself. He was still just as large and angular, his nose was still a prow jutting from his face, but to her mind that was how a man should be. It was everyone else who looked odd.

She stretched and sat up, sand falling with a small prickling sound on to the ancient leather sofa on which she lay. The two men turned to look at her. 'Sleeping Beauty rides again,' said Joe, and came to sit beside her. 'Here, have some beer.' He held the glass to her lips and she sipped. It was delicious, rich and sour and strong.

She took another gulp. 'I don't like beer.'

'Well, I do, so leave some in the glass, woman.'

'You've had a bath,' she said accusingly.

He stretched. 'I have indeed. And if you're very, very nice to me I'll let you have one too.'

'Here, you can keep the beer.' She thrust the nearly empty glass at him and jumped up.

The bungalow was small, with wooden floors and rough plastered walls. This was a remote border station and the accommodation was no more than adequate, but it had a bathroom and the water was hot. Sarah wallowed and scrubbed and soaped and lathered until the water ran cold and when she got out the sides of the bath were coated with grey sludge. She guiltily scrubbed it clean and then faced the problem of clothes.

'Joe!' she called. 'I need you. Quick!'

He lounged into the steam-filled room, which promptly shrank to the size of a cupboard.

'I haven't any clothes,' she hissed. 'I can't put those things back on. Do you think you could ask?'

He twitched the towel from her and cupped one heavy breast.

'Stop it, Joe, he'll hear.' But her nipple was standing taut, betraying her. Joe bent his head and teased it with his teeth until she was flushed and groaning softly. He pulled his trousers open and she reached for him, thrilling at the familiar shock of his size. He entered her as she leaned against the wall, deep-blue eyes meeting tawny-brown ones, her hands behind his neck, her breasts bouncing to the rhythm of their lovemaking. He held back until she came, racked by the spasm, and then he gathered her to him and took his own pleasure.

They parted with guilty laughter. 'I still haven't got any clothes!' whispered Sarah again. 'You'll have to go and ask him.'

'All right, I'll go and ask.' He brushed her shoulder with his lips and went out, leaving Sarah to sponge his semen from her legs. She was happy. Afterwards she wished she had known it was the last time, but there was not the slightest hint of a premonition to darken the day.

He came back with a length of red cotton printed with white leaves. It was what the native women wore, twisting it round their bodies and over one shoulder, but after several tries Sarah could only manage one and a half times round and then an insecure knot over her breasts. It was so long since she had worn a dress that she felt a sudden revival of feminine pride and went in search of a mirror. There was one in the room in which Tanu slept, exhausted after the biggest meal of her life, and Sarah softly knelt and tried to control the wild curling of her hair. Her appearance amazed her, a deep, smooth tan with her teeth and the whites of her eyes gleaming against it. Her cheeks were hollowed beneath high bones; her whole body had a tautness and a lack of surplus flesh that she had never known before. A few lines had etched themselves into the corners of her eyes, and she grimaced at them. Still, she could not expect the face of a child after what she had been through. She went back to the living room with her robe swirling about her. Voices floated to her as she opened the door. She stood framed in the doorway and stared.

Her sister, Susie, paused in her headlong rush of welcome. She saw a tall woman, wand thin, with a cloud of dark hair and the steadiest blue eyes she had ever seen, fragile in her flowing robe, but it matched oddly with her calm. She could have been the Fairie Queene.

'Sarah? It is you? Sarah?'

Still Sarah did not speak. Could this be Susie, this fluffy woman in her crisp clothes, her eyes sticky with make-up? Even at this distance she could smell an overpowering perfume. Surely this was not her sister.

'Susie? I hardly recognise you –' She put out her hands and had them clasped fiercely, and then Susie was hugging her, the scent enough to anaesthetise.

'We thought you were dead, it's been so long – almost a year. Oh Sarah, Douglas has been out of his mind with worry – he flew out twice – and Jerry's been in touch with absolutely everyone –'

Sarah shut her mind to the babble and looked at Jerry. He too seemed strange, pale, too clean, too many clothes. And he smelled appalling, a solid wave of scent. Why ever didn't they realise how repellent the stuff was? Couldn't they smell themselves?

She sought Langeveldt's eye. His nose was twitching and for the first time she laughed.

'I'm not surprised you're happy, it must have been so terrible for you –'

'It wasn't so terrible. Joe looked after me.' Sarah cut quietly across her garrulous sister. She went over to Joe and took his hand.

Susie looked from one to the other and then at Jerry. Alarm bells were ringing peals in her head. She took a step towards Sarah and then drew back; somehow she did not want to get too close to that man Langeveldt. He did not look tame.

'I know you'll be thrilled, darling,' she said swiftly. 'The company's lent the plane, that's why we're here so quickly. We had to come the minute we heard. Benjamin stayed with Nanny, of course, but you won't have seen Benjamin, will you?'

'We have a child. Tanu,' said Sarah. Susie's face became visibly appalled. 'We found her,' explained her sister. 'A native child. We love her very much.'

Jerry joined the conversation. 'Very attractive, these kids,' he agreed. 'But come on, Sarah, we've got to get you back. The papers have been hounding us and then there's Douglas. Your husband,' he emphasised pointedly. 'He's been sent a telegram but he must be in a hell of a state. Come along, Sarah, we've got to go.' Whatever she'd been up to, and it looked like a lot, she was back now and she had to be made to realise it.

'Yes, of course,' agreed Sarah, searching for apparent acquiescence and a way out at one and the same time. 'Will we all fit in?'

'We – were only going to take you,' said Susie.

'Then I can't come.' Sarah sat firmly down on the leather sofa. The grains of sand had gathered in the buttons like little golden pools. A tiny bug crawled in one, his legs moving wildly, trapped. She rescued him on a finger.

'Sarah, you must.'

'Yes, Sarah, you must.'

They were peering at her, their faces very large. Why didn't Joe tell her what she must do. 'Joe?' She looked helplessly at him.

'You're going to have to go and sort things out, honey. Look, Steve here wants a full breakdown of who we saw where: the soldiers, what happened to Bernard, the lot. It's going to take time. You and Tanu go on ahead. I'll follow in a day or so.'

'By ourselves? All alone?'

'Darling, you'll have your family,' cried Susie and threw

her arms round her sister, who was too polite to say that to her mind that was all alone. Joe was the only one who mattered.

Jerry was staring at her. He saw more than did his wife. 'What about the girls, Sarah?' he said. 'Emma and Joanne. You want to see them, don't you?'

Oh, she did. The longing was an ache in her belly, suppressed but not vanquished. She swallowed and got up. 'You will come, won't you, Joe? In a day or two?' He put his arms round her and brushed her lips with his own. 'Two days at the latest. I promise.'

The watchers looked away. Sarah and Joe were making love with their eyes, unaware and uncaring that all they felt was revealed in their faces.

The plane was tiny, you had to stand on the wing to climb in. Susie went first, Tanu was handed up to her and then Sarah turned to say goodbye to Joe. Jerry withdrew tactfully to the far side of the plane.

'Joe, this is awful. We should be going together.'

A travesty of a smile crossed his face. 'We can't, love. We've lived like Siamese twins for so long that it's like being cut in half, but you've got to go and sort things out. Tell your husband, sort out what's to happen about the kids. It's only two days.'

'And will you come?'

'You know how it is with me. There's no way I'm going back to the way I was before. I need you. You are my heart.'

A shiver of fear turned Sarah cold. 'I don't like it, I want you to come. Please, Joe, surely –'.

Her words were drowned by the revving of the plane's single engine. There was nothing to be done. She hugged him as if she would enter his soul, but Jerry was tugging at her arm and Susie was mouthing from the plane. Between them they bundled her through the narrow doorway and strapped her into a seat. One last glimpse of him, his face expressionless, the only signs of emotion a massive fist clenched by his side and eyes that were too bright. How could she leave him when she loved him so much? The little plane bumped furiously over the grass, the engine roared and they were gone.

Chapter 9

A man walking along the street opened a packet of cigarettes and let the paper flutter to the floor. It joined the coke cans and the sweet wrappers in the gutter. A bus passed, filled with laughing gesticulating blacks, but it belched thick smoke into the air. Neither Susie nor Jerry made a comment, yet Sarah was appalled. How could they stay in this filthy place, did they not see how awful it was? Tanu clung to her hand, wide-eyed and silent. She was seeing it all for the first time and perhaps Sarah was too. The flotsam of civilisation. The town was nothing but a badly kept anthill.

Two days since she had said goodbye to Joe and in all that time Susie and Jerry had kept up a steady pressure. They had whisked her to their home, found her a few clothes and taken her on to Harare. Their conversation was all of Douglas and the children, never of Joe and what had passed. Tanu might not exist for all the attention they paid her. Sarah was sure that Joe did not know where she was. Again and again she had asked them to send a telegram but they never said they had done so. She felt helpless and a little mad. Her feet hurt from the pounding of the pavement and they had only been walking for minutes. Everything seemed so close, cars whizzing by inches away, buildings looming where the sky should be.

'I don't like it. I wish Joe was here.' She sounded like a querulous old woman.

'Will you stop talking about that lecherous wife-stealer?

Every other word is Joe this and Joe that.' Jerry had had just about enough of his troublesome sister-in-law.

'Don't, Jerry.' Susie adopted the soothing tone she had decided was appropriate to Sarah's dementia. 'We'll be at the hotel soon, darling. Look at the scenery.'

'Dirt and concrete. Look, there's no point in going on with this. I'm not going back to Douglas so I might as well go and meet Joe now and have done with it. I'll write a letter or something.'

Jerry caught her arm and swung her round to face him. His plump, rather kind face was pink and sweating. 'Like hell, you will! That man's suffered for you. Twice he came out, making enquiries, hiring reconnaissance planes, and against all the evidence he refused to give up. Your husband's a wreck, your kids are in pieces and you want to swan off with some guy who's second cousin to a gorilla. You can't do it, Sarah.'

'I don't need you to tell me what to do, Jerry,' said Sarah mildly. 'You don't know a thing about Joe.'

'You'd be surprised. Everyone's heard of Joe Lange-veldt, and the tales get bigger in the telling. If he's not wrestling wounded leopard he's killing elephant with a birdgun. All very glamorous, I dare say, but I don't know anyone who'd let him in their home and there's hardly a bar in the country that he hasn't been thrown out of.'

'That sounds like Joe,' said Sarah with a grin.

'Then what do you see in him?' asked Susie in desperation. 'You can't possibly want to stay with a man like that. You and Douglas were the happiest married couple I knew. When you see him it will all come back. You're upset; you don't realise what you're doing.'

'You don't understand,' said Sarah patiently. 'Joe and I have to stay together. We haven't even talked about it, it's been so obvious. I know Douglas will be hurt, but really it wasn't my idea to crash in the bush. We didn't mean it to happen.'

Jerry waved an impatient hand. 'That's beside the point. You're infatuated with this guy, it's sex, that's all. You'll get over it. He may have been screwing you every which way for months –'

'Jerry!' exclaimed Susie.

'– but so what? Douglas needs you. And you married him – how did it go? – "For better for worse, for richer for poorer, in sickness and in health till death do us part". Not until Joe Langeveldt horns in.'

'You're disgusting,' said Sarah, but she went hot with longing for Joe and his hard, eager body. Never again to feel his arms around her? Impossible.

They walked to the hotel in tight silence. There was a letter waiting at the desk, addressed to Sarah in Douglas's thick black writing. Douglas. Someone she had once known who had no meaning for her now, he might not even exist. A dim shadow beside the reality of Joe and Tanu. But here was a letter. She felt sick. Alone in her cool, white room she opened it and began to read.

'My darling Sarah,

I can hardly believe it's true. A miracle has happened, but I have been living under a shadow for so long that my happiness is almost painful. I heard from the highest sources – my dear, you are quite famous. A man from the Foreign Office telephoned me at work. I must have sounded a fool, crying and laughing, but he was very kind. I told John Briggs and he opened a case of champagne and the whole office got squiffy. They have all been so understanding for I have done no work worth speaking of for months.

But of course you must be longing to hear about the

children. I will not pretend that things have been easy, for both girls were always particularly close to you. It is usually so with mothers and daughters, I think. Emma's school-work has fallen off so badly and she has become a very nervous child, reacting to discipline almost with hysteria. She starts to pant and the doctor thinks it may be asthma, but to my mind it is simply nerves. As for Joanne, she is quite out of hand. Your mother seems incapable of exerting any control over her whatsoever and if this miracle had not taken place I was seriously thinking about taking her to a child psychologist. I am sorry to worry you with these things when you must still be exhausted but I think it only fair to forewarn you. I am sure that all will come right once you are safe home.

My darling, I will never let you out of my sight again. When I think now of how easily I was persuaded to let you go, I must have been mad. I blame myself for the whole, miserable episode. If I had stood firm we would none of us have had to endure the unendurable. But we must not think of that, either of us. I am coming to bring you home. My wife. My love. My Sarah.

Your own Douglas.'

A thought came to Sarah as she sat holding the letter, a memory of an afternoon in the garden. It had been warm and sunny; she had brought a jug of lemonade out to the table on the terrace and she and Douglas were sitting in the deckchairs in the shade while the girls raced round being cars.

'Emma! Joanne! Stop making that appalling noise – you behave like a couple of slum children,' Douglas had snapped. The girls paused in their game, open-mouthed and anxious. Sarah reached out and touched her husband's arm. 'Don't be mean, darling,' she said lightly. 'You used to be a jet plane when you were little, your mother told me. A Hawker Hunter, that's what you were. Far worse than our two.' And Douglas had grinned, and said it was different for boys, but he had let the children play.

Suppose now, in losing Douglas she lost her children too? Suppose he refused to let them come to her? It could happen, Douglas could be very ungenerous. How would it be with no-one to intercede for them? How had it been for months past? And when all was said and done it hadn't been a bad marriage, it had sheltered and protected her for years when she had wanted nothing else. A chasm seemed to have opened beneath her feet; she had the sensation that she was standing on a very small piece of ground and that whichever way she stepped she would fall. If only Joe were here: she wanted so much to talk to him.

Susie knocked and entered the room. 'Any news?' she asked awkwardly.

'Nothing important. Sue, does Joe know where I am? You didn't send the telegram, did you?'

Her sister flushed, but then met her eye. 'No. We couldn't. Sarah, you don't want that man. What would it be like? Can you imagine having friends to dinner with him around? He can't talk to anyone without upsetting them, you'd be forever ringing people up to apologise. And what about money? Jerry says he's broke and no-one will employ him, he's too uncivilised, and I certainly can't imagine anyone daring to give him an order. And suppose you did stay with him and kept this poor mite.' She waved a dismissive hand at Tanu, asleep on the bed. 'What would she be, black or white? Black skin, white mind. It would be torture for her, living here, or anywhere for that matter. Whatever you decide to do she has to go to an orphanage.'

Sarah ran a weary hand through her hair. 'I suppose you've got all that sorted out too.' Her brain felt numb, incapable of coping with it all.

'Yes, I have,' said Susie briskly. 'It's a Catholic orphanage, very good. They'll write and let you know how she's getting on. She'll get an education and be brought up a Christian. They'll even find her a job when she leaves – they have farms and things where they train them. It is best, Sarah.'

'Is it? Oh God, I wish Joe was here. I can't think straight without him. Susie, please send the telegram: I have to talk to him.'

'If he really wants to find you he will. I don't believe he's that interested. A man like that can always find a woman to sleep with.'

'Honestly, Sue, you pass opinions with no knowledge at all. But you're right, Joe will find me with or without a telegram. I simply have to think of a way to let Douglas down lightly.'

Susan raced across and dragged her to her feet. 'I've had enough of you and your fantasies, Sarah! This is the real world, real life, you have to make your own decisions. What will happen if you tell Douglas you're not going back? I'll tell you what, he'll fall apart. Suppose he lets you have the children. He'll never see them, out here, and he's done nothing to deserve that. And if he keeps them, what will you do? Are you prepared never to see them again? To have them hate you? Because I'd hate you if it was me.'

The vague headache which had niggled since early morning was turning into a solid pounding inside Sarah's skull. 'I've got to rest,' she said tearfully and pulled away from her sister. She crawled on to the bed and curled close to Tanu. When she woke she would come to terms with it all, explain it to everyone and find some way out. Now she had to sleep.

Susie stood looking down at her, borrowed white dress against white bedspread, the only points of contrast the black of hair and eyebrows. Her tan had faded in just two days. She went to the door and turned. 'I'll ask the nuns to call this afternoon,' she said, and waited for a response. When none came she shrugged and went out.

They sat in the coffee lounge, all of them, the two nuns graceful in their flowing grey robes. Tanu perched on Sarah's lap and played with the folds of her skirt. The black nun reached out her arms and Sarah handed the child over with a smile. Tanu played with the folds of the nun's skirt, and swung her thin legs.

The orphanage sounded delightful, caring, concerned, with several country properties. The nuns made them sound like holiday camps. They were lovely ladies, thought Sarah, sweetly innocent and funny. The room began to seem stuffy, although the air conditioning was humming away. She was suddenly conscious of the people all around, so many people, and they were watching her. They looked away when she caught an eye, but she was sure they were watching. 'Just because you're paranoid it doesn't mean they're not out to get you.' Where had she read that? It did not matter, she had to get out. With an excuse that bordered on the rude she scuttled for the garden. There amongst the blossoms and the small, bright birds she calmed. Her breathing steadied and her heart stopped pounding. When she went back the nuns had gone. So had Tanu.

'Susan!' She stared in accusation at her sister.

'It's only a trial. To see if it works out.' She was obviously lying.

'You traitor. I could understand it of someone else, but not you. I never thought anyone could change so much. All you care about is fitting me back into my neat little box with no embarrassing appendages such as black babies that I might have trouble explaining to the neighbours.'

'Or to Douglas. You couldn't wish that on him, Sarah, and besides, you'd never get her out of the country. You haven't thought of the problems.'

'I've told you. I'm not going back.' Even to herself she no longer sounded sure.

Her coffee was cold but she sipped at it regardless. If only she could have time to think about all this, away from the people and the noise. Was Tanu better with her own kind, even if her home was an orphanage? It could be so: to feel a misfit in the only world you knew would be like torture. Look how Joe suffered, an alien in the white man's world, a white to the blacks. His only saving grace was his strength; and his kindness; and his odd, sour wit. Sarah felt herself smiling at the memory. Oh, if only she could be sure she was right in letting Tanu go.

One single thought began to crystallise in the turmoil of her brain. It would not be right, it would not be possible, to let her own children go. There is a tie with the children of one's body that can never be broken and whatever happened she could not live her life in the knowledge that she had deserted them. For months she had been comforting herself with a vision of them leading happy, uncomplicated lives without her. It was hard to accept a picture so very different.

She pulled the letter from her bag and began to read it again, endowing every word with meanings that in all likelihood Douglas had never intended.

'Hysteria.' Was Emma suffering from some sort of fit? Why had Douglas not taken her to a specialist? It was the obvious course. And a child psychologist for Joanne – surely he didn't mean she was deranged? What had happened to her lovely, happy girls, what had he done to them? Whenever she had thought of the future, and it had been rarely, she had seen Joe versus Douglas as a battle with only one result. In the bush, in his own land, Joe was invincible. But here, in town, where law and money held sway – who would win then? She knew, as if Douglas were there and speaking to her, that he would never let her take the girls, and without them there was no hope of happiness.

'You don't have to tell him if you don't want to,' said Susie casually. 'Jerry will do it.'

'What? Tell who?'

'Langeveldt. That you're going home. You must, Sarah. There's nothing else you can do, not if you want to stay sane.'

She was right. All the doubt and confusion in Sarah's head dissolved into grey certainty. There was nothing else to do. 'I'll tell him,' she said bleakly, and even now her throat felt tight with tears. 'But I don't know how I'm going to manage. When he's there the world seems a good place to be. He doesn't baby me or tell me what I should do but – I feel lost when he's gone. He takes the sunshine away.'

Susan reached out a hand to her. 'He's not for you, lovey. I'm sure it seems a real feeling but it's mostly gratitude. I admit, no-one else would have got you out, but that doesn't mean you have to throw your life away. He's a wild man and remember, you've always been the shy one of the family. Why, that's why we were all so pleased when you married Douglas.' Susan smiled fixedly, determined to buoy her sister up with her own certainty.

'Everyone grows up sometime,' said Sarah, and choked

on a sob. All she wanted was Joe, that dear, three-cornered ape of a man, and instead she must have Douglas.

'Sarah! My darling, darling girl! Oh God, Sarah!'

Douglas's voice, made harsh by emotion, drifted into her dream. He was clutching her hand and it hurt. Reluctantly she opened her eyes.

His head was bent but in the thin morning sunshine she could see that his hair was streaked with grey. His spectacles were cast on the bed and when he looked up she saw that his face was grey too, with flaccid folds of skin where once there had been a chunky squareness that sent him on diets. He looked so much older than before, and it was all her fault.

'Oh, Douglas,' she said softly, and held out her arms.

'You look so wonderful,' he said again and again. 'I can't believe it when I think what you've been through.' Even as he spoke he let his hand drift from her shoulder to her breast, and she jumped. But he had waited a long time to make love to her.

'I don't know how to tell you it all,' she said weakly, as he pressed sticky kisses on to her throat.

'You needn't tell me. I shall never ask you and in turn you must never think of it.' He pulled away a little and looked deep into her eyes.

'But Douglas – it happened.'

'And it's over and past. I have you safe again, Sarah, that's all we need think of.' That, and his need of her. He pulled his tie undone – how like Douglas to be wearing a tie, even in this heat – kicked off his shoes and unbuttoned his clothes in embarrassed haste. When he slid into bed beside her she started to cry, letting her tears run into her hair as she lay waiting. Poor Joe. Poor dear Joe. It was all so terribly unfair.

'Don't cry, darling. You're safe now.' Douglas was perfunctory in his soothing, levering himself on top of her even as he muttered words of comfort. He was heavy and his skin felt cold, and there was a faint smell of garlic on his breath, noticeable as he panted trying to get inside. Before she used to help him, but now she could only wait. It was all such a betrayal. A grunt of success and he was floundering on top of her, unaware and uncaring that his wife lay like the dead beneath him, her only sound a long, exhausted sigh when at last he rolled away.

'I'm sorry, darling – I know you're tired.' Douglas was awkwardly trying to apologise, and it was true she was tired. She had only just woken and she was weary to the bone.

'I think I'd like to sleep,' she said and he nodded.

'I'll stay here beside you and sleep too.' He subsided on to the pillow, his eyes fixed on her pale and tear-stained face. She lay quite still for a long time until she was sure that he was truly asleep, then slipped from the bed and went out.

She walked in her white dress through sunbaked streets, out of place and attracting stares. She had the habits of the plains, her stride was too long, her gaze too steady. When she reached the bus terminus she sat under a flame tree and waited. She knew he would come today. The buses came and went, alternately sucking people in and spewing them out into the hot city air. His bus was long in coming. In spite of everything her heart leaped when she saw him, tall, brown, in a set of bush clothes as tattered as the ones in which she had first seen him, his old rifle stuck under the straps of his rucksack. He was smiling.

'Joe!' She ran into his arms and clung, breathing deep of the dear, familiar smell of him, guns and leather and sweat.

'I thought I would die for wanting you. My own dear girl.' He buried his face in her neck and closed his teeth on her, not quite gently. Even now he could make her feel desire. She pulled violently away.

'What the hell's the matter with you?'

'I made love with my husband this morning.'

He went pale beneath his tan. 'I don't believe you. Don't play games, Sarah, please.'

'It's not a game. I'm going back with him. That's what I came to say. If I leave him, I lose my children. There's no way he'll let them go, and Joe – I owe them the sort of life Douglas can give. I never thought about it, you see, I never expected us to be in this situation. I've made a mess of things.'

He swallowed. 'A mess. You make it sound like a badly trained puppy. Look, I see what it is, he's been bullying you. Well, I'm here now and I'll deal with him, arrange about the children and everything. I won't mind about this morning, forget you ever told me. I know you love me.'

'He hasn't bullied me. I decided. I do love you, more than I think you will ever believe, but it simply isn't enough. I have children who need me, and I can't do what I want, I'm not free. I have to go with my husband.'

'You – bitch!' He grabbed and held her, his fingers probing to the bones of her arms. Their eyes met, hers blue and dumb with misery, his on fire.

Slowly he released her, ran his hands over her breasts, her belly, her thighs. She did not move.

'You lying whore!' He took hold of her throat, his face an inch from hers and began to squeeze. He had the tense expectancy of a man having sex and to Sarah it felt like that too, a building pressure rising quickly to an end. She lifted not a finger to help herself. This was the best way out, to die and put an end to all the misery. Let them manage without her, she would be gone.

'Let her go! Let her go!'

Langeveldt's face did not change but now there was another pair of hands, jerking and tearing. The sound of blows. As a black mist rose before her eyes the pressure lifted. She crumpled where she stood, sucking air into starved lungs. After a time, perhaps a long time, she could stand up.

'Sit here, darling. Oh Sarah, your poor throat!' Susie eased her back on the bench. Jerry sat there also, one eye almost closed, blood caked about his nose.

'We thought you might need help,' he said apologetically.

'Where is he?' A crow's voice, and it hurt.

'God knows. He let go of you and started on me. The man's a lunatic, Sarah; you're well out of that one.'

'You don't know what you're saying. He has every right.'

'What? To murder you?'

'Hush, Jerry, she's had enough for one day. Let's get a taxi and get back. With luck we can bathe that throat so the bruises don't show. The finger marks are all under her hair, thank goodnes.'

'What about me?' asked Jerry.

'You walked into a door, stupid. Don't make such a fuss. Come along, both of you.'

That evening they had a celebration dinner at the hotel. Sarah was again in borrowed plumes, a blue silk sheath too tight for her sister and a wide silver choker about her throat. Her voice was still husky, but she said she was getting a cold. The lies and the sense of destiny turned aside served to enhance her feeling of unreality. Soon the dream would end and all would be as it should be, herself and Joe, together. He made her feel whole; with him there was never a need to pretend, there was no part of her that he could not accept. And she had sent him away. It was not to be thought of. She paced gracefully down the stairs to her husband, as elegant and controlled as a swan on still water.

He watched from the bar, drinking glass after glass of whisky, but slowly: he did not want to get drunk too soon. He should be drunk now, but somehow it would not come. There was no peace anywhere. Did she really, after everything, not care? It was ridiculous, he knew she did. During their months together he had used her mind as his own, her every passing thought had been his to touch. He knew her as he knew himself and there had been no lie.

She was so beautiful. Her black hair gleamed against the blue of her dress, with here and there a thread of silver. The signs of strain were showing, not to others perhaps, but his searching eyes saw skin stretched tight across fine bones and a mouth that drooped when it was not smiling. It was all so stupid, he had lost his temper this afternoon; if he had taken a little time he would have got to the bottom of it all. It had to be the children, and a misplaced sense of duty. God, how he had underestimated those two, that podgy sister with her tight clothes and her bossy ways and her terrier of a husband. He had put up quite a fight in the end, and Joe was grateful. Another second or two and he would have killed her.

Glass empty again. He called for another, folding his hands carefully on the bar in front of him and smiling. A model customer, he had even dressed to please – cream slacks and jacket, a dark brown shirt and tie. There must

222

be no fights and no disturbances: tonight he could not afford to get thrown out. He imagined her watching as he lay in the gutter, her neat stereotype of a husband drawing her carefully aside. Douglas. He looked so damned prosperous. They were drinking champagne but he sipped as if it were beneath him. It made Sarah laugh. How could she laugh when she must know what she was doing to him? He half rose and then stopped himself, slipping back on to his seat. Not yet. He had to get her on her own. He would be reasonable and loving, he wouldn't frighten her. Pretend he was interested in Tanu; they had got rid of her quick enough, poor kid.

Douglas reached out and touched Sarah's bare arm, where a bruise showed purple beneath a thin film of make-up. Langeveldt stiffened and whisky slopped on to his trousers. He touched her like a lover, the grey man with his diffident air, and underneath the British conviction that he was so far ahead there was no need to prove it. A picture flashed into his mind: that man naked and Sarah –

'Are you all right, sir?'

Langeveldt looked at the crushed glass in his hand. In a conscious parody of the imagined Douglas he said, 'Goodness me. I don't know my own strength. A cloth, please, and another scotch.'

The man hurried away. God, how he hated towns. It was all so bloody phoney.

But look, Sarah was getting to her feet. She was going to the Ladies. He rushed to intercept her as she left the dining room and instead of meeting as he planned behind a screen he stopped her squarely in the foyer.

She had been white before but she went paler. 'You've hurt your hand.'

'What? Yes, I suppose I have.' Blood was dripping on

to the floor, and some had joined the whisky stain on his trousers. She reached for his top pocket handkerchief and wrapped it round the gash on his palm.

'I thought that was just for decoration,' he said.

'I don't think you're cut out to be a tailor's dummy. What are you doing here, Joe?'

'Casual drink, you know. We footloose hunters – Sarah, I'm sorry.'

'You're sorry? What the hell have you got to apologise for?'

'I nearly killed you.'

'Yes, and I deserved it. I don't really think you should have stopped. But since you did I suppose I'd better make the best of it. We're going tomorrow, on the two o'clock flight.'

He took her hand, but gently, he must remember to keep calm. 'Sarah, don't you remember how it was? Those nights in the swamp, just you and me –'

'– and the flies and the crocs and the hippo! Oh Joe, I do so love you.'

'Then stay!' He clutched both her hands now and his raised voice was attracting stares. 'I'll give you anything you want. You can have a castle to live in and if it's kids you want then damn it we can make a dozen.'

'But I want the ones I've got. I want Emma and Joanne. And I want Douglas to be happy. I owe it to him, Joe.'

It was too much. The veneer of manners, already cracked, shattered and fell away. He was the old Joe Langeveldt, eyes blazing, mouth a straight line beneath a beak of a nose. 'You'd put that walking status symbol before me? You want to go back to your safe little life after what we've known? I should have let those bastards tear you apart like meat on a slab, I should have left you with a fever and let hyena suck your bones. I saved you! I gave you back your life! What have you given me? I'll tell you what, just lies and misery and hate!' He was gripping her shoulders now, shaking, putting bruise on bruise. A phalanx of waiters and reception clerks was advancing on them.

'Joe, you've got to see how it is!' Sarah was screaming now. 'You'll be all right! You'll survive! I've got to look after my family.'

He stopped shaking her and dropped his hands. Spittle coated his lips. She saw realisation dawn in his eyes, watched his fist come back to strike her and waited for the blow. Instead the staff leaped upon him, three to each arm and tried to hustle him towards the door. It was like Gulliver in Lilliput: white-coated men were flung this way and that; one dropped like a felled ox when his jaw met Joe's fist. Sarah hugged herself and sobbed.

'Come away, darling. Pay no attention, it has nothing to do with you.'

The struggling mass of people crashed out into the street. Sarah looked up at her husband. 'But you don't understand —'

'I think you'd be surprised. It's all finished now. Come back and drink this disgusting champagne.'

In a daze, she went. Outside the shouting and the running of feet faded and died.

The next day, Douglas went to buy presents for the children. He would not let her go, he said she needed the rest. It wasn't true. Alone in the room, staring at her locked suitcase, she had only to think. Her body ached for activity, her mind was a rat in a box and she had to do something. A thought came to her. She would go and visit Tanu, say a proper goodbye and take a present. That at least she could do.

She bought a toy pillarbox for posting different shapes. It was perhaps a little young for the child, but then in terms of play Tanu was still a baby. There is little time to play when a child is ill, hungry or frightened, and one or all of these had been Tanu's experience throughout her short and meagre life. If only it would all be different now.

Sarah hailed a taxi and gave the driver the name of the orphanage. He said it was too far, and at once she opened her purse. The man's eyes widened in hope and she had no compunction about letting herself be conned, for however long the journey it was one she was determined to make. The elegant towers and parks of the city soon gave way to streets of tin-roofed houses baking in the sun. The taxi chugged its way along, its passenger too impatient to notice markets crammed with exotic fruit, here a stall selling wooden carvings, there a man holding a live goat. If the occasion had been different she might have stopped, bought something or taken a photograph, but the tourist Sarah had gone, perhaps for ever. Travel, the game for grown-ups, had ceased to appeal. Like Tanu she was past playing.

They came at last to a long, yellow wall, broken by a single door.

'The orphanage?' she queried and the driver nodded. Sarah asked him to wait and he shrugged agreement; he might as well, there would be no other fare to take back to town. She stepped from the car, pulling at her sweat-dampened skirt, and tugged the heavy bell-pull. The sound echoed in the hot, still air, but for long minutes no-one came. The driver pulled his hat over his eyes and prepared to sleep, and Sarah was reaching again for the bell when the door swung soundlessly aside. She stood with her hand in the air, feeling foolish, while the small, black nun in the doorway flashed milkwhite teeth in a smile.

'Er – can I see the Mother Superior?' asked Sarah, wondering as she did so if this might be some sort of enclosed order in which speech was not permitted. That would be very awkward. 'I – er – I have to enquire about a child. My child,' she added, laying claim to Tanu with sudden defiance.

The nun was too polite to express her doubts. 'You have a child with us?' she queried gently.

'She is my responsibility, yes,' asserted Sarah, 'and I should like to discuss her future with the Mother Superior. If that's all right.' She stepped into the doorway, for whether it was all right or not she was going inside.

The nun disarmed her with politeness. 'We are always pleased to welcome anyone who is interested in the children,' she said softly, and Sarah blushed. Living with Joe made one forget that the indirect path is often the quickest. She was in danger of losing her tact.

Her guide led her through cool corridors, adorned only with the occasional crucifix or picture of the Blessed Virgin. It was very quiet and when they did meet another nun the only acknowledgement was an inclined head. They took no notice of Sarah at all. At length the nun paused outside a door.

'If you would wait for just a moment,' she requested, and again bestowed her smile, and in the few seconds of waiting Sarah had time to wish she had never come. This place was apart from all the world and she would never understand it. A murmur of voices came from inside the room and then the nun was there again, holding the door wide, and smiling. Sarah lifted her chin and entered.

The Mother Superior stood briefly and then resumed her seat behind her desk. She had the desiccated appearance of someone who has been in the tropics so long that the flesh has burned from their bones. Even her eyes had lost their colour; they could not always have been as clear and pale as water.

'I take it you are Mrs Hamilton.' She extended a hand and Sarah grasped it, surprised to feel callouses and firm muscle. Hard work and this graceful lady seemed an unlikely combination. 'I am Mother Simone. I wondered if you would take any further interest in the child. Your sister explained everything to me.'

'Oh.' Trust Susie. The tale would not have flattered; as always, her sister would have seized the opportunity for the odd sly dig. Sisterly jealousy should never be underestimated, though fortunately it is often accompanied by a great deal of love.

'I hoped that we should meet. I have heard much of your ordeal – a time of great trial, I fear. You have shown great – resource.'

Sarah grimaced. 'I think that is what everyone wants to believe, Mother. The truth is that without Joe – Joe Langeveldt, that is – I would never have survived. He was so kind.' Her throat tightened and she could say no more.

The nun eyed her thoughtfully and then rose to her feet. 'Come along, my dear. I shall take you to the nursery.'

They stepped from the cool peace of the convent into a courtyard. The sun blazed down on beaten earth, shaded only by a few struggling trees. A class of children was listening to a story, the girls all dresed alike in pink cotton, the boys in grey shorts. They were all black, and every head turned to watch as Sarah walked with the Mother Superior towards the long, low building that was the orphanage itself. It was not a lavish structure, the walls were of concrete blocks and the roof of corrugated iron. Inside it was equally sparse, with bare board floors and no curtains. Sarah reminded herself that trimmings are of little account. She so wanted to like the place, she was determined to persuade herself that she was doing the right thing. Tanu would have a happy life here.

They paused outside a class of eight-year-olds. A nun was pointing to words on the blackboard and each child in turn was reading them. There must have been fifty children.

Sarah turned to her companion and said, 'Isn't it rather difficult with so many children?'

'Yes.' The woman nodded and smiled.

Next they came to a room full of cots. In each was a tiny, black child, a bottle propped against its face.

'Feeding time,' said the nun. 'The only time it is quiet.'

Sarah gulped. It was like intensive farming. 'Where do they come from?'

'Many are refugees, from Mandoto. Some are illegitimate. When a rural culture breaks down and people come to the towns to work then many girls find themselves pregnant and alone. In the past it would be the grandmother who raised them. Now it is us.'

'It's so – uncaring.'

'My dear, we care. But there are too many children.' She swept on down the corridor to the day nursery. Little children crawled and climbed and bumped over the floor. When Sarah entered they at once swarmed towards the unfamiliar figure and she looked in vain for Tanu, one black face amongst so many. Then she heard her shrieking, a high, desperate wail. Swamped by a pink cotton dress, the child stood with arms raised and her mouth wide. Sarah swept her up and tried to calm her. Gradually Tanu's screams turned to sobs and Sarah knew a cold dismay. She could not leave her here.

The nun was watching her. Sarah began to mumble a confused explanation, but she raised a hand. 'I know, my dear, I know. Yes, you may take her. But I want you to understand. Will you come back to my office?'

Holding tight to Tanu, Sarah retraced her steps.

'Now,' said the nun when they were settled. 'I can see that you are shocked. I am glad, because we need help. Too many children, too little money and above all too little interest. We are rearing these children to labour on farms that already have too many labourers, because that is all we can afford to do. You will take this child and give her something better. I want something better for all my children.'

'Er – what did you want me to do?' Sarah began to feel trapped. Just because you're paranoid – this woman was out to get her.

The nun slapped her hand on to the desk. 'Publicity! You are famous, you can tell everyone about us, even the English Sunday papers. They can send photographers. Then we can have a fund, and build new classrooms and a proper nursery wing –' the list went on and on. After a while Sarah rose to try and excuse herself. The nun's pale eyes blazed and her hand clutched Sarah's arm and held her. There was no escape, the woman was out of a Greek tragedy, a fanatic. 'You must help us!' A wisp of hair had escaped her veil; it was grey and wiry. She would not let go of Sarah's arm, and it was getting late.

'I'll do what I can – really – I promise – I'll do what I can.'

'I have your word?' The nun looked positively fierce.

'Yes, yes, Mother. Goodbye. I must go.'

She jerked herself free and ran through the corridors. Behind her the nun could be heard declaiming, 'I have your word! I have your word!'

At last, the street. She fell into the taxi and closed her eyes in relief. The woman was a lunatic, but the abiding sensation was that she had taken a mortgage on Sarah's soul. Tanu began to scramble about on the seat and Sarah unwrapped the pillarbox from its sweat-soaked paper and gave it to her. The child sat absorbed, popping shape after shape through the holes, then taking them out and starting again. Sarah felt utterly depressed. What was she to do with her? How would her own two children feel about mummy turning up with a new black baby, one that needed all the love and care they wanted themselves? How would Douglas feel about it? He admitted to not being at ease with his own two, and Tanu was not an attractive child. Thin legs, big joints, sparse tufts of hair, no language and a desire only to cling. There was no way her family could be expected to cope. 'Oh God,' muttered Sarah to herself. 'You've got to go to Joe.'

One night in the swamp, when the heat was like a blanket and the flies a torment, they had lain and talked of people and places. Joe had spoken of a friend, a one-time hunter, who had given it up and decided to run a whorehouse, saying that he was sick of going hunting and dreaming of making love, it was time to make love and dream of going hunting. He had found a place in Harare. It was called the Wakamba. Sarah leaned forward and gave the name to the driver. He stared and rolled his eyes.

'Wakamba?'

'Yes, please. And quickly.' She dropped a note over his shoulder. He muttered something under his breath and began to drive faster, peeping at her from time to time in the rearview mirror. She supposed it must seem odd, convent one minute, brothel the next, but that was life's roller-coaster for you. Too bad it made you feel sick.

They began to drive through streets where men lounged in dooways and girls in tight dresses sat idly in upstairs windows. The Wakamba was not likely to be missed. Vertical orange letters proclaimed it from one end of the street to the other with the figure of a naked woman sketched in lights above it. The taxi driver did not want to wait. After a brief argument Sarah jumped out of the taxi and ran with Tanu into the building. She had not paid the man so if he drove off he would be out of pocket.

Her speedy entrance did not go unnoticed. There were a dozen men in the bar and they were all looking at her. The walls were covered in photographs and after one startled glance she looked rigidly away, wondering at the extent of human ingenuity. And the unfortunate snake! She looked dubiously at an archway covered by a dirty bead curtain which led into the interior, and speculated on what might be lurking within.

Clutching Tanu as evidence of respectability she advanced on a large, bearded man idly polishing glasses. He was muscle gone to fat. 'Are you Bill Saunders?' asked Sarah.

'That is my name. You want work?'

'Not at the moment, thank you. I'm looking for Joe Langeveldt.'

The man put down his glass and cloth and walked out from behind the bar. He stopped inches from her. 'You the bitch that's caused all the trouble?'

'Er – possibly. I have to see him, is he here?'

'Get out.'

'But is he here?'

'I told you to leave. You must be some hard woman to do that to a man. I don't want you in my place, it's too good for you. Out.'

Sarah sighed wearily. 'I wish you'd stop saying that. It's important, I have to see him and I think he's here.' With sudden resolve she swept past him and through the bead curtain. It was dark and smelled of cheap perfume. Two or three men lounged on sofas, each with a black girl in a tight satin dress. No-one looked up; they were groping each other like teenagers at an all-night party. Joe wasn't there. The fat man lumbered after her.

'You are disturbing my customers –'

'Then where is he? If he finds out you wouldn't let me see him he's not going to be pleased and you know what Joe's like when he loses his temper –'

The ghost of a grin crossed the man's face. 'Lady, you have a point. Upstairs, second on the left. Don't blame me if he kills you.'

'Thanks.'

She ran lightly up the worn carpet, knocked and entered. Joe was lying naked on the bed. Next to him lay a black girl, her breasts huge and pendulous. When she saw Sarah she shot off the bed and out of the door, a reaction no doubt honed by the raids of outraged wives. Joe barely turned his head.

Sarah sat heavily down on the one rickety chair. 'You didn't waste much time, did you? Susie said you were that sort of man and I didn't believe her.'

He yawned. 'Just swapping one whore for another.' He had a bottle of whisky by the bed and he reached for it. 'What have you come for? Don't expect me to feed your ego by doing some more crawling because I've had enough. Go back to your cosy little life and leave me alone. God, how you must be laughing at me, you and that stuffed shirt you're married to.' He took another pull at the bottle.

He looked terrible. The whites of his eyes were stained yellow and the skin of his face seemed stretched to breaking point. It was not as she had ever imagined seeing him. She reached out and touched his arm but he jerked violently away, and lay with his face to the wall. 'Leave me alone. You've had it all from me. If you feel guilty then I'm glad. I want you to feel it, I want you to lie awake in the night and know what you've done. You bitch. You mindless bitch.' Curled up with his bottle he looked like a giant baby. Sarah ached to hold him.

At last she said, 'I've brought Tanu.' There was no reply. 'I've brought her for you to look after.'

He gave no sign of having heard. The child was asleep on her lap. She dropped a gentle kiss on her fuzzy brown hair, leaned over and laid her in the hollow of Joe's body, then added the plastic pillarbox.

'I love you, Joe. Take care of her.' She turned and ran swiftly out to the waiting taxi.

The room was very quiet without her, a place of stillness in the midst of sound; from below in the bar came the chink of glass against bottle and then the high, shrill laughter of women. Outside the traffic buzzed steadily past. The place was as alien to him as any far-off planet and he felt ill and confused and achingly alone. She was gone. It was quite, quite over and it was more than he could bear.

He put the bottle to his lips but he was sodden with whisky and could face no more. With a sudden violent sweep of his arm he flung it against the wall, to explode in a million shards of glass. The baby woke with a shriek and then lay big-eyed and shivering, making little mewing sounds and reaching for Joe's neck. She was wet and smelled sour. The thin brown hair was coarse and wiry, and her knees dug sharp bones into his flesh.

'Christ knows, I don't want you,' muttered Joe, but the child still clung to him, stiff with fear of abandonment. All at once he was very, very tired. With a gentleness he had

234

thought beyond him he eased her arms downwards and cradled her within the curve of his body, holding and rocking until at last they both slept.

Chapter 10

'Will you be home on time tonight, darling?' Sarah buttered toast for the children, gave half an ear to Joanne's reading book and at the same time asked the question.

'I've really no idea. We've these Hamburg people coming over for lunch – it could run on. Why, is it important?'

'Only that I've a Save the Children Fund meeting to go to and I'll have to leave your supper in the oven. You won't mind, will you?'

Douglas lifted a hand to his spectacles, his whole being a study in bewilderment. 'Of course I shall mind. You have all day to attend these meetings and though heaven knows I don't begrudge your charitable activities, indeed it is expected of a woman in your position, there is absolutely no reason why they should affect the day to day running of our lives.'

'Your comfort, you mean. Don't worry, I shall leave you a lovely supper and I'll bake you a chocolate fudge cake. I'm afraid I have to go: they're discussing exhibiting three of my paintings in the library, the ones of the little African girl.'

'Your paintings are all of the little African girl,' said Douglas and his voice held an edge.

'No, they're not,' replied Sarah quickly, but almost all of them were. Even the tutor at the art college had commented on it, and in defence she had dashed off a few studies of lily ponds and trees. In the end though, there she was again, painting Tanu crouched in the dust, or Tanu asleep on the grass or Tanu standing next to an unidentified trousered leg.

Douglas was staring at her and she knew he was going to make an issue of this.

'Darling, it really is time you got over this obsession with Africa,' he began. 'First we endured your crusading zeal when you went and spoke here, there and everywhere about the plight of starving children, neglecting your own two in the process.' He held up a restraining hand as she opened her mouth to object. 'Then came the painting craze, which I thought might be harmless though I should have known better. Now, you have launched yourself into good works like one possessed, and it simply isn't on. If you're not at a meeting then you're speaking at a ladies' luncheon; if you're not there you're at some bazaar, and during your fleeting moments of leisure you're rubbing shoulders with that peculiar man Smithers at the art college.'

'You needn't worry about him, darling, he's queer,' interposed Sarah, but this served only to enrage him.

'How you can associate with someone like that is beyond me! Sometimes I find it impossible to believe you're the same woman I married! I blame myself, of course. I should have made a stand earlier, but I thought it was the shock of your experience. Knowing you as I do, I need not ask how you conducted yourself during your ordeal but –'

'Then why do you keep going on about it?' asked Sarah. 'If you want to know what happened you can ask.' And *I won't tell you* was her mental assurance. Douglas was unhappy enough with only suspicions to work on; he would be frantic if they evolved into certainties. To begin with he had been happy just to have her home. This niggling inquisition had taken time to develop.

'– but leaving that aside I insist you stop all this gadding about. There is no need for you to attend the art college. You paint very nicely as it is, although I do wish you would choose more suitable subjects. And as you know I think more subtle colours might be appropriate – but as for exhibiting your work in the library, you'll be telling me you're selling them next.'

'The price tags will be very discreet,' admitted Sarah, and watched her husband go puce. He rose to his feet and spoke very slowly, as if to a halfwit.

'Do you mean – to tell me – that – my wife – is selling her wares – like any whore in Soho?' He was shouting and in the background Sarah could hear Emma's hiccupping sobs. Raised voices always reduced her to tears.

'Douglas dear, I don't think many whores sell paintings,' she said patiently. 'And anyway it's all for charity; no-one will think you've gone bankrupt.'

'How you can be flippant is beyond me! Enough is enough. I insist that you telephone today, cancel the meeting and explain that you will be unable to release your paintings for exhibition after all. Am I understood, Sarah?'

She was bending over Emma in a vain attempt to stop the child's progression into full-scale hysteria. 'What? Oh yes, Douglas, I always know what you mean,' she said distractedly and since he had lost all his audience except the fascinated Joanne, who sat wide-eyed and eager, there was nothing to do but leave for work. He vented his feelings with a juvenile slam of the door.

Emma was gasping her way into the beginnings of an asthma attack.

'Run and get Emma's inhaler please, Joanne,' said Sarah, and the little girl scampered off. She was a cooperative child, but extremely clever, and strangely this was sometimes hard to deal with. You had to think quickly to keep one step ahead of her, and in Sarah's absence Douglas had too often resorted to 'children should be seen and not heard'. The result had been screaming, biting tantrums of frustration, which evaporated the moment Sarah appeared and listened to what she had to say. If only Emma's problems were so easily put right.

'I shall be late – again!' gasped Emma and Sarah stroked the soft dark hair.

'I'll come in with you. Anyway, I want to talk to your teacher: you're getting too much homework.'

'Don't come in, Mummy, please! All the others manage and if I can't she'll think I'm stupid.'

'I don't care what she thinks. If you must know I would much prefer you to be back at St John's Primary. You were much happier there.'

'Daddy said the other children were vulgar,' said Emma in a squashed voice. 'He said it was all right for the little ones but not for when you got older.'

'Well, I don't agree. Rachel wasn't vulgar, she was your best friend.'

'Daddy doesn't like her.'

'Oh.' There it was again. Daddy shoving his girls into moulds they did not fit. It was starting to worry Sarah, aware as no-one else could ever be of Douglas's insidious autocratic pressure. Why, before she went to Africa she had been completely cowed by him, rendered almost incapable of any sort of separate and responsible existence. It was not that he was unkind, of course, merely that he had fixed views and expected everyone else to share them. The mistake was to give in.

'You won't go to the meeting, will you?' Emma was looking anxious.

'Well – I really should, darling. It's not as if I ever go out in the evening on my own and Daddy does it all the time.'

'But there'll be a row and I hate rows. Daddy starts shouting.'

'And shouting can't hurt you,' said Sarah firmly, knowing that it indeed hurt Emma. Oh, it was so worrying wondering what was to become of this nervous, sensitive little girl who was so ill-equipped to deal with life. Had she always been so, even before Africa? Shy, certainly, but with her mother to shelter and protect her she had managed. Perhaps in time she would manage again.

'Tell you what,' she said suddenly, 'let's drop Joanne off at school and you and me go to the park and feed the ducks. We can take our sketch pads, it'll be fun.'

'But they'll be cross,' said Emma, wide-eyed. 'I'll get into trouble.'

'No, you won't. I'll write a note and say you had a tummy upset. I know we shouldn't but we can't be good all the time.'

'I want to come,' said Joanne, looking stubborn.

'What, and miss science? I am surprised.'

The little girl thought for a moment and opted for school. What passed for science in the baby class was a glorious hour spent mixing sand and sugar or salt and water, with the teacher earnestly trying to explain about things dissolving and the children making mud pies. Still, something might stick even if it was only to their gymslips.

Later, as Emma sat on the park bench and coloured her mother's outline of a duck, Sarah thought about what she should do. The leaves were falling and they rustled about her feet in bronze drifts as she wandered up and down, searching for some sort of compromise. She and Douglas clashed so often these days, over every trivial mark of Sarah's independence. He wanted her back as she had been, a quiet, obedient mouse whose whole existence centred around her husband and her home. Perhaps she should be that again, try to fit herself back into a hole several sizes too small, for after all, that was the woman Douglas had married. He had changed not at all, she far too much.

But what would that do to the girls? Joanne would be all right, it would take a stronger man than Douglas to control that termagant, but who knew what battles would be fought before she clawed her way free. And Emma, gentle, shy Emma, would be crushed.

Foolishly Sarah wished she could talk to Joe about it. He had such a clear mind, or was it simply that with him she could say what she really, truly meant and know that it would not repel him? It was never so with Douglas. Sometimes she felt like the original wolf in sheep's clothing, her teeth always hidden beneath softness and lies.

Emma was playing with somebody's poodle, throwing a stick time and again, enthralled by the little dog's tense and wriggling excitement.

'Come on, darling,' called Sarah. 'It's lunchtime.'

'Couldn't we have a dog, Mummy? A poodle like that one? He's lovely.' Emma's cheeks were pink with the thought of it.

'I'm sorry, darling, we can't. Daddy doesn't like dogs.'

'But you like dogs, don't you?'

'Of course I do. We always had one when I was little.'

'Then we should have one. I hate Daddy, I really do.'

'Now that's being silly. Daddy loves us all and he works

242

very hard to keep us. We can't hate him.'

'Well, I do.'

Sarah sighed. 'Let's go and have lunch with grandma,' she said in grinding exasperation. This day was doomed to annoy her so she might as well put the lid on it.

Mrs Melling was delighted to see them. 'Come in, come in,' she carolled. 'Is Emma not well?'

'Tummy upset,' said Sarah easily. 'But she's getting better.'

Emma blushed and looked at the floor. She would never make a liar, thought her mother ruefully. How different could a mother and daughter be?

'Come in to the fire, darlings, there's a chill in the wind today. They say it's going to be a hard winter. Now, what would you like to eat, though I've little enough in the house, I'm afraid. It isn't easy managing on a pension –'

'It's all right, Mother, I brought some sandwiches. I'm sure you must have the odd tin of soup in the house.' Her daughter was in no mood for a recital of the evils of life on a pension, especially since she was well aware that Douglas had paid a thousand pounds into her mother's account only last month. So he wasn't all bad: there were very few men who could stand extravagance on the scale of Mrs Melling's.

'Oh. Well, yes, I suppose we could do that. Keep warm, Emma, while Mummy and I see to the food. You look quite peaky, child.'

Once in the kitchen the two women got in each other's way. 'Sit down, Mother, I'll do it,' urged Sarah and her mother sat.

'How is Douglas?' she asked pointedly

Sarah shrugged. 'Very well. But he wants me to stay at home all the time.'

'And so you should. That terrible time in Africa seems to have given you itchy feet, my girl. You should count yourself lucky to have a husband like Douglas who's prepared to put up with you. And you don't dress as nicely as you used to either. I haven't seen you in anything new in ages.'

Sarah sighed. 'I haven't the time, I suppose.' Or the will, her inner voice told her. She didn't want to be elegant and charming any more, she wanted to be real.

'Mother,' she said suddenly, 'what would you say if I said I was thinking of leaving Douglas?'

Her mother's mouth dropped open and stayed there. 'You? Leave him?' she said eventually. 'I'd say you were mad.'

'I think I might end up that way.'

'But – is he having an affair or something? I know he's often late home from work but I think it really is work, darling. Douglas adores you.'

'But you see, I don't think he does. He adores someone he thinks is me, yes, someone gentle and loving and well-dressed and efficient. It isn't me at all, and whenever he sees me behaving in a way which he thinks doesn't fit he tries to stop me. And what's worse, far worse, is that he's doing the same to the children. Joanne's tough enough to stand up to him, but Emma isn't. He's turning her into a nervous wreck.'

Mrs Melling fingered her hair, pale pink at the moment. 'Well – I did notice he was very strict when you were away. Smacking them if they didn't fold their clothes and that sort of thing. He takes it all so seriously somehow – but he's always been like that, darling; you never minded before.'

'I did, you know. That's why I insisted on going to see

Susie. It was absolutely the only thing I'd stood firm about in all our years of marriage. Oh, I see now I shouldn't have done, I should have stayed in my little, well-appointed rut and got over feeling restless. But instead I went. And grew up. Mother, I don't need looking after, not in the way Douglas sees it.'

'Darling, no woman can do entirely without men. You don't know how uncomfortable life can be for a woman on her own.' Mrs Melling was agitatedly taking spoons out of the drawer.

'I know that. It's just – Mother, it is possible to be with a man, as a couple, and each of you to be whole, grown-up people. Each needing the other, relying on the other, but still being yourself. It can be like that.'

Suddenly Mrs Melling turned on her. 'It's that man, isn't it? The one Susie talked about, he's the one you want, not Douglas. Sarah, I'm ashamed of you.'

Sarah stared at the floor. There was a sudden hiss as the soup boiled over, and by common consent the conversation was abandoned.

On the way home they collected Joanne and did some shopping. Sarah went to the phone as soon as she got in and cancelled the evening's meeting, rescheduling it for the following morning. It was starting to drizzle and it would be pleasant to spend an evening alone in front of the fire. England might be cold but there was a wonderful, atavistic cosiness about drawn curtains and crackling logs that you could never experience in warmer climes. Joe wouldn't be seduced by the mug of cocoa and the armchair, she thought ruefully, but then you never knew with him. He was always difficult to predict.

It was half past nine before Douglas came in, chilled and irritable. He cheered visibly when he saw his wife.

'I'm glad to see that you can occasionally respect my wishes, Sarah.'

She kissed him lightly on the cheek. 'I always try to, you know that. Would you like your supper on a tray? It's a horrid night.'

'That would be very pleasant, my dear.'

After he had eaten he began to be magnanimous. It occurred to him that since Sarah's paintings would no longer be exhibited in the library it might be nice for her to have one on the wall at home, perhaps on the upstairs landing where it would not be too noticeable. But when he suggested it Sarah looked embarrassed, a flush staining the fine curve of her cheek, the blue eyes dark. He never tired of looking at her, he thought absently.

'I'm sorry, Douglas,' she said uneasily. 'I'm afraid the exhibition is still going ahead. I've moved the meeting to tomorrow morning, that's all.'

He closed his eyes for a moment, raising a theatrical hand to his brow. Then, he sighed. 'I imagine this is my fault,' he said slowly. 'I did not make myself clear. You are not to have an exhibition, you are not to sell your paintings. There is no question of my wife being associated with such things. I said no and I meant no!'

Sarah clenched her fists and made a conscious effort to keep her voice low and reasonable. 'I'm not a child. I don't need your permission and I need not obey your veto. Will you please let me have some little life of my own? I can't bear this continual wrangling whenever I want to do anything. Apart from what it's doing to me, Emma's nerves are in shreds!'

'I think you should see this from my point of view,' remonstrated Douglas. 'I am entitled to have a loyal and faithful wife. I give you everything you want; is it too much to ask that you should fulfil your part of the bargain?'

'Do you mean loyal or faithful?' asked Sarah sharply.

Douglas cleared his throat. 'If you must know, both.'

There was a long silence. 'You said we were never to talk about it,' said Sarah.

'I did not think I would ever have to.'

'I came home. Isn't that enough?'

Douglas would not look at her. 'You are not the woman who went away.'

She laughed, shortly and without humour. 'Well, I did not know that part of the contract was that I should remain as naive and stupid as the day I was married. I know I'm upsetting you, Douglas, and I'm sorry. But – I can't be other than as I am. Let's talk about it tomorrow, I'm going to bed.'

She lay for a long time in the dark, waiting for him to come upstairs. When at last he did so, she pretended to be asleep. It was not a surprise when he reached for her, stuffing himself into her without the slightest attempt at preliminaries. In the past he had at least paid lip-service to her pleasure, but now he preferred to punish her. It might also be that he needed it that way. There was something about the suddenness and the lack of conversation that Sarah knew excited him, as if for Douglas sex was better with a stranger, with no fuss and no care, just the act. Once when she had persuaded him to go slowly, after all the kissing and touching he could not go on. It had been terribly embarrassing, that. Douglas pretending that he had suddenly lost interest, Sarah bewildered until she realised what had happened. 'So much for your ideas,' he had muttered, like a schoolboy whose conker string has snapped. And it was back to the lunges in the dark. There seemed no answer to it.

In the morning the unresolved row hung like a cloud over the breakfast table. Emma could not eat but Joanne more than made up for it, demolishing a plate of toast with lightning speed.

'Can I go out to play?' she demanded.

Sarah glanced at the clock. 'Yes, darling, I think there's time. You too, Emma.'

'You will both remain at the table until everyone has finished,' said Douglas, not bothering to lower his paper.

'Does it really matter, darling? They'll have to go in five minutes anyway –' wheedled Sarah, but no further comment was forthcoming. They all subsided into unhappy silence, Joanne kicking the chair leg, Emma's breath starting to rattle.

'Go and get your inhaler, Emma,' said Sarah.

The paper descended. 'The child doesn't need all this stuff you keep giving her; you mollycoddle her. A little discipline would go a long way with you, miss.'

Emma's cheeks were pale and the shadows under her eyes looked like soot.

'I'm sorry – I'll try –' she gasped, fright making her worse.

'All you need to do is concentrate on breathing normally,' said Douglas firmly. 'Like me, keep in time with me: watch.' He took several deep, gusty breaths and Emma tried vainly to match him, the sweat starting on her brow. Then she was panting again, noisily, desperately, her fear of Daddy's wrath only adding to it all.

Sarah ran for the inhaler and thrust it into Emma's hands. The child sucked at it thankfully but all of a sudden Douglas snatched it away.

'The child doesn't need it! She was managing, and if I say she shall not have it that is what I mean.'

Sarah held out her hand. 'Give it back, Douglas. There's no need to bring the children into this argument. You can't win by making them suffer.'

He slipped the inhaler into his pocket and sat down again, pretending to read the paper. Emma gasped and panted, stark terror in her eyes at the loss of her comforting, lifesaving inhaler. Joanne was starting to cry, putting pudgy hands to her cheeks and whispering, 'Daddy's hurting Emma. Daddy's hurting Emma.'

'Douglas, give it back!' shrieked Sarah, suddenly desperate.

He looked up, deliberately casual. 'But I thought you had somewhere to go this morning, my dear.'

'You can't mean to blackmail me! Douglas, you're hurting your child.' The veins in Emma's neck were bulging with her struggle to breathe.

'I think the blame lies at your door, my dear. You're the one who puts your own concerns before anything else.'

Emma coughed and for a desperate moment stopped breathing altogether. Then the ghastly tearing noise began again. It was as much as Sarah could stand.

'I won't go! I won't ever set foot out of this house again if you will only give me the inhaler. I'll do anything you want but let me have it! Please!'

'I hope this is a promise you will stand by, my dear. I should hate to go through this again.' He was enjoying it. There was triumph in his eyes.

'I won't ever, ever do anything you don't like again, Douglas,' said Sarah and held out her hand. After a moment Douglas dropped the inhaler casually into her palm, and at once she was bending over Emma, soothing and comforting.

A teaspoon flew across the table and hit Douglas on the cheek.

'Joanne!' The little girl pouted in defiance, her lip stuck out, her eyebrows squashed together.

'You're horrid,' she said and Douglas hit her, once,

across the arm. Joanne shrieked and dived under the table, bawling with rage and hurt.

'Come out at once, you little devil,' roared Douglas and reached for her legs, two chubby pistons flailing at him.

'For God's sake, go to work,' yelled Sarah. 'I'll deal with her. Just go away and let me sort things out.'

Douglas stood up, his tie askew and his hair on end. 'This place is a madhouse!' He looked around at the devastation before him and knew he had gone too far. It was all Sarah's fault, she was the one to blame. If she had behaved properly none of this would have happened and his children would not look at him with eyes of fear and hate.

'I hold you responsible for this,' he said shakily, pointing a finger at his wife. 'I remind you of your promise. Be careful, Sarah. Be very careful.'

'Just go away. We can talk about it tonight.'

Sarah waited until she heard his car leave the drive and then sat back on her heels and sobbed. If there had been a gun in the house she would have shot him for torturing Emma so. How could he? That he should use the children to fight their personal war seemed to her beyond everything. Nonetheless it had worked, and would work again. He had only to threaten and she would do exactly as he wanted.

Joanne still crouched under the table, peering balefully from under a corner of the cloth. 'Come on out, horror,' said Sarah and took her on to her lap. You could not punish such courage as Joanne had shown.

'I'll be late – for school,' puffed Emma, much better now that Douglas had left.

'You're not going, either of you. Put your coats on and play in the garden. We'll be going out later.'

'Where?'

'I don't know yet.'

Alone, Sarah sat and drank a cold cup of coffee and wondered what to do. After this morning they could not stay. She supposed they could go to her mother, but that would be Douglas's first port of call when he came home and found them gone. If she went anywhere within easy reach this morning's scene would be repeated time and again, and none of them could stand it. But where else was there to go, except Susie – and Joe. Dear, wonderful, capable Joe. She had once accused him of cruelty but he never would have done as Douglas had today. You could be so wrong about people.

She had a sudden, violent longing to be near him, and to know that she was safe. Strangely enough, she had not once felt safe since coming home, she was constantly in danger from Douglas's questions, threats and demands; and also from her own longing for things to be different. She had felt all along that there was no permanence in her life, that all was changing and unsure. Sometimes, alone in the big, sumptuous house she had felt waves of panic rising within her and she had stamped on them, tensing her whole being to fight off whatever might happen if she let her feelings show. She had been living a lie and it was time to put an end to it.

She went upstairs and began to pack, one giant suitcase for the three of them and a couple of flight bags for their immediate needs. Thank God the children were on her passport – it was foolish of Douglas to have overlooked that most obvious shackle. And the stamps and things for her last trip might still apply; if not she would bluff her way through. As for injections, they would see to all that when they got there. Susie always sneered at 'the pincushion English' as it was and if they were careful about water and food it should be all right. Money was a problem but if she paid for the ticket by credit card and cleared out the housekeeping account she might just have enough for a few weeks. She had no illusions about Douglas's generosity once they were gone. He would let them starve before he paid her a penny, and he would certainly fight her for the children. Yes, they were safer by far in Africa.

When she rang the travel agent she had a moment's panic that there would be no seats available, and she almost cried with relief when she learned they could leave on a lunchtime flight. It would mean a dash to Heathrow but they had no choice but to make it.

She called the girls and looked at their anxious faces. 'We're going away,' she said awkwardly, trying to radiate certainty and confidence.

'Without Daddy?' asked Joanne, looking belligerent.

'Without Daddy. We're going to see Auntie Susie in Africa, and I want you both to behave very well indeed. We're going on a plane. Do you understand?'

'Will we come back?' asked Emma nervously.

'I don't know yet, darlings. I don't know what we're going to do, but I promise you'll be all right. I'll take care of you and you'll love Auntie Susie. We'll manage, I'm sure we will.'

'Daddy will be awfully cross,' said Emma and Sarah thought that was the understatement of the year.

She left Douglas a note. It read: '*Dear Douglas. After this morning I think it best if we both have a little time to think. I have therefore taken the girls on holiday. We might go to Scotland, I haven't decided. Anyway, I will write and let you know what we plan to do. Please believe me when I say that I am terribly sorry for the way things have turned out, and I am sure that on reflection you will see that this is the best solution. Sarah.*'

There. That hinted at a parting forever and also gave her a breathing space. He would track her down eventually but the last thing she wanted was Douglas hot on her heels across the world. She left the note on the table, put the key under the mat and closed the front door behind her.

Chapter 11

Sarah looked pale and tired, thought Susie, and her nerves were as taut as the string of a violin. There was a restlessness which had never been there before, and a nervous habit of pausing in mid-sentence as if to check that whatever she was about to say was watertight, as though she were giving a statement to the police.

'But what did Douglas do?' she asked again, and Sarah shook her head wearily. She did not want to detail the petty squabbles of her life, to have her sister weigh whether this or that was bad enough to have forced her to leave.

'It was just that we couldn't get on,' she said eventually. 'We were fighting all the time, and in the end Emma's asthma got so bad because of it that I decided we had to go.'

'But you could have stayed in England, surely?'

'Er – no. Douglas would have been difficult. I don't want him to know where we are.' There was a little silence and then Sarah hurried on. 'But I don't intend to land on you indefinitely. I thought I might get in touch with Joe, though I've no idea where he is. I don't suppose he'll be very pleased to see me but I think he might help. I need him and he's never let me down.' It sounded plaintive and she despised herself for it, but if he failed her now there would be nothing in all the world for her to trust. And she had failed him so badly.

'Does Mother know where you are?' asked Susie

sharply. Whenever Sarah mentioned Joe she shied away like a frightened horse.

'No. I didn't have a chance to tell her and anyway Douglas would shake it out of her in no time. I thought you might write something vague, say you'd had a letter . . . I don't know.'

'If you ask me you don't know a lot of things. What are you going to do for money? What about schools for the girls? I don't really know how you got in at all without proper papers. You don't seem to have done any planning – I mean, where are you going to live?'

Sarah felt confused and unhappy. Susie always seemed to be badgering her; why had she forgotten that about her sister? She took a deep breath.

'I don't know what I'm going to do,' she said firmly, 'and going on about it isn't going to help. All I need is some sort of idea where to find Joe Langeveldt. I could always ask at the Wakamba I suppose but it would be embarrassing. The man might offer me a job.'

'It might be the best offer you'll get,' snapped her sister. 'Anyway, you can forget Joe Langeveldt, he's back in Mandoto up to his ears in refugees. The place is a war zone and they're building up to the worst famine in years. It's a mess and just the sort of place for your friend Langeveldt. He must be the only white man in the country.'

'But – the relief agencies are there, aren't they? I thought by now it would all be organised.' She had heard nothing at all in England about Mandoto's problems and had somehow assumed that it was all over. But then the media tended to ignore long-running wars.

Susan shrugged. 'There's no proper government to tell anyone anything and the fighting is still so bad that nothing gets through. We only know because a reporter friend flew over and saw the crops and things, but he turned tail when he got shot at. No-one wants to repeat your experiences, Sarah.' She gave a sudden grin and added, 'The only news comes from Joe Langeveldt. Furious letters demanding that people do something. I think the government loses them in someone's in-tray.'

For a moment Sarah was taken aback. 'Do you mean – but that's awful! Are you telling me that Joe is in there all alone and that no-one can be bothered to help him? Why don't you do something, Susie? People could be starving.'

'Well – yes. But what can I do? What can anyone do?'

'A lot. An awful lot. I bet Joe isn't standing by with his hands in the air.' Sarah got to her feet and began to pace the room. Imagine what it must be like for the people there, for the children. Still without help after all this time. No wonder Joe had gone back. She thought of Tanu and shuddered. To think of her in the middle of it all once again, perhaps hungry, terrified, plunged back into a nightmare. Although Joe wouldn't allow that, she was sure. And to think he was asking for help, and it must choke him to do it, and no-one at all would listen. Could she too turn a deaf ear? It would be easy. She had her own problems, her own responsibilities, and as Susie said, what could anyone do – except what they knew was right.

She turned to her sister. 'Susie, will it be all right if I leave the girls with you? It won't be for ever, I promise, and you can probably get them into school here. It would be lovely for them, they seem so settled already – Emma hasn't had one attack since we arrived. All I ask is that you don't tell Douglas.'

'I don't mind having the girls, you should know that. But where will you be?' She read the message in her sister's eyes and turned pale. 'Sarah – you can't!'

'Oh yes, I can. I'll leave the day after tomorrow.'

The ensuing hours were a jumble of people, questions and forms. By some wonderful chance she had brought a copy of a leaflet the Save the Children Fund had printed to accompany the library exhibition. It showed Mrs Sarah Hamilton, artist and member of the committee, and from there it was only a short step to announce herself Sarah Hamilton, Save the Children Fund representative with responsibility for Mandoto.

'Since my time in Mandoto I have been very concerned about conditions there,' she told the manager of the mining company, having inveigled herself into his office on the strength of Jerry's name. 'We have reason to believe that there have been deliberate attempts to gloss over the problems there and I have been asked to make a full investigation. It may well be that a television crew will be here shortly.' And the manager, visualizing a World in Action exposé of the callousness of mining companies, perhaps even latching on to wage levels, was only too happy to lend a Land Rover, complete with driver and supplies.

'You'll lose Jerry his job,' complained Susan. 'I wish you'd stop and think, Sarah.'

'I haven't the time. Look, are there better maps than this? So far I can only establish that Joe is somewhere in this large lump of brown, an area about three hundred miles square. We have to do better than this, Susie.'

Her sister was showing signs of nervous collapse. 'You cannot possibly go!' she wailed. 'For goodness sake, I think you're deranged, leaving Douglas only to go off into the middle of a war, complete with a Land Rover obtained entirely on false pretences –'

'Not entirely,' objected Sarah. 'I am on the local committee. We hold jumble sales.'

'– and not even sure where it is you actually want to be.

No wonder Douglas couldn't get along with you, no-one could.'

'Joe seemed to manage,' said Sarah absently. 'Tell me, how did these letters of his get out?'

'Some blacks brought them. But really, Sarah –'

'Would Jerry know who it was? Could he find the man for me?'

'Well – I don't know. You really intend to go through with this, don't you?'

'Yes I really do.'

The Land Rover roared its way along roads thick with dust, bouncing from pothole to pothole. Sarah clung to the seat, her map long since abandoned, relying solely on the directions of the weird individual who was rattling around in the back. An old, thin man, wearing tattered shirt and shorts, his sandals the last resting place of part of a car tyre, ingeniously cut and shaped. He said little but every now and then he would tap Sarah's shoulder and gesture left or right, his hands and fingers loose and mobile like those of many an African. He looked fairly benevolent, she thought, and Jerry had assured her that he knew where Joe was. Still, Sarah was grateful for the pistol her brother-in-law had given her, stowed now beneath her seat, for heaven knew where they might end up.

It was the only support Jerry had given her, for he was totally opposed to her plan. He had even threatened to inform the authorities that she was a subversive and prevent her leaving the country, but his impossible sister-in-law had threatened to bash him over the head if he dared. And she left, before dawn, the family still asleep, and crept throught a border post before it was light.

They said she did not realise the danger but she did, oh,

she did. She felt sick with the fear of it, and in her dreams, two perhaps three times a night she saw the face of that man, the one who killed poor Duffy. If they caught her this time – her hand searched for the pistol. There were times when it was better by far to be dead.

She wondered why on earth she had come. The air held the heat of an open oven, a Yorkshire pudding heat, sapping strength and will. She had forgotten that heat like this existed, drawing the sweat into pools on the seats. Her bush shirt clung to her shoulderblades and her khaki trousers felt like sacking against her legs. But the driver seemed not to feel it, grinding on for hour after hour. They communicated in sign language for the most part, and she rarely felt the lack of a common tongue. Her two companions guided and fed her, gave her water and said when to stop. At night they erected a little bush tent into which she scurried, grateful for privacy. They observed a strict decorum in camp, trained she thought on safari, and they pushed her inexorably into the role of memsahib. She was to do nothing but accept all that was provided. It irked her and on the third evening she gently but firmly pushed the driver away from the fire and began to cook. She looked up to see his face puzzled and hurt – she thought his cooking was bad!

'I'm sorry, I didn't mean – I only wanted to – here, you do it!' She moved quickly away again and the man resumed his place, but stiffly, letting her know she had offended. After that she let them do things their way.

At night they always pulled well off the road and camped behind trees or dunes, once cuddling uncomfortably close to an ant hill. Twice they heard gunfire to the east and on a clear, still night they heard other travellers, a convoy of trucks moving steadily through the dark, their headlights spiking the velvet night sky. Without a word spoken they doused the fire and crouched in readiness, the pistol heavy in Sarah's hand. Both her companions were nervous; they murmured to each other and said 'eeeh, eeeh' as the trucks came nearer. The moon was so full – would their tracks be spotted? But the trucks rumbled on and what they were or where they were going Sarah never knew.

Their route was a winding one, chosen she thought to avoid the soldiers. They meandered along rough road and game track, startling antelope and guinea fowl more often than people. Four days, five days, a week. Sarah toughened in mind and body, for the first time in months able to accept what the day had to offer without any need to do anything about it. She could only wait and sweat, scratch at a million fly bites and think about Joe.

Did he hate her for what she had done? It was possible. Everything he did was wholehearted and when he loved he held nothing back. His hurt had been terrible, she had thrown his love back in his face and at the last taken even his pride. If only he could have tried to understand – but that was not Joe. In his own world, in the bush, it was she who lacked understanding, but the problems of a little, civilised life were beyond him. She deserved all the misery of this last year if only to pay for what she had done to Joe.

The hand of the guide tapped her shoulder, motioning to the left, and she nodded, passing the signal to the driver. Blacks had pink-palmed hands, the colour staining only the lines, like a tie-dyed shirt. Joe's hands were huge and very brown, the backs covered in fine gold hairs. So strong and yet so very gentle. She thought of those hands on her body during the long, starry nights and she almost gasped aloud. Desire had been asleep in her since she left him, those struggles with Douglas no more than childish fumblings. It was only Joe that she longed for, only his hard flesh that made her feel empty and alone. She burned and her rough bush trousers rasped against her skin. No use thinking of love: she had forfeited all right to his kindness. All she could do was offer her help.

The country was brown and parched under the sun. Near the border there had been people, small poor villages with a few cattle and thirsty fields. Here they saw no-one and what villages there were had been burnt or abandoned.

'Where has everyone gone?' she asked, spreading her hands wide and looking around. Some refugees had crossed the border but there had been no mass exodus. The guide nodded his thin, creased head, the fuzzy hair grizzled at the temples.

'Langeveldt,' he said simply. 'Langeveldt.'

She assumed he had misunderstood and after another attempt, which elicited the same reply, she gave up. 'Soon Langeveldt,' said the man. 'Soon.' And he nodded and smiled, showing a mouth of broken teeth. She smiled in return and looked ahead across the parched plain, for it could hardly be very soon she thought, there was nothing there. Ant hills. Scrub. A thin line of trees away to the left, at the base of a little fold of hills. The guide tapped her shoulder and gestured towards them, and at once their driver obeyed.

They drove across earth cracked from lack of water, sending a plume of dust into the air. As they drew nearer Sarah could see the outlines of huts, set amongst the trees and going back into the hills, and she realised that the trees marked the course of a river. Two birds rose heavily into the air as they passed and she saw that they were vultures, their black, coarse feathers rattling as they flapped upwards, their necks naked and grotesque.

Ghastly creatures she had always thought them, arriving like rowdy guests at a funeral, anticipating a party. And those two looked full fed. For the first time she felt real apprehension at what she might be going into. Famine, Susie had said; war; and Joe's fierce pain.

Dimly, peering through the dust, she could see figures amongst the trees. The guide slapped his hand against the seat, his signal to stop, and the Land Rover lurched to a halt. The little party climbed stiffly down, much alike despite the difference in race, their faces a dust-caked mask in which only teeth and eyes showed life. They walked the last hundred yards with slow, deliberate steps, carrying nothing although Sarah longed for her pistol. Ahead she could see the long slim shapes of guns. A man stepped forward and shouted something, she had no idea what, and the guide ran forward, surprisingly agile for one of his years, calling a greeting. Sarah stopped and shaded her eyes with her hand. No sign of Langeveldt. She walked on and entered the welcoming shade of the trees.

Rondavels were everywhere in little groups of six or eight, their thatched roofs blending completely with the surrounding foliage. Men stood and watched her, their faces blank but expectant, and she realised that these were warriors. Everyone was armed, with a gun or with a spear, and there was an order and purpose about the encampment that spoke of military discipline. Here an ammunition belt, there a camouflage jacket, the detritus of some army or another. In Mandoto the differences mattered little unless you were about to be shot.

'Langeveldt,' she said suddenly. 'Joe Langeveldt.'

A man glanced sideways at her. He was almost a boy really, without the muscle and weight that age would bring. 'You come to help?' he asked cautiously, and she jumped at the unexpected English.

'Yes. I'm from Zimbabwe. I want to help the children.'

At once he was by her side. 'Over the river. Langeveldt, children, over the river. Come.' He clutched determinedly at her arm and almost dragged her through the trees until they came to the river bank. Once this was a wide and flowing stream, now it was barely knee deep and they splashed and floundered their way towards the other side. The water was murky and sluggish, but people knelt on the far side, washing clothes in a weary, desultory way. They would be no cleaner when they finished, thought Sarah, staring nervously at the hollow faces around her.

She stopped to catch her breath and look about, disregarding the urgings of her guide. How could she have thought that there was nothing here? Hidden beneath the trees were people, the place was seething with people, everywhere she looked there were people, sitting, lying, standing, crouching, old men with sticks, girls with narrow, large-eyed faces. An old woman was lying in the dust, her eyes closed, oblivious to the flies that clustered on her face. Sarah wondered if she were dead.

'Children. Come see the children.' The man was tugging at her again, pulling her onward and although this was why she had come she hung back. She had come upon all this too quickly, it was hard to take it in. So many people and yet it was so quiet, when Africans must be one of the noisiest peoples of the world. No laughter or singing, not even the dull murmur of talk. There had once been grass here, near the water, but the people had trampled it away. The earth was bare and hard, and over it all hung the stench of bodies, and vomit and excreta. They passed a long, palm-roofed shelter where people lay in rows, a dull, soft moaning coming from nowhere. A boy of about twelve sat in the dust and clutched his knees and sobbed, the tears rolling into a sore at the corner of his

264

mouth. Why should he cry and why did no-one comfort him? And then they came to the children.

They were grouped, the mothers, within a compound made of thorn and they sheltered from the sun beneath thatched screens. Perhaps a hundred women, thought Sarah vaguely, perhaps more, and every one had a baby. She could not look at them. One glance and she tore her gaze away, walking through the bodies looking this way and that and everywhere the same. Tiny, wizened babies, more like monkeys than anything human. Stick arms and legs, heads too big for their necks, and always the pouched, unhealthy stomach. They wailed in voices too weak for comfort and again and again were offered empty breasts. Here, everything was empty: there was no hope in the faces and no food in the bowls. Sarah looked and saw only death.

A hand tugged at her trousers and she looked into the face of a girl, the skin tight and grey across her cheeks. Her baby mewed and flailed in her arms, so thin that even this little strength seemed remarkable. The mother held out her hand for food, and Sarah turned away. There was no recrimination, no loud, insistent begging, merely a dull acceptance of the inevitable. The youth who had led her there stood patiently by.

'How long?' asked Sarah faintly. 'How long have these children been here?'

He shrugged. 'Every day come more. Many die. That way –' he gestured east '– they fight. The people come here. Now, we have nothing. Langeveldt good man,' added the youth. 'He take them, he feed them, he bring the men to guard. But all hear of Langeveldt, all come. And we have no food. Now, no food.'

'Yes. Yes, I see.' Her mind reeled from the enormity of it all. One saw pictures, everybody did, of starving children the world over. One stick-like baby the mind can accept, but this – how many had died before now? How many of these would be dead before morning? Bile rose in her throat and she pushed her way out, wanting to run but forced to pick her way over people.

Outside it was not so bad, she thought, seeing wasted faces that were yet still recognisable as human. Then she saw a man sitting on the ground. He had no feet. And a woman, old, with a bandage on the tattered remains of her arm. Her guide followed the direction of her eyes. 'They fight,' he explained, and turned his hand into an aeroplane, making engine noises exactly like Joanne. Then his hand became a bomb, falling *poof!* to the ground. 'Big bang,' he added, wide-eyed.

'I see. Yes,' said Sarah and wondered why on earth she had thought she could help. She could hardly look at what was here without feeling sick. The logic behind the camp's concealment became obvious, for dead men tell no tales and bombs here would wipe many a slate clean. Trust Joe to find somewhere like this.

'Langeveldt!' she said again. 'Langeveldt?' She needed to see him, longed for him to say that all was well. He would have it in hand, of course he would, the shock made it seem worse. It could not possibly be this bad. Joe would explain it all.

The young man pointed up the hill, to where a track was winding its way between the trees, and the unlikely pair set off towards it. He led the way, bare feet careless of the thorns that littered the path, his toes strong and square as befits a man who has rarely worn shoes. He was naturally gregarious, turning now and then to point out plants and stones that might interest her. Sarah smiled and pretended to notice, but in her mind's eye all she could see was a child, tiny, wizened, its future turned to dust.

They came upon a clearing on a small plateau on the hillside. Men were digging in the earth, the shrouded shapes of bodies lying nearby. Four, five, six neat parcels and one was so very, very small. A figure straightened and looked to see who came. It was Langeveldt.

She knew who it was even before he raised his head; she could tell from the way he bent over the shovel. A crippling weight seemed to lift from her mind. Her last sight of him had been in that squalid little room, stinking of drink and misery, and it was the one scene that she had never called to mind. It hurt too much to remember him thus. It made her want to cry, and still it could; in fact she was crying now, the tears running softly down her cheeks. She scrubbed at them, unaware that she left fingermarks clear in the grime. She looked like a grief-stricken child.

'Sarah!' He felt no surprise at seeing her; there had been so many unexpected things of late. Like the locusts and the bombs, and still another failure of the rains.

'I saw – down there – the children.'

He nodded, slowly. His whole frame, massive as a tree, drooped with weariness. 'There are too many. We can't feed them and they're too weak to go on. And I ask for help and nothing comes.'

'I've come. I knew you wouldn't ask if things weren't desperate.'

He wondered if she were real. Sometimes in the night he had dreamed of her so vividly that on waking he had reached for her and felt surprise to find her gone. And when he remembered the hurt was still as fresh, it was a wound that never seemed to heal. But these past weeks he had not felt it – he had felt nothing, could allow himself to feel nothing when sanity lay only in the endless struggle for food.

'Have you brought any food?'

She nodded. 'Some. Not enough. I had no idea there would be so many.'

He laughed, without humour. 'None of us thought there would be so many. Like a river of people, flooding out of the bush. We should let them die, I suppose. No-one wants them. An expensive drain on someone's economy, that's what those children are. That's why no-one will help.' He swayed and almost fell, and Sarah clutched at his arm, thrusting her shoulder against him to keep him upright. The smell of him was just as she remembered, striking echoes and chords in the shadows of her mind. It was almost evening and she was exhausted. How much more tired must he be who had endured this camp for day after terrible day.

'You must sleep, Joe. It will do no-one any good if you collapse. Let the others finish here, you've done enough.'

'I've done nothing. I do everything I can and it isn't enough. Do you remember those prayers we said over Duffy, that pathetic, useless little man? Who did we say those to Sarah? Can you look at those children dying down there, can you look at those people who know they're going to die and still think there's a God? I can't. I can't think there's anything but hell and this is it.'

'Come now, and sleep,' she said gently. 'I'll give out the food I have and then in the morning we'll see what to do. It will be better in the morning.' It was something she said to the children, and Joe's mouth twitched as he recognised the phrase. 'I don't need mothering,' he said with a tinge of sourness and began a weaving, staggering progress down the path.

Joe slept in a hut on the hillside, a little apart from the people, where the hot wind raised ghosts in the leaves. A child played in the doorway, scooping the earth into tiny mountains and gulleys, a child with smooth and shiny skin, her hair the densest black.

'Is that – is she – Tanu?' asked Sarah, her eyes wide in disbelief.

'That she is,' said Joe and collapsed through the door of the hut.

Sarah heaved and tugged him on to a thin straw mattress, all the while watched by the child. When Sarah reached a tin mug into a clay pitcher of water and held it to Joe's lips, she filled it again and offered it to Tanu. The child bent her head and drank, never once taking her eyes from Sarah.

'I'm going to get food,' said Sarah, not knowing if she could possibly understand. 'Wait here. I will bring food.' She went swiftly down the path and into the camp, wondering how long it would be before you could look and feel no pity. The horror had dulled a little even in so short a time, but she kept away from the children. You could never get used to the children.

In her absence the Land Rover had been brought under the sheltering canopy of trees. She splashed her way across the river towards it, and found her faithful driver standing guard over the supplies. They had brought so little – most of their stock had been petrol, stowed in cans strapped to the sides and roof of the vehicle. The flour, dried meat and a few luxurious tins stashed in what space remained seemed an insult when set against the sufferings of these people. Sarah found a bag and took enough for Joe and Tanu and herself, knowing as she did so that it was wrong. They had no more claim to life than any one of thousands and yet because she cared she would give them their fill and leave others with nothing. Was it better for some to live and others to die, or for all to have too little? One thing was sure, Joe had done without for many days past; it caught at her heart to see him.

Her driver helped to sort the food for distribution. The patience of the people surprised her. They stood and watched silently as the sacks were carried across the stream and cups found to measure out each portion. It was only when they saw the food that the reality seemed to dawn, and then they became a pushing, jostling horde. Sarah screamed at them, desperately trying to hold them back. The ones at the front held out a forest of bowls, shouting, pleading, their teeth huge in faces that had lost all flesh, while the ones behind, fearing that there would be none left, clawed and fought to come closer. The food would be trampled, it would all be lost! Then came the sound of blows, and cries of pain. Gradually the crowd fell back, shouting and gesticulating, as four of the soldiers forged a path for themselves through the mob. They carried short, thick sticks and they left a trail of groaning bodies behind them. Sarah put her hands to her face, appalled, yet aware of the necessity. This was no place for the niceties of life.

The men ranged themselves around her little feeding station, and under their watchful eyes Sarah was able to give each person a measure of flour and a measure of meat. Some tried to come round twice but a blow from a stick discouraged them. Sarah could not like these men with their practised, casual violence. They did not starve.

Soon everything was gone and still people waited to be fed. They were the old people, forced to the back of the line, and they stood with their bowls, resigned and hopeless. One old woman mumbled through toothless gums a jumble of words that must have been a curse. She had iron rings set into her ear lobes but the flesh had shrunk and now the heavy metal swung on what seemed like pieces of leather. Sarah took her bag of food and scurried away up the path.

The child sat waiting within the hut. She crept to a corner when Sarah entered, as nervous as any wild creature.

'Tanu, it's all right,' said Sarah. 'Look, I've brought food.' She opened the bag but the child stayed where she was. She was as wary as an antelope, thought Sarah and turned her attention to Joe. He slept like the dead, the skin of his face stretched tight. A harsh face, always that, but now it looked almost wild. She felt a shiver go through her, of apprehension mixed with longing. Did she want to love Joe again? It hurt when you loved like that, it laid you open to pain that was more than you could bear, until you had to bear it. It took away your soul and gave it to another. There was no harm in holding back a little, in giving less than everything to keep something for yourself. It was safer that way.

She opened a tin of spam and gave the child some slices. Tanu crouched in her corner while she ate, and afterwards Sarah fed her biscuits, stale and crumbled but edible. She ate little herself, wondering if she would ever eat again without feelings of guilt. It was nearly evening and soon the child slept, her face shiny with grease. Sarah sat and watched the end of the day, seeing the bats begin their darting forays through the trees. The mosquito hum was deafening; there is no famine for a fly.

'Is that really you or are you a ghost?'

She turned, her face a blur in the darkness of the hut. 'It's me. I brought some food, but it isn't enough – I don't know what to do.'

Joe pulled himself up on his elbow. 'You can go away, that's what you can do,' he said furiously. 'I've had enough of you and your lies. Don't you get enough excitement in England that you have to come and sight-see a famine? I don't know what makes you think you'll get any welcome from me.'

Sarah gulped. 'You haven't eaten. Here, I've brought food.' She held out the remains of the tin of spam, but Joe did not take it.

'I can't eat that. There are babies dying.'

'The babies can do nothing to help. You can.' When still he did not take it she screamed, 'Eat it, damn you! I've come all this horrible way to bring you this and the least you can do is eat it!'

She heard him snort in the dark but he reached for the food. 'Lady Bountiful doesn't like difficult peasants, I see. What else is there?'

'Some more tins, only a little flour – I gave the rest out – and some powdered milk for Tanu. I felt terrible taking it when everyone else had so little but when it comes down to it there's no point in everyone dying. And I'd rather you two lived.'

'Very worried about us all of a sudden, aren't you? You weren't so concerned a year ago. You shook us off like leeches in a swamp!' His voice cracked, whether with anger or tears Sarah did not know.

'I paid for it,' she whispered, but he gave no sign of having heard. She handed him the biscuits and he finished the packet.

'These are disgusting,' he commented, firmly back in control.

'That's why I didn't eat them. Look, what is going on here? When I came up here just now there were more people arriving. God knows where they'd come from. A dozen of them and not a piece of bread between them. Why do they come?'

Joe sighed and she knew without seeing that he was running his hand through his hair. She knew his gestures better than her own. 'They come to escape the fighting,

272

it's very bad further east. It's relatively safe here because
the camp is under the protection of a local band of
freedom fighters – you probably saw them, wandering
about with guns. They're not a bad lot, they don't shoot
refugees, but if it's a case of who gets what they make sure
they're first in line. Still, it's worth it not to be massacred
by the government forces; they stop at nothing. And a
week, two weeks ago, we had food. I've seen this coming
for months but no-one listens. Do you know I slogged it
all the way to Zimbabwe only to get thrown out of some
twit's office before I could halfway explain what was
happening here? So I brought back what I could, begging
for it, and it was enough for the people we had then.
When the rains failed more people came, there wasn't
enough. The crops blew away and we'd long since
slaughtered the cattle. I wrote letters, dozens of them – at
least some should have got through. Nothing. Nobody
gives a damn.'

'Yes, they do. You haven't done it right, Joe.'

He erupted into fury, lunging at her across the dark hut
and grabbing her arms. 'You say I haven't done it right?
How much harder could I try, you stupid bitch, how much
more can I do? I work till I drop and those fat cats sit in
their plush offices and do nothing! Do you hear me,
nothing!'

His fingers were biting into her arms and she struggled
to be free but he hung on. 'Why can't you talk to people,
Joe?' she gasped. 'The newspapers, the charities, the Red
Cross? You go and see the government and of course they
don't care – they won't until they're forced to. Why, I bet
you didn't take one single photograph. How do you
expect people to believe you? You're that lunatic Joe
Langeveldt who never does anything normal.'

The smell of her hair came to him, warm and sweet and

remembered. 'I fell normally in love,' he said softly, and his hold on her slackened.

'That doesn't count.' She pulled quickly away.

After a while he said, 'Would it have made a difference? Photographs and things?'

'Joe, of course it would. It would have made all the difference if you'd gone to one newspaper. They would have loved it, tough guy Langeveldt giving his all for starving children. Oh, by the way, did you know that I'm the Save the Children Fund representative in Mandoto?'

'You're not!'

'Well, no, I'm not really. But people think I am, otherwise they wouldn't have let me in.'

He laughed, genuinely amused this time. 'God, but you amaze me. When I think of the way you used to be, frightened of your shadow, I wonder if you're the same person.'

'Douglas didn't think I was,' said Sarah, and found she was choking on tears. She sprang up and ducked out of the door of the hut. It was all too much; for months past she had struggled and suffered and endured and she had kept on because she had to. Now she felt ill and unable to cope, especially with Joe. One moment hurting, the next his voice husky with need. Chaos inside and out, nothing anywhere to cling to. The sky was almost hidden by the trees, but in one clear space the stars were brilliant. So far away from all this misery and death.

Joe stood in the doorway of the hut. 'Have you enough fuel to get back to Zimbabwe?' he asked thoughtfully.

'Well – yes, just about. It took days and days though, Joe.'

'You went the long way round. Tomorrow you and I go back. I can do nothing here as it is except wait for us all to die. We'll do it your way and see what happens.'

'What about Tanu?'

He looked surprised. 'What about her? Where I go she goes, because unlike you I take my responsibilities seriously.'

Sarah was stung. 'You bastard! As if you didn't know that the one reason I left was because I do take my responsibilities seriously. What if somebody asked you to abandon Tanu while you swanned off somewhere more interesting? What would you say? Exactly what I said but you're too stubborn to admit it.'

He sighed. 'Sarah, I'm in no mood for a fight.'

'It must be the only time in living memory, then.'

'Can't we just, for now, calm down and go to sleep. We've a lot to do tomorrow.'

'You sound exactly like Douglas,' she said waspishly and pushed past him into the hut.

They lay only inches apart. The hut was not built for three people, and Tanu sprawled over more than her fair share. Joe stared unseeing into the darkness and longed for the woman beside him. He had had many women since Sarah, he had spent himself in body after body and never once felt satisfied. It had been the final irony, for Sarah to leave him with a thirst he could not slake. He tried whores and ladies, black girls and white, leading them as willing partners into every excess he could think of. And not once did it compare with slow, sweet, ordinary loving with Sarah. He remembered the first time, and how she had cried, and there had been almost more pleasure in the comforting than the sex. Without meaning to do so he reached out his hand and touched her, feeling the swell of her breast beneath his fingers, the flesh warm and soft. Gently, almost holding his breath, he felt for her nipple but she grumbled in sleep and turned over. Langeveldt lay and burned.

He woke her before it was light. 'Let's get going. We don't want women shoving their babies in the windows.' He picked up his gun and began stuffing bullets into his pockets.

'Why would they do that?' asked Sarah, still fuddled with sleep.

'To give them some chance of living, of course. God, but you can be so stupid.'

She recoiled and went to shake Tanu into wakefulness. Joe was in a foul temper today and she did not begin to understand the reason.

Tanu rode on Joe's shoulders as they walked through the sleeping camp. She was such an obedient little thing, she made no demands at all, as if already aware that there was no use asking for something no-one could give. She knew that what Joe had he would give her. Sarah passed a figure slumped in unnatural repose. Dead, she thought and felt a shiver run through her. It would be disease that took them in the end; such wasted bodies could resist nothing. If cholera or dysentery came this place could be a graveyard in days. She hurried after Joe as if even the seconds she was wasting were important, for if help was to come it must come quickly. They splashed across the river together and the smell of the water, tainted as it was, came as a relief after the miasma that hung over the camp. Day was breaking, the horizon was stained with a thin orange glow that set the trees in silhouette and from somewhere nearby came the croaking of a frog. Foolish of him, surely, to make himself known. Someone would eat him.

Joe went to put Tanu in the Land Rover, stowed the gun behind the seat and then walked to one of the huts. He called a greeting and a man came out, yawning and stretching. He was young and fine-featured. Joe seemed to be trying to persuade him about something. At last he nodded, they shook hands and Joe turned to go.

'What was that about?' asked Sarah.

'He wants to pull his men out and move into the hills. He thinks things are hopeless here. I've asked him to wait until I get back, in not more than a week.'

'Joe! We can't do it in that time.'

'We have to.'

He started the Land Rover and shoved it into gear. There was a sudden yelling and bellowing and from under the car there struggled Sarah's driver.

'Oh dear. I'd forgotten all about him,' she said vaguely, as he bawled and complained, obviously objecting to being abandoned in this terrible place, and they'd nearly run him over, after all he'd done! Didn't they know he was asleep under there? Not a word did Sarah understand but she knew just what he wanted to say. 'Can we take him, Joe?' she asked and he sighed.

'I suppose we'll have to. He's certainly not going to shut up.' He jerked a thumb towards the back of the vehicle and the man scrambled thankfully aboard.

Joe rammed his foot on the accelerator and the car lurched forward. Damn it all, now they had a blasted chaperone; that was all he needed.

Chapter 12

Journeying is all a matter of speed. Pleasure comes from slow and peaceful wandering. There was no pleasure in this desperate dash for help. It was not long before the radiator sprang a leak under the strain. They could drive for no more than two hours before the engine boiled, and in the middle of the day it boiled every twenty minutes. Joe stopped in the shade of some scrubby, dry-leaved trees.

'We'll stop till it's cooler. We'll have to drive through the night.'

'We'll wreck the car,' said Sarah resignedly. Joe had been absolutely stinking all morning, snapping at every passing comment. He probably wanted to wreck the car.

'If you prefer to sit on the bonnet and pour a never-ending stream of water into that radiator then you can,' said Joe and climbed stiffly out. He rattled a few words of explanation to their unemployed driver, who promptly lit a fire and began to make tea.

'He was like this on the way out,' said Sarah. 'A sort of African version of Jeeves.'

'And I bet you played Lady Muck to perfection,' said Joe, hiding a grin at Sarah's look of outrage. What was she doing here, he thought yet again. Where were Douglas and the kids? He was damned if he would ask her – he had finished asking her for anything – but why on earth had she come? He glared at her and sipped his tea and exchanged insults.

In the night, Joe and the driver took turns at the wheel, the headlights picking an unsteady path across the land. They hit a main road shortly before dawn, stretches of pock-marked tarmac interspersed with dirt.

'If we meet anyone unpleasant just remember you're the Red Cross,' said Langeveldt. 'Say it and keep on saying it. They'll know who I am, it's no use pretending.'

'What will you do?' asked Sarah, but he did not reply. She glanced across at Tanu, asleep with her thumb in her mouth, and felt her stomach turn over. Heaven knows what would happen to her.

They met a convoy of lorries as the sun came up, and Sarah and Joe crouched on the floor while the driver waved and shouted to the soldiers. Afterwards he and Langeveldt laughed and chatted about it, and Sarah felt left out. No-one talked to her. When they pulled off the road to rest in a dry gulley, everyone was tired except Tanu. She ran around, playing and singing, and kept them all awake.

'Damn it, Sarah, can't you make her shut up?' complained Joe, who found it impossible to be tough with the little girl.

'I thought you said she was your responsibility.'

'You found her.'

'You kept her.'

'And whose idea was that? I didn't volunteer if you remember, though I don't suppose you gave much thought to us after you'd swanned off to your cosy little nest –'

'God, Joe, if you only knew! Come here, Tanu. Look, you can draw.' Sarah took a stick and sketched in the dust, Tanu, Joe, Sarah, the driver. Then she gave the stick to Tanu and settled down to doze. After a while she looked to see what the child had drawn and there in a row were lots of matchstick people lying down. 'Who are they, Tanu?' she asked innocently.

'Dead. All dead,' said Tanu, and went on drawing.

They set off again with the sun low in the sky, and when night fell, before the moon came up, they crashed. They were bumping along on the unmade road when the nose of the vehicle pitched into a crater, catapulting them all this way and that. Tanu began to shriek.

'What is it? Tanu, are you hurt?' There was real alarm in Joe's voice. He loves that little girl, thought Sarah, he loves her to distraction.

'A petrol can landed on her head. But you're all right, darling, aren't you?'

Tanu was not all right, there was a gash on her forehead that filled her eyes with blood and she bawled with mingled fear and pain.

'Is she bleeding? Here, let me have her.' Joe reached over and cradled her on his lap, and at once the child began to calm. Sarah soaked a rag in water and bathed her cut, stabbed by an emotion she did not care to label. You could not be jealous of a child.

The driver was prowling round outside, peering at the front of the car with the aid of a flash. The Land Rover had dropped a wheel deep into a shell hole and there it stayed, with a somewhat quizzical look on its face, caused by a dent in the radiator grille. Joe gave Tanu to Sarah and went to look at the damage.

'We'll have to lift it out,' he said shortly.

'That's impossible.' No-one could lift a car, thought Sarah, and knew that if anyone could it was Joe.

'Get in and start it up,' he urged. 'Put it in four-wheel drive. We only need to lift the front for a second. As soon as the back wheels touch the ground you can reverse it out. Get a move on.'

Sarah did as she was told, and at the given signal sat with her foot ready on the clutch. Joe and the driver settled themselves at the depressed corner of the vehicle. 'Ready – now!' yelled Joe, and he and the driver heaved till their muscles cracked. Sarah slammed the clutch in, stamped on the accelerator and the car raced backwards.

She looked up to see Joe and the driver face down in the dust. 'Are you all right?' she asked nervously. Joe got up slowly and the driver groaned and sat on the ground rubbing his elbow. Both men glared at Sarah.

'If you want to kill me I wish you'd get on with it,' said Joe with ice. 'I do not need dragging across Africa hanging on to a Land Rover. I find it tiring.'

'I didn't know you wanted me to go slowly,' objected Sarah. 'You can't complain when you don't tell me what to do. Anyway, we're wasting time.'

Joe and the driver climbed aboard, grumbling and rubbing at their arms. They exchanged comments which Sarah was not so naive as to think complimentary.

'I wish you wouldn't talk about me when I don't understand.'

'Learn the language,' said Joe, taking his turn behind the wheel.

'Don't worry, I intend to,' she retorted, and Joe's hands gripped the wheel with sudden force. What in God's name did Sarah mean to do? He glanced at her, sitting in the dark beside him, her hair caught up in a scarf, her shirt open to a hint of cleavage. In the heat of the afternoon she had taken a cloth and bathed her face and neck, letting droplets of water run into her shirt and onto her breasts. Yet when she saw him watching her she turned away and he knew that she was blushing. Sarah, to blush when he and she knew each other's bodies as well as they knew their own. Better, in fact, for he could plot every mole and tender place of hers and had never even thought about his own. Her legs, so long and slender that even now sprawled apart . . . Desire surged in him and he knew that if they had been alone he would have stopped the car and loved her, whether she wanted it or not. As it was, when Sarah reached across for a cloth to wipe the window he snarled and struck her hand aside.

'You bad-tempered bastard,' she said crossly, but he would not look at her.

They reached the border as it was getting light. It was none too soon: they had emptied the last can of petrol into the tank and food was so short that only Tanu had eaten her fill. The border guards were agitated, expending their officiousness on the driver and treating Langeveldt with awed tact.

'We hear – things very bad – in Mandoto,' said one man cautiously.

'I don't know why more refugees don't come this way.' Sarah thought it politic to be chatty.

'They die before they get here,' snapped Joe and the guard retreated back into his hut. He had heard about this man Langeveldt and what happened to those that upset him.

They were bothered about Sarah – she had no official papers and no-one was quite sure how she had got into Mandoto in the first place. They deliberated and made telephone calls until eventually Joe got bored.

'You want us to take root here?' he asked with gentle menace. 'How many more hours is it to be before you decide she isn't a spy? You know who she is and where she's going, and what is more we're leaving now.' He grabbed Sarah's arm and hustled her to the Land Rover.

'Suppose they arrest us?' she asked nervously.

'I'd like to see them try.'

Hours later they stopped at a roadside filling station on the outskirts of town and Sarah spent some of her little hoard of money on petrol. The driver was appointed to babysit for Tanu and Joe threatened him with murder if he dared get drunk. Amidst a babble of promises the man wandered off in the direction of a café, some more of Sarah's money jingling in his pocket and Tanu skipping by his side.

'She looks so well,' said Sarah, shaking her head in surprise.

'Doesn't she just?' agreed Joe and they glanced at each other like proud parents. It was on the tip of Joe's tongue to ask about Sarah's own children and above all about Douglas, but she was going through her pockets, counting money.

'I haven't much left,' she said anxiously and Joe just grunted. The moment was gone.

There was nothing to do but make for their respective washrooms and try to render themselves presentable. Eventually Sarah emerged in khaki canvas skirt and clean white blouse, Joe in a pair of trousers little better than the ones he took off and an ancient crumpled shirt.

'Don't you ever buy any clothes?' asked Sarah incredulously.

He scratched his head. 'Well – no. For one thing I never have any money and for another it's bloody hard when you're my size. Anyway, won't this do?' He looked down at himself, a huge brown man with even now his white shirt coming untucked from his trousers. Her heart melted towards him and she put a hand to her mouth. 'I think, Joe – I think you'll do,' she said breathily, and set off down the street.

Their first port of call was a newspaper office. The foyer was beautiful with marble pillars and the wealth of plants that grace so many of Africa's public places, and Joe could not have been more conspicuous if he was still toting his gun. Heads turned towards them, the lovely slender lady walking with a barn door of a bushman, but neither Joe nor Sarah was concerned. They had more important things to worry about.

'I want to see the editor,' said Joe to the reception clerk, a synthetic blonde in a pink silk blouse.

The girl gave him a practised smile. 'Do you have an appointment?'

'No. But we must see him, it's important.'

'If you will give me your name I'll telephone his secretary and ask,' she said vaguely, 'but perhaps you'd prefer to see Mr Matthews –'

'The editor,' said Joe and fixed her with a steely glare. 'My name is Langeveldt.'

'Er – would that be – Joe Langeveldt?'

'It would.'

The girl coloured, cast him a glance of admiration not unmixed with awe and rang the editor's secretary. Within minutes they were travelling skywards in the lift. 'You see, Joe, you do have appeal,' said Sarah.

'You didn't find me so irresistible.'

The lift doors opened. 'I'm here, aren't I?' she said over her shoulder, and led the way into the editor's office.

The editor of the *New Africa Chronicle* was a man who was used to riding the storm. Revolutions came and went, governments rose and fell, but he and his newspaper would go on forever. A thin, understandably anxious man with thinning hair and watchful, bulbous eyes, he disliked having to antagonise people. Freedom of the press was all very well but freedom was not likely to be served if the paper disappeared altogether. He stood and offered a hand to each of his guests.

'Do sit down. I'm Mark Tomlinson.'

'How do you do?' said Sarah, smiling and crossing her long, tanned legs.

Joe wasted no time in pleasantries, casting himself into a chair and saying:

'We've come about the famine in Mandoto. I'm running a camp of sorts down there and people are starving. The government's not interested so we need publicity to get international aid. Now, I've got a few photographs of the children, and if you look you'll see –'

'Hey, hold on a minute,' said Tomlinson with a patronising chuckle, holding up a hand to stop him. Joe was rummaging in a folder and his head lifted.

'Yes, Mr Tomlinson?' he asked gently, the tawny eyes holding Tomlinson's pale grey ones.

Tomlinson adjusted his tie. 'It's just that – we're not doing anything on Mandoto at the moment. Politically sensitive.'

The folder slapped down on to the table. 'I think it might well be politically sensitive,' began Joe. 'Thousands of people are being allowed to starve and governments the world over are turning a blind eye, not to mention all you tinpot newspapers. It was made pretty clear at the border that reporters don't get in and they're even more nervous who comes out. If you think that I'm going to stand by and –'

'Joe!' Sarah caught his arm as he rose to his feet, towering over a pale Mr Tomlinson. She willed Joe to calm down. 'Let me,' she insisted, and with a tense nod he agreed. He knew he shouldn't lose his temper but when he thought of those children . . . He clenched his teeth and waited.

'You see, Mr Tomlinson,' said Sarah, 'I'm from England. I have visited Mr Langeveldt's camp and things are indeed desperate. Now, obviously when I go home in a day or two's time I shall be visiting our own newspapers as well as the charities, and aid will be forthcoming, but it may seem a little odd if the local papers over here, as well as such a prominent one as the *New Africa Chronicle*, have refused to cover the story. As a matter of courtesy we felt we should give you the opportunity to participate.' She smiled at Tomlinson and idly began to trace the pattern of threads in her skirt with a long, slender finger. No-one said anything at all.

Tomlinson awkwardly cleared his throat. 'Well –' he said stiffly. 'I think in that case it might be as well if I called in one of my reporters – my senior reporters –' he added with a nervous glance at Langeveldt's hawk-like face '– and see what we can make of the story. It might not be quite as big as you'd like it to be –' he wanted to get the row over now rather than be frightened to leave the building for a week – 'and we might centre on the personal aspects. You're quite well known in the continent, Mr Langeveldt.'

'That will be perfect,' soothed Sarah.

'You print a photograph,' said Langeveldt and tossed a picture on to the desk.

Mr Tomlinson glanced at it and blenched. Not one of his readers would be able to eat their breakfast after that. Still, if he could add a picture of the amazing couple seated before him now it might be worth it. If by some miracle this was the woman Langeveldt had been stuck in the bush with all that time ago then he really was made, government disapproval or not, for she was a cracker and no mistake. And Langeveldt was always newsworthy, even if bloody uncooperative. As far as he knew no-one had ever managed an interview with him before, although there was a tale of a reporter maimed for life. He hoped it was apocryphal, but since you never could tell he rang down for one of his older members of staff.

When Sarah and Joe emerged an hour later they were ebullient. 'See what a bit of blackmail does,' she said triumphantly. 'Now, if we visit all the other papers and tell them the *Chronicle*'s running a story they'll all want to get in on the act. And after that the charities and tell them the papers are on to it and are going to ask questions – why don't the carers care, that sort of thing – and then we go to the government and offer them the chance to help before the world points the finger. By tomorrow night something should be happening.'

Joe chuckled. 'I don't believe you're real, Sarah Hamilton. Why couldn't I do it this way?'

She looked at him speculatively, one finger to her lip. 'I think – it's a matter of practice,' she said thoughtfully. 'If you talked to people more you'd learn to use the rules.'

He had the sudden feeling that he had no idea of the rules of any of the games he was involved in. He had never before wanted to play by any rules except his own, which he knew to be highly individual. And now, when he wanted to say things and ask things and did not dare to do it wrong, he had no idea where to start. If he did it wrong she would be gone again. It seemed to him as if he had been living in a box these last months, walled in by misery and despair. Why it should be he did not know, but with Sarah he was free, even though he knew he was her prisoner. He could hate her for making him love her so. When she was there he saw the world through her eyes, even this city became manageable instead of the alien steambath he knew it to be. They were like travellers in dark tunnels and she held the light. He would have been amazed if he had known that for her the light was in his capable grasp.

'Let's get going,' he said gruffly and took her arm, a seemingly casual gesture that was very much intended. He touched her as often as he could without her noticing, unaware that every brush of his hand made her skin tingle.

They trailed from place to place, reciting their story until they were bored by it. A charity worker promised immediate supplies and one woman actually cried when Joe, for lack of anything new to say, told her about the death of an eight-year-old boy. She had a boy about that age herself, she said, and as Joe told her what a happy, helpful child the dead boy had been until he fell ill she sat and muttered, 'Yes, yes, yes,' as if it was her own son he was describing.

'She'd be a lot of damned use in Mandoto,' he said disparagingly when they emerged, but Sarah could see he was surprised. People did care about what was happening, but to believe it the experience had to become real to them, something they could understand in terms of each little piece of suffering, not statistics and number of camps. And they had to be told, exactly, how they could help.

Here Joe excelled. He knew precisely what food and medical supplies were needed, and he stamped on projects that did not fit in with what he knew should be done. Without intending to do anything of the kind he impressed people simply by talking about what he understood. Not for him the small-talk and evasions of civilised life; he said what he meant and was liked for it.

'You're quite a man, Mr Langeveldt,' said a charity director as they shook hands at the door.

Joe raised a quizzical eyebrow. 'Let's get some results before we start patting each other on the back. Come on,

Sarah.' He slipped an arm around her waist and led her out, leaving the charity director chuckling.

'You didn't have to snap at him,' complained Sarah as they strode down the street.

'Another minute and he'd have given me a cuddle and a kiss, and there are some things that even I won't do to get what I want.'

'Will you slow down, I'm exhausted.' Sarah stopped breathless against a lamp post. 'I hate African cities. They're worse than anywhere else because they're so hot.'

Joe glanced at his watch, currently a battered wind-up affair he had acquired in exchange for setting up somebody's gun. His watches never lasted long and sometimes he did without for months on end, but in town they were useful. 'Time to get back for Tanu. Everywhere's shutting up shop now anyway; we can't do any more today.' They began to wend their way through the streets, weary in body and mind. Help was coming, aid would get through, but the continual effort of asking for it was draining.

Soon they came to the place where they had left the driver and Tanu, but there was no sign of them. 'Might be in the cafe,' said Joe and went to look. They were not there.

'Perhaps they're at the Land Rover,' said Sarah, but it was still where they had left it, parked in a side street, all by itself. Joe began to worry.

'What in God's name has he done with her?' he asked, striking his forehead with one huge fist. 'I should never have left her – we could have brought her with us. She could be dead!'

'She could be but she probably isn't,' said Sarah, just as worried but with a little more experience of looking for lost children. There had been the heart-stopping moment when Emma disappeared in Littlewoods and took ten minutes to find, hidden amongst the racks of clothes, and Joanne's stroll along a beach to be returned a full half-hour later by a man who had found her wandering. Both times she was sure they were dead, and the sight of them, tearful and penitent, had been like a glimpse of heaven. She looked up at Joe's tense face. 'We'll look in the bars,' she said firmly, and began to walk.

'You're taking this bloody well,' snarled Joe.

'Only because it's not going to help if two of us get hysterical.'

'I am not hysterical! But when you think what he could have done to her –'

'Don't think! He's a nice man, he probably has hundreds of children of his own; he could have taken her somewhere to play – or anything.'

'Or anything,' echoed Joe. 'God, I knew I should never have kids, it's murder from start to finish.'

'You can say that again,' agreed Sarah. 'You look in there and I'll go in here.'

They poked their heads round door after door, stopping a dozen conversations, but there was no Tanu and no driver. Now it was Sarah's turn to panic, and she started to cry. 'They could be anywhere! We should go to the police but I know they won't do anything, and she isn't really ours at all so even if they find her they'd probably take her away. Joe, what can we do?'

He sighed and gathered her to him. 'I don't know. Keep looking, I suppose. Let's go back to the Land Rover and work down the back streets from there. If we don't find them in an hour we'll go to the police.'

Sarah snuffled into his shirt front, then realised it was the only one he had and rubbed at the marks.

'What are you doing?' He held her close and knew a

gentle soothing of his soul, even in the midst of his anxiety.

'Making a mess of your shirt. Let's hurry, Joe, please.'

They retraced their steps, working systematically up and down the hot and dusty streets. The shops were mostly run by Asians with half the stock stacked outside. They passed a barrelful of melons and Sarah longed for one, but every second mattered. She found she was almost running.

'Slow down, you'll make yourself ill. Look, let's try up here.' Joe pulled her into a tiny slip of a road, past the rubbish-strewn back doors of the shops.

Halfway along she saw a child playing in the dust. 'Tanu!' She and Joe ran together and Sarah got there first, scooping the little girl into her arms and holding her close. 'Tanu, Tanu, Tanu, where have you been, you naughty girl? I was so worried. I could squeeze you to death for frightening me so.' She was almost in tears again and for his part Joe felt weak. He leaned against a wall and felt his head spin and wondered if he would ever know joy like this again.

He had Tanu and he thought he might have Sarah. His heart thumped against his chest and he longed for a drink. Just then he noticed the prone figure of the driver slumped on some steps. He poked him hard with his toe and the driver groaned and mumbled. 'I should have known he'd get drunk,' he commented. 'But at least it saves us having to pay him. We can leave him here and he won't dare come and ask for what we owe.'

Sarah was dubious. 'It seems a bit mean.'

'After the fright he's given us! Like hell it is.'

But Sarah pulled out her remaining money and counted it carefully, then she slipped one single note into the sleeping man's pocket. 'That's all I can afford,' she said and turned to go with Joe.

'You're too soft,' he muttered.

'And you are far too hard.'

Hours later Joe lay in a bed in a cheap little hotel and couldn't sleep. He was hurt, bewildered and confused. What on earth was going on in Sarah's head? She appeared, with no explanation, and behaved as if she had never been away. And then today they had been so close – why, she had gone into his arms for comfort and she had found it. But tonight when he wanted her, needed her, and she knew how much he needed her, she had turned her back on him, huddling next to the baby on the hard, smelly bed and shutting him out. She pretended to sleep although he knew she was awake and he longed to touch her: but there was a wall between them as solid as if he had seen her build it. She risked her very life to come to his aid and then she turned her back. He could have strangled her.

He let his mind dwell for the littlest possible time on how he would like things to be. It was a luxury he rarely allowed himself, for he found it sapped his strength. A little farm in Mandoto, trying to help the people rebuild something of their lives. There was so much that needed doing and the fighting was dying down, largely due to the famine which was an irony of sorts. A small, pretty house under the trees by the river, but with high ceilings and big beds – he was sick of living in a world built for midgets. And Sarah. He caught his breath just thinking about her: she would lie in his bed and he would feast on her, making her cry out in an agony of joy. Come to think of it he'd better have a bigger house or the children would hear. Damn it all, there he was again, longing and hoping when he knew quite well it would all come to nothing. But surely he need not give up hope quite yet.

The room was hot and stuffy, full of the sounds of a city. Suddenly he could bear it no longer, lying in this stinking hole with his thoughts running round and round in his head like a rat in a box, he had to have air. He flung out of the too short bed, pulled on his clothes and stormed out. Sarah sat up and looked after him, her eyes lit by the glow of traffic in the street outside. She had hurt him but it was better this way. If she had let him love her he would have taken it as proof that all was well, and it was far from being so. All right, she loved him, she admitted that now, he was like water to her thirsty soul. But he had no future. If love alone was all it took then she would throw in her lot with his and never look back, but she needed more than that. She needed a future, if not for her then for her children, and Joe lived only for the present. What would Emma make of this huge, irascible man, nervous, sensitive little Emma? And when strong-willed Joanne met implacable Langeveldt there would be storms such as the world had never seen! But strangely children always loved him, they knew where they stood and they felt safe. Perhaps if he had a home it would be all right, they would manage somehow for money, but Joe had nowhere he could call his own. He was a gypsy and it bothered him not at all. It bothered Sarah a lot.

Tonight had been terrible; he had burned for her and she could not look at him. How could he not know that she longed to hold him, to lie crushed beneath his weight as he sank his hot and aching body into hers? But he did not know it and she did not tell him, for tomorrow's decision had been made today. She was leaving.

Joe returned to the room when even the city was quiet. Sarah lay asleep, one arm over Tanu, her flesh strangely pale against the black and shiny skin of the child. He knew then that he would never let her go. To hell with what she wanted – half the time the blasted woman did not know what she wanted, as if he would not give her the world if only she would stay. Why would she not talk to him, tell him what had happened in her life? He reached a hand to wake her and then drew back. If she was with him there was nothing he needed to know.

In the morning they were heavy-eyed and crumpled, not one of them with anything clean to wear. Sarah rinsed a pink cotton frock for Tanu and let it dry on the child, which it did in minutes, but she herself felt like a tramp, dirty and messy both inside and out.

'I'm tired of feeling ugly,' she said crossly, and Joe stared at her in amazement. He always thought she was beautiful. To him she was more lovely now than in yards of silk and satin, because she looked real.

'Don't be so stupid,' he said witheringly, and Sarah coloured. Did he have to be so horrible on their last day together? It wouldn't cost much to say she looked all right, but when Joe lost his temper it was no holds barred. Still, it might be for the best; anger gave you strength.

'Breakfast. Breakfast,' Tanu was saying hopefully, and Sarah seized her hand and marched towards the door.

'Since I'm the only one with any money around here I'd better go and buy this child some food,' she snapped, and flounced out. Joe blinked and followed more slowly. Sarah was certainly building herself a considerable head of steam.

During the morning it came clear that they had started something. Their picture was all over the *New Africa Chronicle*, wherever they went they were chased by telephone calls and best of all one charity was arranging to send an advance team with supplies that very afternoon.

'We can assess the situation and report back,' assured the organiser, a young, keen individual determined to change the world overnight.

Langeveldt met his naive smile with a glare like brown steel. 'I think you'll find that what I have told you is true,' he said grimly. 'What arrangements have you made to guard the convoy, lorries and food? They are very tempting.'

The man swallowed. 'We haven't made any arrangements. We thought, with the crosses on the lorries –'

'So. Unlike you I do not hope for the best.' The younger man's face was a picture of nervous indecision and suddenly Langeveldt chuckled. 'I see that you are coming with us. Don't worry, I'll look after you. What's your name?'

'James Morrison. I've never been on anything like this before –'

'I doubt it will be nearly as exciting as you'd like. Well, James Morrison be ready to go at two or we leave you behind.' He looked at his watch and saw that the face was cracked. He cursed inwardly. The civilised world simply did not make things for people like him.

At two o'clock he and Sarah stood staring at the little convory of four ageing lorries, each crammed with food.

'It's a start anyway,' said Langeveldt.

'It's a very good start; they've even brought some tubes and things to feed the weakest babies. Here, you'd better have my brother-in-law's pistol. Did you remember to get the bullets?'

'Yes. Got any money left?'

'Not a bean. Have you?'

He shook his head and then grinned. 'Good thing we're

getting out of this city. If there's one thing you need in this place it's money.'

Sarah took a deep breath. 'I'm not getting out, Joe.'

So. At last she came to it. She had certainly taken her time. 'What do you mean to do then?' he asked, and marvelled at the calmness of his voice. His stomach was in a knot so tight it hurt.

She shrugged. 'I don't know. Go back to Susie's and get the children I suppose, then find some sort of job. I've left Douglas, you see. But I need a home – for the children.'

The lorries were starting up. 'And you think I can't give you that?'

'I didn't know you even wanted to.' She was shaking, but this time at least he seemed calm. He must have known this was coming, after last night he must have suspected.

James Morrison leaned out of one of the cabs, the little black face of Tanu by his side, sucking a lollipop. 'Are you ready, Mr Langeveldt? We're about to move out.'

Joe nodded. 'I'm coming. Right away.' He turned to Sarah, and slid his arms around her waist. 'How about saying goodbye properly?' He bent his head to kiss her, she reached her arms up and around his neck, and suddenly she was flying through the air to land with a thud in the back of one of the trucks.

'Off you go then, James,' bellowed Langeveldt, and climbed in beside her as the lorries began to move.

'I'm not coming,' shrieked Sarah, and tried to struggle out of her bed of sacks. Joe caught her waist and flung her back again, pinning her down with the length of his strong, hard body.

'The only place you're going is with me,' he murmured, nuzzling her neck, oblivious of her flailing arms and legs. 'I don't know what you're up to and I don't care, but it's time you realised that I am not a nice man, Mrs Hamilton, and I make a habit of not being reasonable. You are staying with me.' He pulled her blouse aside, bursting one of the buttons, and bent his head to her breast. Sarah tangled her fingers in his hair and heaved, but he took no notice.

'Stop doing that, you brute!' she panted, trying to kick, but her leg was pinned under his iron thigh. Shudders went through her, radiating out from her breast as he mouthed her nipple. The lorry stopped at traffic lights and she could hear people talking. 'I want to get out,' she said softly, pulling his shirt up and clawing at his back, like a cat that is being stroked. 'I'm not coming with you.' He lifted his head and laughed in her face, his teeth as white and strong as any lion's.

'I love you, Sarah, but if you don't take your clothes off I will tear them in shreds. Be quick about it, I'm desperate.'

'Not here! Someone might look in.'

'I hope they enjoy watching it as much as I'm going to enjoy doing it.' He reached up her skirt and dragged at her panties and Sarah let him, too weak with needing him to care about later. The lorry started up again as he opened his trousers and Sarah groaned with relief and anticipation. Perhaps it was wrong to love him when she knew that she would leave but the feelings that swept her were delicious and remembered. How had she lived without this heaven?

'Don't think this means I'm staying,' she murmured, as he lowered himself on to her, holding back for the briefest possible second before he pushed himself inside. She gasped and clung to him, and for a moment she thought of Douglas, until Joe and the terrible painful pleasure of him drove thought from her mind.

A long, peaceful time later Sarah pulled herself up in her bed of sacks and said, 'Even if I come to Mandoto with you now, I'll leave in the end.'

Joe lay back and looked at her, her breasts swaying slightly with the motion of the lorry, her nipples still wet from his kisses. 'What did you come for if you didn't intend to stay?' His voice cracked and Sarah hid her face from his anger and hurt.

'I came – because I thought it might work out,' she said slowly. 'You see, I had to leave Douglas. You and me, Joe – well, you know how it was. We didn't have to pretend anything, we still don't. Not many people can be like that together. When I married Douglas I was a child, and when I was with you I grew up. Douglas wanted his child again, that was all there was to it, and when he couldn't have her he took it out on Emma and Joanne. So I left. And the only place I could think to come was here. I needed to see you, Joe.'

'You say that and in the next breath say you won't stay! Sarah, I'm not your local service station – pop in for some sex and a psychological boost every time life gets depressing.'

'The sex wasn't my idea, you made me!'

'Oh yes. I noticed how hard you were struggling.'

Sarah sniffed and fought against tears. 'All right, all right, it was good! But just because you screw me to perfection it doesn't mean there aren't any problems.'

'Tell me about them. I'm listening.' Joe linked his hands behind his head and waited, knowing what was coming, like a tennis player about to demolish an inferior opponent.

'It's the children. I need a home for the children and God damn it, for me. I can't live like this always, I need a house and a little bit of safety. All I want is the knowledge that when I go to bed beside you I can expect us all to be more or less alive in the morning. My children, the girls . . . Emma's nervous, you see, she has asthma, and with all this trouble over Douglas – I worry about her so. And Joanne – she's a tough nut, you and she would get on fine, but little girls can't take on soldiers. And Tanu, my girl just as much as yours, where's her home? She hasn't got anywhere. And I haven't got anywhere and I want somewhere safe and sure that's mine. And that isn't what you want.'

'Now that's where you're wrong!' Joe leaned over and caught her hand, already needing her again and thinking that in a minute they would make love. 'Of course you want a home. Did you think I expected you to bring up your children in a tent somewhere? Oh God, if you knew how much I've longed to have you with me! I'll build you a house, a beautiful house, overlooking the river, and what's more I'll build a bed that's a decent size. I'm sick to death of sleeping on a glorified shelf, and the bed that our children are made in will be vast. I want a son, Sarah. I want to plant my seed in your belly and watch you swell. And if it's money you're worried about, the only reason I haven't got any is because I never bother to make it. I never need to. When I need it I shoot a bit and hunt a bit and there it is, but when we've got our farm –'

Sarah couldn't stand any more. 'What farm? Where are you going to build this wonderful house?'

Joe stared at her. 'In Mandoto, of course. Where did you think?'

'But Joe – no!' The lorries were stopping at the border, and half-blinded by tears she pulled her blouse together and stuffed it into her skirt, kicking the remains of her pants under a sack. Joe was moving also, holding on to her arm, and she fumbled with the fastenings of his trousers,

300

her hands shaking too much to do up the buttons.

'Here, I'll do that. Sarah – what's wrong with Mandoto?'

She flung up her hands to cover her face. 'There's nothing right with it! People murder people, rape people, everybody starves! How can you ask me to live there, to take my children there and bring more babies into the world so they can suffer too? I love you, Joe, surely even you must see that, but please don't ask me to live in Mandoto.' She almost fell out of the back of the wagon, into the arms of the border guard they had met two days before.

'Mrs Hamilton? You go back to Mandoto?' he said cheerily, apparently oblivious of her dishevelled and desperate appearance.

'No! No! I'm never going to Mandoto again, it's a terrible place. He wants to kill my children, that's what he wants to do –'

Joe slid one arm around her waist, grabbed hold of her hair with his other hand and pulled her to his chest, almost smothering her against him and at the same time saying, 'There, there, darling, it'll be all right. She's a little tired,' he said to the guard with a conspiratorial grin. 'Pregnant. Worried about what might happen to the baby with all this bouncing. Come along, darling, the road's not that bad and you can ride in the cab.' He led her away and out of sight behind the lorry before letting her come up for air.

'I'm not coming,' gasped Sarah, red-faced and breathless.

'One word out of you and I shoot us both,' hissed Langeveldt. 'You are staying with me.'

'You can't do this to me! It isn't fair!'

'You want your children to have a mother, don't you? So keep quiet.' He looked round to see the startled face of

James Morrison watching them. 'Keep out of this,' snarled Langeveldt, 'or I'll swing for the lot of us. I warn you, Sarah, I mean it.'

She did not doubt him for a moment. When Joe lost his temper he would bring the world down around his head and think it right. When he calmed down it would be different, but by then they would be over the border. She went to sit with Tanu in the front of one of the lorries and closed her eyes wearily. Half an hour later Joe swung up beside her and the convoy trundled slowly into Mandoto.

Chapter 13

The charity workers were a friendly lot, full of the enthusiasm and righteousness of people doing what they know to be admirable. In his present mood of boiling, murderous anger, Langeveldt found them irritating, but heaven itself would have got on his nerves at the moment. Even Tanu recoiled from him and went instead to Sarah, leaving Joe to brood by himself. On this journey they drove quite late into the night before stopping, and rested during the heat of midday. Sarah thought they would take two, perhaps three days to get there. Joe made no comment at all.

At night the charity people erected a tent or two, and slept around the lorries, but Joe took no chances with Sarah. He made a bed for them both in the back of a lorry and made sure he was nearest the exit.

'I'm not likely to run off in Mandoto,' she complained, but he made no reply. She had stamped on his dream and he could not talk to her. Once, in the night, he made love to her, silent and angry, wanting to hurt but even now holding back. She cried just the same, sobbing into his shoulder in an agony of grief. At last she whispered to him, pleading, soft, 'Anywhere that isn't like Mandoto. Anywhere that's safe.'

'If you wanted Douglas you should never have left him,' said Joe and turned his back. He had definitely decided to shoot them both. The man Morrison would take Tanu and look after her; he would find her some sort of life. He felt calmer now, he could accept it and be glad. Once he had seen to his people, done all he could for them, it would be over. Sad, perhaps, never to see another dawn, but he had seen enough. It was a little price to pay for peace.

On the second night they pulled off the road quite late, and because the moon was new it was very dark.

'There's no cover,' said Joe, looking about him as though it were daylight.

'No-one will see us,' said Morrison. 'It's like a blanket tonight.'

'We should go on and find somewhere safer,' muttered Sarah, and Joe laughed at her, showing his teeth in a wolfish grin.

'No. We'll stay right where we are,' he said happily and every hair on Sarah's body stood on end. He could smell danger, Joe could, and it excited him. A night like this was tailor-made for a fight, and he knew something was going to happen.

'Damn you, Joe, damn you for ever,' she cursed, rummaging for the pistol.

Morrison looked bewildered. 'But it's all right, isn't it? There's nothing wrong.'

'Not in Joe's eyes, there isn't. Tanu love, you sleep in the lorry. It's all right, I'm here and so is Joe.'

'I thought you didn't trust me to look after her,' said Joe, counting cartridges in the light of a headlamp.

'Of course I trust you! God, if I can't trust you, who can I trust?' It was true. Out here, in danger, there was no-one better to put your faith in and if she would rather be safe and secure that was beside the point. She loaded the pistol and weighed it in her hand.

'Are we going to be attacked?' asked Morrison, his voice rising in panic.

'No. Yes. Ask Joe,' said Sarah, but Joe was making a

comfortable nest for himself on the ground behind the front wheel of Tanu's lorry. 'Go to bed, James,' urged Sarah. 'But don't sleep too sound.' She found a blanket and crawled in beside Joe. 'We might as well be warm,' she muttered, and curled up to go to sleep.

She woke in the dark, silent time before dawn. 'Are they coming?' she whispered.

'Yes. Only half a dozen, I think – they don't expect any trouble. I heard a jeep or something a while ago. They stopped a mile up the road. Can you see that shadow over there? He's the nearest: I'll let you shoot him.'

Sarah breathed on a giggle. 'It'll take me till lunchtime.'

'I thought you were scared.'

'I am. But less than before. You get used to this sort of thing. I think.'

She pulled her pistol up and slipped off the safety catch, sighting along the barrel as best she could. If only there was some light; it was like looking into a solid wall of black.

Suddenly Joe levelled his rifle and fired, the crack painful in the silence of the night. There was a single shriek, high, ghastly, then nothing. Sarah's skin crawled. The shadow, her shadow, was moving, and there was a rattle of gunfire, humming in the air like a swarm of flies. 'Oh God,' she muttered, rested the barrel of the pistol on the tyre and pulled the trigger. The shadow moved rapidly to the right and she fired again, and then Joe's rifle cracked and it fell and lay still.

'What's happening? What's going on?' The charity workers were popping up like rabbits, noisy and dangerous.

'Get down and shut up, all of you,' roared Joe. 'Morrison, put on the lights of this lorry, and don't get yourself shot in the process.'

There was a mad, panicky scramble and the lights made a wavering yellow path through the night. Sarah saw a pair of legs and fired at them, but Joe was shooting beyond, into the dark. A few more desultory poppings from the darkest shadows, and it went quiet.

'Sarah? Sarah?' called a voice from the lorry and Sarah called out, 'It's all right, Tanu, it's over. Stay there, I'll be with you in a minute.' She lay very still and searched the blackness with her eyes.

'I think that's it,' said Joe and crawled carefully into the open, taking care to avoid the light.

'Did anybody get shot?' asked Morrison in a nervous, excited voice.

'I bloody hope so,' said Joe, 'or I'm losing my touch. Put the safety catch on that thing, Sarah. You know what you're like with guns.'

'What am I like?' she asked, affronted.

'Vague.' He went off to have a scout around.

The charity workers were agog with excitement, as delighted with their little skirmish as it was possible to be.

'Mr Langeveldt is amazing,' said one to Sarah and she just grunted. They seemed so young and so new to it all. The little convoy set off as soon as it was light, leaving three dead bodies in the dust.

'They may come back for them,' said Joe. 'We can't waste time on funerals, I want to get to that camp. If my little army's pulled out we're in trouble.'

'Those men last night,' said Sarah. 'They waited until we were well away from the border. A bit worrying, that.'

'As long as they haven't taken the camp. Two hours and we should be there.'

It was a relief to see the little line of trees that marked the river, but Joe approached with caution. 'Three lorries stay here,' he ordered. 'Sarah and I will take the first one in.'

'We both get shot together, is that it, Joe dear?'

'You said it, sweetheart.' He grinned at her and all of a sudden she had to grin back. You could only take so many precautions, and she was tired of the tedium of being afraid.

'Me come,' said Tanu and Sarah shrugged and put her in the lorry. She was getting very fatalistic in her old age.

Figures ran this way and that beneath the trees as they approached. Sarah waited for a rattle of gunfire, but none was forthcoming. A little distance from the camp Joe stopped and got down, walking slowly and confidently forward, his rifle held with deceptive ease in his hand. Suppose he was shot. Suppose, now, some lunatic lifted a gun and shot him. Sarah knew she could not bear it, she could not live if the world did not hold Joe. She dragged at the door handle and tumbled out, running to catch up with him.

'What are you doing?' he asked in surprise.

'Keeping you company.'

They walked on, and from the sheltering belt of trees there came a shout of welcome as they were recognised.

'Thank God,' said Sarah, and went back to bring in the lorry.

There seemed to Sarah to be fewer soldiers than before. Many of the rondavels were empty, and the men that remained seemed very relieved to see them, laughing and slapping each other on the back. She saw the youth she had spoken to before, grinning at her shyly. 'Where are the soldiers?' she asked, spreading her hands wide and looking about her.

He looked apologetic. 'They not stay without Lange-veldt,' he explained. 'They safe with Langeveldt.'

She gave a reluctant grin and nodded.

The camp itself seemed no less crowded, bodies lay everywhere and the children's enclosure had been invaded by others. That annoyed Joe. He set about reorganising it with a rattle of instructions that were obviously funny as well as pointed, because those evicted laughed as they went. Sarah could not laugh and neither could the charity workers, facing the scene for the very first time. The faces before them were tinged with grey, and that under black skin resulted in a thick, muddy colour that had nothing to do with health. And dysentery was present, inevitable with so many crammed together. People were exhausted and without strength. An old woman lay on a thin rush mat, her lips barely parted. Joe bent and spoke to her, touching her cheek with his huge, spatulate fingers, and she tried to smile. Joe nodded and moved on.

James Morrison was white and shaking. 'This is terrible,' he kept saying. 'These people are dying.' And even in this last week many had died. Sarah looked for the baby she had noticed before and could not see it, and though she comforted herself with the thought that amongst so many one was hard to find, she knew that the baby was dead. Others would die soon too, because for some the food came too late.

All day they worked, making hospital tents and feeding stations, digging more and yet more latrines. 'So many people,' the charity workers said one to another. 'I wouldn't have believed there were so many.' Joe was tireless, moving from group to group sorting out problems. This was his place, thought Sarah suddenly. This was what he was good at. He understood these people and they accepted him.

For her part she worked with the babies. It was not so bad, she found, when there was something you could do.

To look and know yourself impotent was like a torture, but to look and know you could help was another matter entirely. Some would die, and so be it, you could not be in Africa and not know death, but others would live and that must be her triumph.

That night the camp was festive. Everyone had eaten and what is more they would eat again in the morning. All of a sudden the quiet of despair was gone, people sang, a drum was beating in celebration. Victory was crawling out of the mire of defeat, still weak and shaky, but alive.

Sarah went and stood on the hill beside Joe's hut and looked down on the lovely yellow lights of the fires, glowing like spirits in the dark. One moment she was alone, the next Joe was beside her.

'What will happen to them?' asked Sarah. 'After the war and the famine and perhaps another war, what sort of life is there for them?'

He sighed. 'None at all if people like me abandon them. That's what you'd like me to do, isn't it? Go to some place where things like this don't happen. And I can't, I just can't leave them. I thought I could, I thought if I brought the food that would be enough, but it's hardly a beginning. If I go now there could be an army here tomorrow taking even the little they have, even their miserable, sickly lives.' He put a hand to his face and Sarah knew that he was crying.

'If you want to go back with the lorries then you can,' he said thickly. 'I said I'd kill us both first and I meant it, but in the end there's no point. You'd better take Tanu: she needs a mother. Write and tell me how she gets on. Send a – photograph!' His voice broke on a sob and he turned to blunder up the hill, crashing through the undergrowth, barely seeing what was in his path.

'Joe! Wait!' Sarah raced after him, but he would not

stop, striding up the hill as if it wasn't there while she panted and struggled in his wake. 'Joe! For God's sake, stop,' she gasped and at last he turned and saw her. He slumped on to a fallen, rotting log.

'You shouldn't sit there – snakes,' puffed Sarah.

'I hope there's a bloody family of them. Go away, Sarah, you're torturing me! I know you're right, this isn't any place for your children and it isn't any place for you.'

'Yes, it is.' She seized his hand in both of hers and cradled it against her cheek. 'All right, it's dangerous and uncomfortable, I grant you that, and it scares me a lot of the time. But it's your home and it's where you belong. You were the one who said if I'd wanted Douglas I ought to have stayed with him, and you were right. I don't want Douglas, I want you. And if having you means living here, then I will.'

'You don't mean that. You'll be sorry tomorrow, you'll tell me I'm killing your children.'

'If I say it you can hit me. Anyway, you don't kill children, you save their lives. My children will be safe with you, I know they will. If all these people can trust you to take care of them when they have so little, how can I not trust you when I have so much?'

Joe looked incredulous. 'But you don't have anything! We had more between us the day that aeroplane crashed.'

Sarah looked at him, at his dear, craggy, beautiful, tear-streaked face and knew she had more now than ever before in her life. 'I've got you,' she said simply, and went into his arms for his kiss.

VOYAGE

ELIZABETH WALKER

VOYAGE

On a luxury liner where too much champagne makes dowdy Harriet easy prey for handsome, heartless Jake.

VOYAGE

To the Caribbean on a borrowed yacht, as sexual initiation at Jake's experienced hands wakes Harriet to beauty and self-confidence.

VOYAGE

Ending in shipwreck on the exotic but voodoo-ridden island of Corusca, where Harriet finds the riches that will give her untold power, but also makes a deadly enemy.

VOYAGE

From the grey coast of England to the sin and sun of Nassau, from a shabby boarding house to ownership of America's most elegant and luxurious hotel chain.

VOYAGE

Of self-discovery where even the Caribbean surf pounds to the heartbeat of an extraordinary pair of lovers: Harriet and Jake – impossible together, unthinkable apart.

FICTION/GENERAL   0 7472 3131 1   £4.50

More Compelling Fiction from Headline:

ROWAN'S MILL

Elizabeth Walker

**bestselling author
of VOYAGE**

At sixteen she wouldn't have had the nerve. At eighteen
she would have known better. But at seventeen Rowan
Judge was prepared to tackle the toughest job in town
single-handed: saving the family woollen mill from
closure. Bradford's hard-headed business community
had seen nothing like it since the rise of James Barton,
the textile baron who had broken up Rowan's family
and blighted their lives. Determined to prove herself
more than his equal, in the space of a few years Rowan
achieves the impossible – she drags the mill from the
brink of disaster to Stock Exchange success. But at what
cost to herself and those she loves?

Saul, Rowan's husband, bears the brunt of her driving
ambition. Charming, mercurial, a supremely successful
salesman, he finds himself in constant clashes with her
over the development of the business. And when she
meets Richard, son of her arch enemy, Rowan sees in
him her perfect match in talent and temperament.
Which will she choose? Or does Rowan's mill mean
more to her than either?

A finely meshed and enthralling saga, *Rowan's Mill* is
the powerful novel of a remarkable woman whose
desire for revenge unleashes an invincible ambition.

**Also by Elizabeth Walker from Headline
VOYAGE**
'Once you start reading, you won't be able to stop.
A memorable book, and refreshingly different.'
Woman's World

FICTION/SAGA   0 7472 3237 7   £4.99

A selection of bestsellers from Headline

FICTION

THE EIGHT	Katherine Neville	£4.50 ☐
THE POTTER'S FIELD	Ellis Peters	£5.99 ☐
MIDNIGHT	Dean R Koontz	£4.50 ☐
LAMPLIGHT ON THE THAMES	Pamela Evans	£3.99 ☐
THE HOUSE OF SECRETS	Unity Hall	£4.50 ☐

NON-FICTION

TOSCANINI'S FUMBLE	Harold L Klawans	£3.50 ☐
GOOD HOUSEKEEPING EATING FOR A HEALTHY SKIN	Alix Kirsta	£4.99 ☐

SCIENCE FICTION AND FANTASY

THE RAINBOW SWORD	Adrienne Martine-Barnes	£2.99 ☐
THE DRACULA CAPER Time Wars VIII	Simon Hawke	£2.99 ☐
MORNING OF CREATION The Destiny Makers 2	Mike Shupp	£3.99 ☐
SWORD AND SORCERESS 5	Marion Zimmer Bradley	£3.99 ☐

All Headline books are available at your local bookshop or newsagent, or can be ordered direct from the publisher. Just tick the titles you want and fill in the form below. Prices and availability subject to change without notice.

Headline Book Publishing PLC, Cash Sales Department, PO Box 11, Falmouth, Cornwall, TR10 9EN, England.

Please enclose a cheque or postal order to the value of the cover price and allow the following for postage and packing:
UK: 60p for the first book, 25p for the second book and 15p for each additional book ordered up to a maximum charge of £1.90
BFPO: 60p for the first book, 25p for the second book and 15p per copy for the next seven books, thereafter 9p per book
OVERSEAS & EIRE: £1.25 for the first book, 75p for the second book and 28p for each subsequent book.

Name ....

Address ....

....

....